HEALTH POLICY
IN CANADA

HEALTH POLICY
IN CANADA

Second Edition

TOBA BRYANT

Canadian Scholars' Press Inc.
Toronto

Health Policy in Canada, Second Edition (previously published as *An Introduction to Health Policy*)
By Toba Bryant

First published in 2016 by
Canadian Scholars' Press Inc.
425 Adelaide Street West, Suite 200
Toronto, Ontario
M5V 3C1
www.cspi.org

Library and Archives Canada Cataloguing in Publication

Bryant, Toba, author
Health policy in Canada / Toba Bryant. -- Second edition.

Includes index.
First edition published under title: Introduction to health policy.
Issued in print and electronic formats.
ISBN 978-1-55130-924-8 (paperback).—ISBN 978-1-55130-926-2 (epub).—
ISBN 978-1-55130-925-5 (pdf)

     1. Medical policy—Canada. 2. Medical policy. 3. Medical care—Canada. I. Title. II. Bryant, Toba . Introduction to health policy.

RA395.C3B82 2016   362.10971   C2016-905141-2   C2016-905142-0

Text design by Brad Horning
Cover design by Gordon Robertson
Cover image by iStock by Getty Images/wildpixel

Printed and bound in Canada by Marquis.

For Alexander and Dennis

TABLE OF CONTENTS

PREFACE TO THE SECOND EDITION*

There are many books on health policy and public policy that have been designed for the policy specialist. This book was developed with the intent of making health policy accessible to students and practitioners in a range of health sectors. These include health professionals such as nurses, physicians, social workers, and other allied health care professionals who are on the front lines of health care delivery. The second audience is post-secondary students in these same areas, as well as those studying health policy and public policy.

This book is not a compendium of every health policy or health policy initiative undertaken in Canada. Rather, the book explores some of the key developments in health policy in Canada and elsewhere. It does not regard health policy as a process that simply requires management of facilities and human resources. It recognizes health policy as a public policy area that is driven and influenced by social, political, and economic forces.

The book draws upon the approach taken by Gill Walt in her excellent book *Health Policy: An Introduction to Process and Power*. In that 1994 book, Walt presented a framework of health policy focused on process and power. She was specifically interested in the political, economic, and social forces that shape how policy is developed and implemented. While it is a highly readable text, Walt focused largely on health policy in the United Kingdom.

The aim of writing this second edition is to consider health policy in Canada within the context of recent international developments in economics and public policy, including economic globalization and free trade agreements. Therefore, an important theme in this volume is the impact of economic globalization on health policy and health care in Canada, and of the market on health policy, not only in terms of health care provision, but also on the health-related public policy that shapes the health of the population—the social determinants of health. While it is true that the major health problems in the world today are found in developing nations, this volume focuses primarily on health policy among developed economies such as Canada, the United States, the United Kingdom, and others. An important theme is health equity and how it can be addressed through public policy and other collective action. Where possible, boxed inserts present case studies on specific health initiatives, especially in the area of primary health care reform. A number of Canadian provinces and territories have undertaken primary health care reform by innovating new models of delivering care.

Much of the existing health policy literature in Canada focuses on health care policy to the exclusion of public policy that shapes the health of the population in a jurisdiction. Public policy that influences population health through the provision of economic, political, and social resources is also health policy. This recognition—that what are now termed the social determinants of health strongly influence health outcomes—appeared in the 19th-century writings of Rudolph Virchow and Friedrich Engels. The implications of this knowledge have been integrated into health policy in Europe, but less so in Canada. This book therefore considers the political, economic, and social forces that shape both health care policy and health-related public policy in Canada. By doing so, it aims to make understandable the processes and means of producing health policy in the service of health. This second edition addresses key changes that have occurred since the publication of the first edition that have influenced health policy and the health of populations.

The first few chapters of this book serve as a road map to this inquiry. The book first lays out the theoretical terrain that underpins health policy by examining key public policy frameworks and various paradigms of health and knowledge. It outlines four health lenses: (1) biomedical; (2) lifestyle; (3) socio-environmental; and (4) critical/structural. It also discusses how the dominant research and theoretical approaches in the social sciences—positivism, interpretive/hermeneutics, and the critical social science perspective—can help explain how health policy comes about and its philosophical underpinnings. The paradigms consist of different assumptions about the world and how it can be understood and studied, with clear implications for understanding how health policy is understood and made and the types of health issues that are identified and addressed.

The book then discusses how health care delivery is organized in Canada by examining federal legislation on health care financing and administration from 1958 to the present day. It details how health care reform has dominated health policy discussions since 2000. Some of the emerging themes in health policy are examined, including issues of public versus private financing and delivery of health care services, global epidemics such as Ebola, the changing roles of the public and private sectors in health care, public health, the impact of economic globalization on health policy, and how various sectors come to shape health policy. How these developments shape health-related public policy related to income, housing, and other social determinants of health is also examined.

Each chapter contains boxed inserts that illustrate the key concepts discussed. Tables and figures further clarify the concepts examined in each chapter. In addition, each chapter concludes with critical thinking questions, URLs for resources available on the Internet, and recommended further readings. These resources are intended to help extend discussion on the issues and enhance students' conceptual understanding of health policy concepts and issues.

Understanding health policy and how it is developed and implemented is an essential skill for those concerned about health care and health in Canada. I hope that those reading this book come away with a better understanding of these processes and how they can be influenced in the service of health.

*The first edition was published in 2009 under the title *An Introduction to Health Policy in Canada*.

ACKNOWLEDGEMENTS

Few books are written without the support of many people. I would like to thank Natalie Garriga, developmental editor. I would also like to thank the reviewers for their insights and constructive comments. All helped to strengthen the prose and the content of the book.

The beginnings of this book are found in my doctoral thesis on health and social policy change. The supervision and constructive contributions and insights of David Hulchanski, my thesis supervisor, and my diligent committee members—Ron Manzer, Sheila Neysmith, and Irv Rootman—also helped to shape this volume.

Finally, I would also like to thank Dennis Raphael, my husband and scholar, and my son, Alexander, for their support. Also thank you to my employer and colleagues in the Faculty of Health Sciences at the University of Ontario Institute of Technology, who provided the space for me to prepare the second edition of this volume.

Toba Bryant
Toronto
November 2015

Chapter 1

INTRODUCING HEALTH POLICY AND POLICY STUDIES

INTRODUCTION: WHAT IS HEALTH POLICY?

Policy refers to plans and procedures developed and implemented by governments, agencies, organizations, and associations to achieve desired goals. *Public* policy refers to a course of action or inaction chosen by *public* authorities to address a given problem or interrelated set of problems that is anchored in a set of beliefs about the best way to achieve those goals (Pal, 2006). Public policy is about many things and is shaped by a wide range of factors, such as individuals or groups taking action on a public issue through advocacy, political ideology, and politics, or the give and take between stakeholders, political representatives, and government. Also among these dynamics are what is known about an issue by experts, community members whose lives are directly affected by an issue, government action or inaction on a given issue, and other stakeholders. The idea of public policy is that an issue is not a private affair, but one that needs to be addressed by the larger society in the public domain (Pal, 2006).

Health policy is a subset of public policy. On another level, it is also about politics, power, and process (Walt, 1994). In other words, who has power and who does not have power to influence health policy and health policy outcomes? Who benefits and who does not benefit from health policy change? What is the nature of the political or policy change process? For example, in Canada, the medical doctor or physician is usually the gatekeeper to many aspects of the health care system. This includes, but is not limited to, being seen by medical specialists, physiotherapists, and other allied health care providers. The dominance of the medical profession creates particular dynamics that affect the nature and delivery of care and the ability of other health professionals, such as nurses and pharmacists, to influence health policy and how they deliver care to patients.

Medical dominance also influences the public's ability to influence health policy. It does so by persuading governments to address or ignore certain issues. Alternatively, this dominance can lead governments to intiate particular kinds of action on an identified issue that benefit some but adversely affect others. Many health policy issues are of special importance to the medical profession. Its dominance shapes whether and how governments decide to address them. This dynamic also influences the nature of health policy itself and leads to an emphasis on health care organization and delivery. It can preclude consideration of developing public policies to promote health equity. Health equity means that all residents have access to the resources and health services they need to maintain and improve their health (Bryant & Raphael, 2010). Health *in*equity refers to a situation in which unequal health outcomes across the population are a result of unfair or unjust systemic practices, such as racism.

Various groups and stakeholders all attempt to influence health policy debates and outcomes, but clearly they do not all participate on a level playing field. Therefore, politics—in all its meanings—permeates the study of health policy and the nature of health policy and health practice (see Box 1.1).

Box 1.1: What Is Politics?

Politics is multidimensional.

- Politics as government: Politics is primarily associated with the art of government and the activities of the State.
- Politics as public life: Politics is primarily concerned with the conduct and management of community affairs.
- Politics as conflict resolution: Politics is concerned with the expression and resolution of conflicts through compromise, conciliation, negotiation, and other strategies.
- Politics as power: Politics is the process through which desired outcomes are achieved in the production, distribution, and use of scarce resources in all areas of social existence.

Source: Bambra, C., Fox, D., & Scott-Samuel, A. (2005). Towards a politics of health. *Health Promotion International, 20,* 187–193.

Politics is also about political parties and civil society organizations, such as movements and coalitions that mobilize to address a particular issue and to seek specific changes in public policy. Canada has a multi-party system. Its political parties include the Conservative Party, the Liberal Party, the New Democratic Party, the Green Party, and the Bloc Québécois. This is similar to the political landscape in Western European countries. As will be seen, the Conservative and Liberal parties have tended to dominate the Canadian political landscape, making it harder for newer and smaller parties to gain a presence in the political system.

All political parties are driven by their political ideologies. *Political ideology* refers to a system of ideas about what are the key issues and what should be done about them. Table 1.1 shows the main themes of Canadian political parties' platforms during the October 2015 general election.

THE SCOPE OF HEALTH POLICY

Health policy encompasses both health care and other health-related public policies. The state, represented by the government of the day, determines the organization of health care and resource allocations for the delivery of health care services to the population. In countries that have public health care systems, such as Canada, the state has a very central and direct role in this. In other words, Canada has a publicly financed system of public health care insurance. But the state also shapes health policy in nations in which the governmental role allows the private sector to have a larger role in policymaking.

For example, the United States' public policy is dominated by market-driven approaches, so that its health care system consists primarily of a wide range of private health insurance plans (Navarro, 1994). As will be discussed in chapter 6, President Barack Obama implemented the Patient Protection and Affordable Care Act in 2010. While the legislation did not create a single-payer system similar to Canadian medicare, it helped to make people who were uninsured eligible to receive Medicaid (Hall & Lord, 2014). Medicaid is an assistance program that provides health care to low-income Americans of all ages. US Medicare provides health insurance to seniors aged 65 years and over. The 2010 act expanded Medicare to include people with disabilities. Medicaid and Medicare are in and of themselves single-payer systems, since the federal government pays for these programs. But even then, American health care continues to be dominated by a for-profit model provided by a multitude of health care institutions.

Table 1.1: Canadian Political Parties and their Ideological Commitments

Conservative Party of Canada	Liberal	NDP	green PARTY OF CANADA	BLOC QUÉBÉCOIS
• Lower taxes for families and businesses • Balance budget • Expand international trade • Increase health transfers to provinces and territories by 6% until 2016–2017	• Lower taxes for middle class • Increase infrastructure spending • Renegotiate health accord and include long-term funding agreement	• Reduce income inequality • Invest $500 million to hire more health professionals • Introduce universal drug coverage	• Green, sustainable economy • Create jobs • Expand medicare to include drug coverage	• Separate Quebec from Canada • Promote socio-economic interests of Quebecers • Change health care funding arrangements

Health policy has a broad scope and encompasses health care financing and delivery, as well as improving and maintaining the health of the population (Canadian Population Health Initiative, 2004). In North America, this broader approach to promoting health is less developed than it is in other nations. In Canada, consideration of health-related public policy beyond the purview of the health care system is rare. For example, Canada's concern with health status indicators is usually focused on the effects of health care access and delivery (Canadian Institute for Health Information & Statistics Canada, 2002). Even though Canadian policy documents have argued that there are many factors that lie outside the health care sector—the social determinants of health or people's living and working conditions—that influence these indicators and hence the health of a population, there has been little policy action in support of these arguments (Raphael, 2008). Indeed, since the 1970s, Canada has achieved greater reductions in income-related health inequalities in acute conditions, which are usually the most amenable to medical treatment (Bryant, Raphael, Schrecker, & Labonte, 2011). It has been less successful in reducing income-related inequalities in mortality from factors amenable to public health measures.

In contrast, many European nations have a broader understanding of health policy as involving more than the delivery of health care services (Mackenbach & Bakker, 2002). In many European nations, health policy is also concerned with addressing the broader policy issues associated with various social determinants of health, such as income, housing, and education (European Policy Health Impact Assessment Project, 2004). This concern is grounded in frameworks that consider the provision of income, housing, and food security as ensuring that people have access to the resources necessary for health. As a result, governments focus on how the provision of citizen security shapes health status indicators (such as infant and adult mortality rates) and influences the incidence of and mortality from a range of diseases (such as cardiovascular disease, diabetes, and other chronic diseases) (Mackenbach & Bakker, 2003).

In these jurisdictions, governments are considered to have an important role in promoting the health and well-being of their citizens, not only through the provision of health care, but also by addressing these social determinants of health. In this volume, this broader definition of health policy is applied to understanding health care and health issues. Health policy is concerned with a range of issues that affect health and well-being in addition to its obvious concern with health care organization and provision.

THE EVOLUTION OF HEALTH POLICY

The provision of health care as an entitlement in many industrialized nations began in earnest following the end of the Second World War (Teeple, 2000). By the mid-1970s, virtually all industrialized nations, with the exception of the United States, developed public health care systems as components of the postwar welfare state. In terms of health-related public policies—which are normally defined as comprising the welfare state, such as providing income, employment, and other forms of security—the postwar period was also a time of expansion. This was especially the case in nations such as Canada, the US, and the UK. Interestingly, the seeds of the welfare state were planted much earlier in many European nations, especially in the Scandinavian nations (Einhorn & Logue, 2003). Indeed, the Scandinavian nations have tended to rank high on life expectancy and human development indicators, and also have lower income inequality.

The driving value in health care developments was the provision of health services on the basis of need rather than the ability to pay. (This principle eventually became enshrined in Canadian health policy statements.) The creation of a public health care system, similar to developments in other public policy areas such as public education, was an expression of societal will to share the cost of health care across the population. This sharing would ensure universal access to health care services for all citizens regardless of their incomes or place of residence. In short, health care would be free at point of access. Relating back to the definition of public policy provided earlier, health care in Canada had become a public issue to be provided by the state on the basis of need. It was no longer a private matter. The guiding value was universality, whereby all Canadians were entitled to receive health services without user fees, and the same quality of care regardless of where they lived.

Prior to the development of medicare, many people did without health care or, in some cases, lost their homes in order to pay medical costs, especially during the Depression of the 1930s. At that time, health care was considered a responsibility to be borne by the individual or family. Despite the fact that Canada's health care system was created during a period of economic prosperity, some argue that Canadian medicare was developed as a response to poverty, not affluence (Yalnizyan, 2006). The experience of the Depression (1929–1939) convinced the Canadian public—with politicians coming on board rather later—that a health care system based on universality provided the preferred solution to meeting the health care needs of the population. In addition, returning veterans who had fought in the Second World War wanted something in return for their sacrifices overseas. The initial establishment of a medicare system in Saskatchewan by Premier Tommy Douglas reflected these influences.

Box 1.2: Tommy Douglas: The Greatest Canadian

My friends, watch out for the little fellow with an idea.
—Tommy Douglas, 1961

For more than 50 years, his staunch devotion to social causes, rousing powers of speech, and pugnacious charm made Tommy C. Douglas an unstoppable political force. From his first foray into public office politics in 1934 to his post-retirement years in the 1970s, Canada's "father of medicare" stayed true to his socialist beliefs—often at the cost of his own political fortune—and earned himself the respect of millions of Canadians in the process.

The child of Scottish immigrants, Douglas spent his formative years in Winnipeg, Manitoba, in a home where politics, philosophy, and religion were side dishes at the dinner table. His father, a veteran of two wars, worked part-time in an iron foundry. When money was tight, Douglas and his two sisters had to drop in and out of school as they worked occasional jobs to help pay the bills.

His family's socialist leanings were solidified after Douglas was hospitalized at the age of 10. Due to a bone infection suffered four years earlier, Douglas's knee required several operations, none of which were successful.

Without the money to pay for a specialist, his parents were told that the only option was to amputate their son's leg before the infection spread to the rest of his body. But before that could happen, a visiting surgeon offered to operate on Douglas for free, as long as his students were allowed to attend. The surgery saved Douglas's leg—quite possibly his life—and would serve as his inspiration for his dream of universally accessible medical care.

Not long after this, Douglas would witness first-hand the violent end of Canada's first general strike on a day known as "Bloody Saturday." In the summer of 1919, a teenaged Douglas watched from a rooftop as officers fired on participants in the Winnipeg General Strike and killed two men. The forceful and violent end of the strike further mobilized his dedication to the working man.

During his youth, he tried many different occupations: amateur actor, boxer, and apprentice printer. Douglas found his true calling in 1924 when he enrolled in a liberal arts college run by the Baptist church. It was here that he refined his notion of the "social gospel," a vision of religion-in-action that he would carry through his life. Following several post-graduation years working as a minister in Depression-era Saskatchewan, Douglas made the move to politics in 1935 when he was elected as an MP in the Co-operative Commonwealth Federation, or CCF.

After nine years in the House of Commons polishing his fiery public-speaking talent, Douglas was elected the leader of the provincial CCF in Saskatchewan. With interest in socialism peaking in postwar Canada, the party won a landslide victory in 1944 and Douglas found himself an instant celebrity as the head of North America's first-ever socialist government.

Amid widespread skepticism, Premier Douglas mobilized aggressively, passing more than 100 bills during his first term. He introduced paved roads, sewage systems, and power to most farmers and managed to reduce the provincial debt by $20 million. Over the next 18 years he weathered Communist fear campaigns and a province-wide doctors' strike. Elected to five terms, he introduced Saskatchewan residents to car insurance, labour reforms, and his long-standing dream of universal medicare.

But the years spent reforming his home province worked against him when he made his transition to national politics. By the time he was elected to the leadership of the newly formed national New Democratic Party in 1961, many provincial governments had already adopted many of his ideas, diluting his progressive lustre. That, combined with a fervent anti-medicare campaign by Saskatchewan's medical professionals, helped to deal him his first significant defeat in the 1961 federal election. The NDP won only 19 seats, and Douglas lost his cherished seat in Regina.

Douglas continued to promote his socialist policy through the 1960s, but never managed to secure the highest office in the land. The adoption of national medicare and a pension plan by Lester B. Pearson's Liberals gave him hope.

He took his final and most controversial stand during the October Crisis of 1970, when he voted against the implementation of the War Measures Act in Quebec. The move was devastating to his popularity at the time, but he would be heralded years later for sticking by his principles of civil liberty.

He stepped down as leader in 1971, but he stayed on with the party. In 1979, he resigned his seat in Parliament and retired to a house in the Gatineau Hills, just outside Ottawa, where he devoted himself to reforesting his land. He continued to make appearances at NDP functions where he gave his trademark speeches. Douglas died of cancer in 1986.

Tommy Douglas's legacy as a social policy innovator lives on. Social welfare, universal medicare, old age pensions, and mothers' allowances—Douglas helped keep these ideas, and many more, watching as more established political parties eventually came to accept these once-radical ideas as their own.

Source: http://www.cbc.ca/greatest/top_ten/nominee/douglas-tommy.html. Site no longer active (2004).

The form that public health care takes in Canada reflects a policy approach that is grounded in particular principles and values. The public provision of health care is financed through taxation rather than fees for services. Since wealthier people generally pay more taxes and the less wealthy require greater health services, public financing of a universally accessible health care system effectively serves as a form of redistribution of resources from high- to low-income groups (Teeple, 2006, 2010). Despite the potential of this transfer serving as a source of conflict among the Canadian public, surveys consistently find medicare to be Canada's most prized social program (Yalnizyan, 2006).

Box 1.3: The Two Phases of Medicare

When we began to plan medicare (35 years previously), we pointed out that it would be in two phases. The first phase would be to remove the financial barrier between those giving the service and those receiving it. The second phase would be to reorganize and revamp the delivery system—and of course, that's the big item. It's the big thing we haven't done yet.

—Tommy Douglas

Source: Tommy Douglas, from the 1982 film *Folks Call Me Tommy*, as quoted in Saskatchewan Health (1992). *A Saskatchewan vision for health: A framework for change.* Regina: Saskatchewan Health.

GOVERNMENT IN CANADA

Canada has a bicameral system of government at the federal level. Bicameral refers to the two houses at the federal level: the House of Commons (Parliament) and the Senate, the "chamber of sober second thought." The House of Commons consists of the governing party seated on one side of the House, and the Opposition parties seated on the opposite side. The governing party as of this writing is the Liberal Party, led by Prime Minister Justin Trudeau, elected in the October 2015 election.

As of the October 2015 federal election, the Opposition parties include the Conservative Party, the New Democratic Party (NDP), the Green Party, and the Bloc Québécois. The Official Opposition is the Conservative Party.

Figure 1.1: The Institutions of Our Federal Government

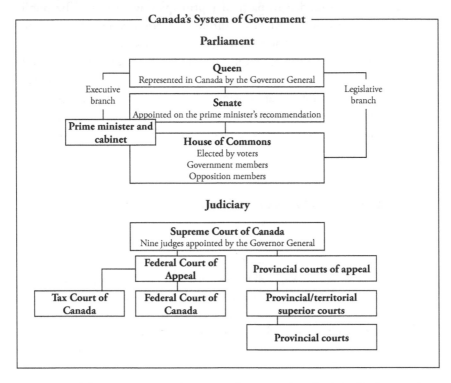

Source: Adapted from Forsey, E. (2009). *How Canadians govern themselves* (8th ed.). Ottawa: Library of Parliament, Canada.

After the 2015 federal election, the distribution of seats is:

- Liberal Party—184 seats
- Conservative Party—98 seats
- NDP—44 seats
- Bloc Québécois—10 seats
- Green Party—1 seat

THE ROLES OF FEDERAL AND PROVINCIAL GOVERNMENTS IN HEALTH CARE

Canadian federalism is a key institutional concept necessary for understanding the development of medicare. Federalism refers to the division of legislative authority between a central or national government and regional governments. In Canada, these regional governments are the provincial and territorial governments.

In Canada, the federal and provincial governments share responsibility for health care. Section 91 of the Canadian Constitution Act enumerates the powers of the federal government with emphasis on its spending power (Government of Canada, 1867/1982). Thus, the federal government pays some of the costs of provincial and territorial health care programs, sets some of the rules for health service provision by the provinces and territories, and provides health care services to some groups, such as Indigenous Canadians on reserves and members of the military (Brooks & Miljan, 2003).

Section 92, subsection 7, of the Constitution, specifies the powers of the provincial governments and, most notably, invests responsibility for the administration and delivery of health care in the provincial and territorial governments. The specific wording of Section 92, subsection 7, assigns provincial—and territorial—legislatures exclusive power to make laws concerning "The Establishment, Maintenance, and Management of Hospitals, Asylums, Charities and Eleemosynary Institutions in and for the Province, other than Marine Hospitals" (Government of Canada, 1867/1982). The wording reflects the state of health care in 1867, when governments played a minimal role in financing, regulating, and funding health care (Brooks & Miljan, 2003). Private organizations and charities built hospitals, which derived revenues from fees paid by patients for the services they received. Hospitals for those with mental illness received a small sum from the provincial governments. In addition, doctors billed patients directly for their services.

Public health issues, such as epidemics and sanitary conditions that adversely affected health, eventually led to the development of public health boards at the local or municipal level. The position of Minister of Health at the provincial level of government did not emerge until the 1880s. Provincial boards of health were also created at this time. At the federal level, the Dominion Department of Health was created in 1919. The much larger state presence in health care did not occur until the middle of the 20th century. In 1944, Health and Welfare Canada was created. It combined health and social services that can be seen as promoting public health. In 1993, then Prime Minister Kim Campbell created two separate departments: Health Canada and Human Resources and Labour Canada. The latter is now Employment and Social Development Canada. Health and social policies remain separate federal departments.

Together, sections 91 and 92 of the Constitution determine that federal influence upon health care occurs through its control of revenue transfers to the provinces. These transfers support provincial health care programs. In turn, the provincial health care plans must comply with the five principles of medicare articulated in the Canada Health Act of 1984.

Consistent with this analysis and the structure of the Canadian welfare state until approximately the 1990s, the federal government attempted to use its spending powers to enforce national standards for medicare and other social programs. These powers and their associated attempts to influence public policy have been a source of ongoing conflict between the federal and provincial and territorial governments. From the 1960s to the 1980s, the federal government played a significant role in financing health care services. The 1980s, however, saw the federal government reducing its health transfers—that is, financial resources, as well as other related transfers—to the provinces and territories while attempting to maintain control over health care. During the 2000s, federal, provincial, and territorial ministers of health met and signed health agreements in 2000, 2003, and 2004. These accords are examined in chapter 10. Of note is that the 2004 Health Accord, also designated the 10-Year Plan to Strengthen Health Care, expired March 31, 2014. There has been little discussion between the two levels of government to renegotiate this agreement. Advocacy organizations such as the Canadian Health Coalition and others are concerned about the future of medicare in the absence of a formal agreement between the federal government and the provincial and territorial governments. Chapter 10 explores these issues.

In short, federalism is key to understanding the nature of Canadian government and the organization of health care financing and delivery. As an institution, Canadian federalism can obstruct change, but can also lead to innovations such as the creation of medicare. These issues are also explored in chapter 10.

THEORIES OF PUBLIC POLICY

In order to understand the various dimensions of Canadian health policy, it is necessary to lay out various theoretical approaches that attempt to explain how health policy is made and implemented. As an introductory overview, most fall within one of two camps: consensus or conflict/critical approaches (Walt, 1994). Consensus approaches are concerned with how various groups compete to influence public policy, including health policy. These public policy theories assume that policy is made based on a rational consideration of various alternative courses of action, with choices based on a cost and benefit analysis and solid information on the various public policy options available to government to address an issue.

Consistent with this approach, many applied models of policy development and change are built on assumptions drawn from the physical and natural sciences and adapted to examining public policy issues. This was an attempt by early public policy theorists to make the world of policy analysis and politics more like science (Brunner, 1991; Albaek, 1995). The intention was to improve the quality of policy decisions by applying scientific principles of rationality and objectivity. In essence, Lasswell (1970), credited as the founder of the policy sciences, attempted to remove consideration of values and politics from public policy inquiry.

These consensus models tend to focus on technical issues such as the day-to-day organization, financing, and delivery of health care and analysis of the roles that various groups and professions play in delivering care and influencing policy development (Walt, 1994). They say little about the economic, political, and social forces that shape the overall organization and delivery of health care services and other public policies that shape health. Indeed, these models tend to neglect the raw politics that shape public policy decisions (Raphael, 2015).

Consensus models are important as there are always significant activities intended to provide minor improvements to existing services and other policies that shape health (Walt, 1994). But how useful are they for explaining broader issues of how health care is organized and delivered, and the factors that influence these issues? How useful are they for understanding whether there is adequate provision of income, housing, and food security, which are known to be the primary determinants of the health of the population? Can rational cost-benefit analyses explain how the broad strokes of health care and health-related public policy come about? Or, can they explain the impact of neoliberalism, the dominant political ideology, on public policy decisions and on income-related health inequalities?

In response to these concerns, some see consensus models as sorely neglecting the important role that political ideology, values, and power play in shaping complex issues such as public policy in general, and health policy in particular (Teeple, 2000). Political ideology is a system of ideas about how problems should be addressed. This includes issues such as whether government has a responsibility for social provision to the population, and whether such provision should be carried out by the public or private sector. Ideologies influence the issues on which governments decide to take action.

Values are beliefs that influence political ideology and come with a significant emotional investment to add to its ideas component. Since it is apparent that ideology and values play important roles in shaping policy, it makes sense that conflict should exist among various competing constituencies who are interested in shaping public policy.

Why would we expect that large for-profit health care corporations and working-class, financially insecure Canadians would share the same ideology and values with regard to the provision of health care? Why would we assume that both groups would support income redistribution to ensure health equity? And why would we assume that these two groups would have equal ability to influence the development of health policy? Conflict models consider the role that ideology and power and their different manifestations among differing groups play in shaping health policy.

Conflict models, therefore, usually consider broader macro issues in the organization and development of health care policy in particular, and health-related public policy in general (Armstrong, Armstrong, & Coburn, 2001). There is particular emphasis on the extent to which health policy debates are influenced by social class politics and inequalities in influence and power. Differences in power associated with gender, race, social class, disability, or sexual orientation, among others, have implications for not only the ability to influence policy development (Grabb, 2002, 2007), but also who will be affected—for better or worse—by public policy decisions.

Canadians with less power—working-class Canadians, women, populations with low income, and people of colour, among others—not only have less influence upon policy development, but are more likely to lack access to health care, as well as resources such as income and employment security that support health. These populations are also more likely to have poorer health and may require more health care. As one example, the organization of health care is especially important for populations with health conditions such as HIV/AIDS. Yet, these groups have less power and influence in society. How would these differences in power and influence affect their ability to influence health policy? And how do these differences influence their health outcomes?

Each model has its place in explaining the development and implementation of health policy, but it may be that some issues are best understood by drawing on one model rather than another. It is argued throughout this volume that health policy issues in particular are driven by strong ideological convictions—shaped by political, economic, and social forces—about how health should be maintained. Health policy—and other public policy decisions—is driven by raw politics and ideological beliefs about various health issues that should be addressed (Raphael, 2015).

INDIVIDUALISM IN HEALTH

Another key issue in understanding policy development is that of individualism as an explanatory discourse on health. Individualism is the belief that the focus of attention with regard to health care and health policy should be on the individual rather than on environments and societal institutions or structures (Hofrichter, 2003). With respect to health care, it provides a narrow lens focused on treatments and remedies. It may also focus on individual screening for biomedical indicators and identifying individual risk factors such as poor diet, lack of exercise, and alcohol and tobacco consumption (Nettleton, 1997). Within this approach, concern with broader aspects of the health care system and the political, economic, and social forces that shape health care services and delivery and other health-related public policies tend to be neglected.

Similarly, with regard to health-related public policies concerned with health maintenance or promotion, the focus is again on individual characteristics and individual behaviours (Hofrichter, 2003). Attention is given to public policies that may influence biomedical indicators or risk factors such as cholesterol, glucose levels, or weight. Policy actions that shape the incidence of risk behaviours such as poor diet, lack of activity, or tobacco and alcohol use also tend to dominate attention. Health policy comes to be narrowly conceived as a means of changing such behaviours. The end result of individualist approaches is a narrow health care focus on individual treatment plans and remedies and ways of shaping individual health-related behaviours. This focus allows for little consideration of broader contextual factors that influence these behaviours.

Individualism can lead to victim-blaming, whereby poor health outcomes are attributed to individual "lifestyle choices" rather than the environments and societal institutions that are known to have primary influence upon health outcomes (Hofrichter, 2003). In Box 1.4, Hofrichter succinctly states the problem with such an approach for both health care policy in particular and health policy broadly.

Consistent with Hofrichter's analysis, individualist approaches to health dominate policy activity in Canada. Broad questions about health policy give way to the management of health systems and concerns with wait times. Rather than considering the provision of a program to provide prescription drugs to all citizens as a matter of entitlement, the focus is on whether to provide one drug or another to patients undergoing chemotherapy for cancer, or heart patients undergoing life-prolonging surgeries.

Box 1.4: Individualism in Health

With exceptions, few decision makers examine the relationship of inequalities in health status to racism or social, political, and economic inequality. None suggest the need for major political and economic transformations to eliminate health inequities. Many analysts and policymakers instead focus on symptoms and treatments, microanalysis of individual risk factors, and changing people's behavior and lifestyles, not conditions or places. They present options primarily through a biomedical model and remedial solutions, mostly associated with health care, rarely stressing social transformation.

Individualism, a powerful philosophy and practice in North America, limits the public space for social movement activism. By transforming public issues into private matters of lifestyle, self-empowerment, and assertiveness, individualism precludes organized efforts to spur social change. It fits perfectly with a declining welfare state and also influences responses to health inequities. From this perspective, each person is self-interested and possessed of a fixed, competitive human nature. Everyone has choice and the potential for upward mobility through hard work—ignoring how we develop through the process of living in society (Tesh, 1988). Individualism presumes that individuals exist in parallel with society instead of being formed by society.

Source: Hofrichter, R. (2003). The politics of health inequities: Contested terrain. In R. Hofrichter (Ed.), *Health and social justice: Politics, ideology, and inequity in the distribution of disease* (pp. 25, 28). San Francisco: Jossey Bass.

In the health-related policy arena, governments at all levels promulgate messages that promote individual responsibility for reducing the risk of developing chronic diseases, such as heart disease and diabetes, through proper diet and exercise. There is less attention to health-related public policy issues such as income, housing, and food security and how these issues increase the risk of developing these chronic diseases (Raphael, Anstice, & Raine, 2003; Raphael & Farrell, 2002). Some argue that governments foster these approaches to justify less government involvement in the provision of social and health services (Raphael, 2008).

Narrow views of health policy also neglect the conflicts and politics endemic to policy discussion. This volume therefore emphasizes that health policy is not exclusively about health care and its provision to the larger population. Rather, it is also about politics, values, and conflict among groups in society and arguments about what contributes to health and well-being. Consistent with Rudolph Virchow's (1848) famous dictum "Medicine is social science and politics is nothing else but medicine on a larger scale," full attention is provided to these issues throughout this volume.

EMERGING ISSUES IN HEALTH CARE POLICY IN CANADA

As noted, Canadian federalism has shaped the organization and delivery of health care in Canada. It also shapes the distribution of responsibilities for health care between the two levels of government. It helps explain the continuing debates between the two levels of government in the health care policy arena. Much has been written about Canadian federalism and its implications for health care. These key issues characterize health care and health-related policy and must be considered in any analysis of health policy.

For example, the vertical fiscal imbalance is considered to lie at the heart of the current debate on the future of health care in Canada and has been a source of ongoing difficulties in intergovernmental relations for many years (St-Hilaire & Lazar, 2003, p. 60). The imbalance refers to the division of powers for health care and the different revenue-generating capacities of each level of government. In other words, the federal government has the revenue capacity (i.e., the ability to raise money through tax collection), and the provinces and territories have the responsibility to respond to health care needs. The Constitution has thus created a situation in which the taxing powers of the two levels of government do not always match their responsibilities for service provision to the population.

The greater revenue-generating—and funding—power of the federal government has enabled it to exert control over the provinces and territories by dictating in part how they should deliver health care services. In short, at the heart of vertical fiscal imbalance is the capacity of each level of government to generate its own revenues to finance its own expenditures (St-Hilaire & Lazar, 2003). Some observers see advantages to this arrangement. For example, having more taxation occurring at the federal level of government promotes tax harmonization and reduces economic inequalities among provinces and territories.

However, the downside is continuing intergovernmental wrangling over the financing of health care and increasing concern about the future of medicare. Such toxic intergovernmental relations and the resultant perception that governments are unable to respond to pressing public policy needs may prompt calls to remove health care from the realm of government responsibility and privatize health care financing and delivery. Some would argue that we have a parallel private health care system in the form of private clinics that cater primarily to the health needs of high-income groups. As will be discussed in later chapters, the federal government has contributed to this situation by reducing its health transfers to the provincial and territorial governments.

THE CHANGING ROLE OF GOVERNMENT IN HEALTH CARE

Recent funding changes have altered the role of the state in health care and health-related policy. During the 1980s and 1990s, federal spending declined, and the provinces and territories had to pick up the slack (Bryant, 2015; Teeple, 2000). While this trend began to reverse with greater federal contributions, there has been growing interest in creating a third level of governmental responsibility in health care by devolving responsibility for health care and other health-related matters to municipal governments. All provinces and territories have devolved some health care services to regional bodies (Church & Barker, 1998).

Regionalization is an organizational arrangement that sees the development of more locally based administrative and governance structures (Church & Barker, 1998). This structure is authorized to perform functions or exercise authority that was previously the responsibility of provincial or local governments, such as cities. For example, regionalization could involve the transfer of responsibility for public health activities such as sanitation and prenatal care from local health boards to a regional agency. At the same time, it could devolve health care authority from a central governing agency, such as a provincial government, to these same regional bodies.

Regionalization activity stems from a belief within governments that a regional health care system runs more effectively and can be more responsive to local health needs (Church & Barker, 1998). Church and Barker suggest that advocates of regionalization believe that regionalized health care systems are better able to respond to many of the problems currently associated with health care. They do so by promoting better service coordination and realizing economies of scale. Greater equity in service delivery of health care expenditures may occur.

On the downside, the organization and management of regionalization may fail to involve citizens in health care decision making, and can reduce accountability to citizens and the larger community even more than may have been the case previously (Church & Barker, 1998; Sutcliffe, Deber, & Pasut, 1997). This transfer of power to these regional authorities is an important trend in health care in Canada. What are the implications of these kinds of transfers of power for access to health care and the quality of health care provision?

HEALTH CARE REFORM

Most Canadians agree that medicare can be improved. Several commissions on health care reform have garnered much attention. The predominant reports on health care reform were *A Framework for Reform*, prepared by former federal Minister of Finance Don Mazankowski for the Alberta government, Senator Michael Kirby's *The Health of Canadians: The Federal Role*, and former Saskatchewan Premier Roy Romanow's *Building on Values: The Future of Medicare*, prepared for the federal Liberal government of Prime Minister Jean Chrétien (Mazankowski, 2001; Kirby, 2002; Romanow, 2002). Mazankowski favours user fees and an expanded role for the private sector's involvement in health care delivery. Mazankowski considers health care to represent a "rich commercial opportunity" (Grieshaber-Otto & Sinclair, 2004).

Romanow, in contrast, calls for the renewal of medicare around the key principles of public financing and not-for-profit delivery. He rejects an increased role for the private sector in health care itself. Yet, he is open to an expanded private sector role in the delivery of ancillary health services such as food services, cleaning services, maintenance services, and other services that are critical to the health care system (Armstrong et al., 2003; Grieshaber-Otto & Sinclair, 2004).

One outcome of all of these activities and commissions has been the federal, provincial, and territorial governments agreeing to focus their efforts on reducing wait times for various medical procedures and devising a health care guarantee (Government of Canada, 2007). Indeed, such a guarantee was recommended by the Mazankowski and Kirby reports (Mazankowski, 2001; Kirby, 2002; Grieshaber-Otto & Sinclair, 2004). This guarantee and its implications suggest another important theme informing Canadian health policy: that of public versus private financing and delivery of health care.

HEALTH CARE REFORM AND THE PUBLIC VERSUS PRIVATE HEALTH CARE DEBATE

As noted, the 1980s and 1990s saw—ostensibly to assure the sustainability of medicare—Canadian governments reducing the role of the state in health care by reducing their financial commitments to the provinces and territories. This reduction has been associated with increasing private sector involvement in the financing and delivery of health services. Indeed, Canada now has one of the largest proportions of such private sector involvement in health care among developed nations (Organisation for Economic Co-operation and Development, 2013). Its current public spending on health is just 11.2 percent of GDP, ranking as the fifth-highest health spender among OECD member countries. Canada's health spending growth slowed by 0.8 percent between 2009 and 2011.

Interacting with these cutbacks, the outlining of a move toward health care treatment guarantees has influenced debate regarding public versus private financing and delivery of services. These health care guarantees involve establishing a maximum wait time for each type of major procedure or treatment. When the maximum time has been reached, the insurer (government) would be required to pay for the patient to receive the procedure in another jurisdiction.

It has been suggested that this arrangement could lead to more locally managed and delivered private for-profit care if the publicly financed and managed systems become unable to meet these guarantees and the private sector becomes mandated to step in (Rachlis, 2005). Privatization can assume many different forms, such as establishing public-private partnerships (P3s) to build a new hospital, allowing private specialized clinics to provide cataract surgery or hip replacements, or allowing private insurance schemes to support a new tier of health services, thereby substituting for the publicly managed system.

Supporters of private health care argue that it is more efficient and has shorter wait times for care. However, studies show that the quality of private care is poorer and has been associated with worse outcomes, in some cases even higher mortality rates (Woolhandler, Campbell, & Himmelstein, 2003). Part of this may be related to lack of sufficient staff to provide quality care in for-profit health care settings.

In reality, claims that allowing a parallel private health care system would relieve wait times in the public system are not accurate. Only people of wealth who can afford to pay will jump the queue by seeking private care, while others who cannot afford private care will remain in the public system (Rachlis, 2004). But since these private clinics will draw physicians from the public system by

Box 1.5: The Chaouli Decision and Private Health Care in Canada

The decision by the Supreme Court that struck down a Quebec ban on private health insurance has fuelled calls for a parallel private system (Rachlis, 2005). Many medicare supporters view this decision as a nail in the coffin of medicare. If banning private health insurance to protect the public health care system is seen as violating the Charter of Rights and Freedoms, how can medicare be preserved and protected? What are the key costs and benefits associated with public versus private health care? Is increasing privatization going to create more problems than currently exist?

Source: Rachlis, M. (2005). *Public solutions to health care wait lists.* Ottawa: Canadian Centre for Policy Alternatives.

enticing them with higher salaries and other incentives, waiting lists would increase, not decline. These issues are taken up in later chapters of this book.

There is much evidence to support the view that the public health care system could be improved in some ways. Many of the problems with the system can be attributed to under-resourcing by governments (Armstrong & Armstrong, 2003). However, there is also a need for an emphasis within the public system on preventative care consistent with the vision of Tommy Douglas, the father of medicare. Provincial and territorial governments can explore, as some already have, different models focused on primary care reform. In addition, use of the broader definition in this book of health policy as including other health-related public policies would assure consideration of these broader issues and their implications for the future of the health care system.

POLIS VERSUS THE MARKET

One way to consider how issues such as economic globalization and increasing privatization of health care can be understood is presented by Deborah Stone's dimension of the polis versus the market in public policymaking. This dimension runs through many themes discussed in this chapter. The distinction also lies at the heart of many debates in the Canadian health policy field.

In *The Policy Paradox*, Deborah Stone defines two models of political society: the polis and the market (Stone, 1988, 2012). *Polis* is the Greek word for city-state and the term that Stone applies to a model of political society whose primary objective is to act in the interests or welfare of the collective. The focus of the polis is community well-being, rather than the individual. Political activities are organized around providing for the common good. Such activities may create conflicts among various sectors and groups, but communal, rather than individual, interest is always seen as paramount (see Table 1.2).

In contrast, the market is defined as a social system in which individuals engage in various activities, usually economic, to enhance their welfare (Stone, 2012). They do so by exchanging goods and services with the expectation that such trades will be beneficial to both sides. It works as follows. Participants in the market compete with each other for scarce resources. Each individual attempts to obtain goods and services at the lowest possible cost and to transform raw materials into more valuable items to be sold at the highest possible price.

In the market model, then, individuals engage in activities for the sole purpose of maximizing self-interest, defined in whatever ways they wish for themselves. In this context, self-interest can also include acting to protect the welfare of family and friends. Stone (2012) argues, however, that the market as a social system can profoundly distort political life by neglecting the role that ideology, politics, and values may play in shaping the organization of society. It also fails to consider the inequities that emerge in this type of society.

Stone notes the launch of what she terms "the rationality project," which is dominated by the market as the model of society (Stone, 1988, 2012). She sees the fields of political science, public administration, law, and policy analysis adopting a common mission to save public policy "from the irrationalities and indignities of politics" (1988, p. 9) in order to imbue public policy with rational, analytical, and scientific methods.

In essence, the rationality project depoliticizes inherently political activities, such as policymaking, by removing values and conflict from consideration. Society is conceived as a "collection of autonomous, rational decision-makers who have no community life" (Stone, 1988, p. 9). As defined above, individuals maximize self-interest through rational calculation of the options before them, whether they are buying a car, a house, or health care.

The polis and the market signify two different models of society. While they are polar opposites, they are useful for understanding and explaining the tensions in the health policy field. These tensions are explored in chapter 7.

There is evidence that the increasing emphasis on the market has shaped policymaking in Canada. The restructuring of the global economy has

Table 1.2: Concepts of Society

	Market Model	Polis Model
1. Unit of analysis	Individual	Community
2. Motivations	Self-interest	Public interest (as well as self-interest)
3. Chief conflict	Self-interest vs. self-interest	Self-interest vs. public interest (common problems)
4. Source of people's ideas and preferences	Self-generation within the individual	Influences from outside
5. Nature of collective activity	Competition	Co-operation and competition
6. Criteria for individual decision making	Maximizing self-interest, minimizing cost	Loyalty (to people, places, organizations, products), maximize self-interest, promote public interest
7. Building blocks of social action	Individuals	Groups and organizations
8. Nature of information	Accurate, complete, fully available	Ambiguous, interpretive, incomplete, strategically manipulated
9. How things work	Laws of matter (e.g., material resources are finite and diminish with use)	Laws of passion (e.g., human resources are renewable and expand with use)
10. Sources of change	Material exchange, quest to maximize	Ideas, persuasion, alliances, pursuit of power, pursuit of the public interest

Source: Stone, D. (2012). *Policy paradox: The art of political decision making* (3rd ed.) (p. 35). New York: W.W. Norton & Company.

contributed to growing insecurity for citizens. The rise of neoliberalism—the belief that the marketplace should be the arbiter of the creation and distribution of various resources—has driven this and other public policy developments in recent years (Coburn, 2001). At a broad governmental level, powerful interests have urged governments to consider health services as an area for investment and trade opportunities. What does this mean for the development of health care policy and the survival of the health care system in Canada? The distorting nature of public policymaking under such a market view is considered in later chapters.

> ## Box 1.6: Neoliberalism, Public Policy, and Population Health
>
> Neoliberalism has also influenced health policy as more broadly conceived. One aspect of neoliberalism is a withdrawal of the state from involvement in the delivery of health services. It has also led to significant reduction in government support of important social determinants of health, such as income, housing, and food security, among others. To what extent has the resurgence of neoliberal ideology associated with governmental withdrawal of resources affected the health status of Canadians? What are the implications of neoliberal ideology for developing and implementing health care policies and health-related public policies that maintain health?

While all of these health care issues are critical in the study of health policy, they are not the only health-related policy issues that need to be considered. Governments also set health-related policies that have differing impacts on the health of different populations. These include issues that affect the incidence of poverty and social exclusion.

Indeed, it is increasingly evident that the way a society organizes the production and distribution of economic and social resources within it fundamentally shapes health outcomes (Marmot & Wilkinson, 2006; Raphael, 2008). These processes can lead to social and economic marginalization, which has been associated with adverse health outcomes. Interestingly, the economic, political, and social forces that affect health care policy are frequently the same forces that influence health policy as broadly conceived here. It is the intention of this book to define and explain how these forces influence health care policy, health-related policy, and the health of a population as a whole.

HEALTH POLICY AND PUBLIC POLICY

Health policy is often considered separately from public policy theory, and this has limited understanding of how health policy is made and how it can be changed.

By linking health policy to the broader public policy literature, it becomes possible to articulate the influences and differential impacts on health policy by different societal groups. Such an analysis illustrates how health policy reflects the ideological commitments—and action in support of such commitments—of governments and various interests, sectors, and society (see Box 1.7).

Box 1.7: Medicare Needs a Culture Change, Not More Money
By André Picard
The Globe and Mail

"Canada is a country of perpetual pilot projects," Monique Bégin famously wrote in the *Canadian Medical Association Journal*. The former minister of health and welfare pithily described a long-standing, frustrating problem in our medicare system: We have solved every single problem in our health-care system 10 times over, but we seem incapable of scaling up the solutions.

This inability to learn, to share and embrace innovation across jurisdictions, is explored thoughtfully in the new report of the Advisory Panel on Healthcare Innovation. The panel, led by David Naylor, a physician and former president of the University of Toronto, stressed that "Canada has no shortage of innovative healthcare thinkers, worldclass health researchers, capable executives, or dynamic entrepreneurs who see opportunity in the health sphere."

But innovation is stifled by the structure and administration of the health system, and a dearth of leadership. Medicare—the name we give our publicly funded health insurance scheme—is, in fact, not a system at all; it's a collection of 14 federal, provincial and territorial programs that are neither integrated nor coordinated. Worse yet, within those programs, there is a near total absence of vision and goals.

The role of our health bureaucrats is to hold the line on spending as best they can and, above all, ensure that the names of their political masters don't appear in damaging headlines. Improving patient care is rarely the No. 1 priority. The way our system is funded—predominantly with block transfers to hospitals and fee-for-service payments to physicians—encourages volume of procedures and the status quo. It does not reward quality of care, or responsible stewardship. In fact, when an individual or a program goes out on a limb and makes changes to improve efficiency or cost-effectiveness, the benefits often accrue to others; perverse disincentives are commonplace and counterproductive.

These problems and frustrations are not new. The Naylor report cites an example from 1974, when Canadian researchers published a landmark paper showing that nurse practitioners could do 70 per cent of doctors' work with no difference in outcomes or patient satisfaction. Using NPs also saved money, but hiring more nurse practitioners was hampered by the fact that, generally speaking, doctors are paid on a fee-for-service basis and nurses are salaried. Four decades later, that same bureaucratic hurdle remains. Most other Western countries acted on the research: NPs are an integral part of health-care delivery and most physicians are salaried. But in Canada, NPs are still grossly underused—except in pilot projects, of course.

We still negotiate physician and nurse contracts separately and our management of health-care human resources is a mess. Until you get workers with the right skills in the right place at the right time, you will never deliver seamless, patient-centered care and you will never control costs, because labour accounts for two-thirds of all spending. As the NP story and countless not-acted-upon research findings since illustrate, innovation is hampered by policy gridlock. The managers of the system, who are largely powerless and beholden to the whims of politicians, are with few exceptions profoundly mistrusting of entrepreneurship and pathologically risk-averse.

For decades, we have produced reports about the need to transform health-care delivery and funding while, simultaneously, clinging to the same old way of doing things. It's a fundamental disconnect between evidence and action. If you don't take risks, you will never innovate. So how do we break the logjam?

According to the Naylor report, it has to begin with leadership, and it should come from Ottawa. One of the panel's central recommendations is the creation of an independent health innovation agency to not just fund pilot projects, but promote scaling-up, using searchable repositories of successful programs, financial incentives, regulatory change, all with the aim of spurring innovation. More resources alone will not ensure the scaling-up of good ideas. There needs to be partnership, commitment and monitoring to ensure implementation. In short, it's not more money the system needs, it's culture change—a shift from perpetual pilot projects to embracing best practices.

Source: Picard, A. (2015, July 28). Medicare needs a culture change, not more money. *The Globe and Mail.* Retrieved from www.theglobeandmail.com

CONCLUSIONS

Health policy is frequently narrowly conceived as being concerned with health care, but should be conceived more broadly. Health policy is a vehicle for governments to respond to health care needs, and provides means for supporting a population's health through the development and implementation of health-related public policies. An important issue is the extent to which these activities are best carried out by the public sector or turned over to the private sector as a source of investment and profit.

Understanding of health policy can be advanced by placing it within the broader domain of public policy. Various models for considering public policy are available, and these can be designated as consisting of consensus and conflict models. Conflict models consider the role that political ideology, values, and power play in shaping the development and implementation of health policy in particular and public policy in general. These frameworks help to make sense of some of the emerging issues in health policy in Canada: funding and financing, organization and delivery of services, and emphasis upon public versus private organization and delivery of health care. These models also illuminate how public policy in the service of maintaining health is created.

CRITICAL THINKING QUESTIONS

1. What does the term *health policy* mean to you? What has informed your understanding of health policy?
2. How does the media report health policy issues? What issues do they highlight? What is missing from these reports?
3. In your other courses, how is health policy defined? What issues have been highlighted?
4. How has what you have read in this chapter about health policy and health care in Canada been consistent or inconsistent with your understandings prior to reading this chapter?
5. If you consider recent federal and provincial election campaigns, how have health issues been presented? Which political party or parties have discussed health policy in broad terms?

FURTHER READINGS

Brunner, R. (1991). The policy movement as a policy problem. *Policy Sciences*, *24*(1), 65–98.
    The author examines the problem of applying a technical definition to complex policy problems. While it is not focused on health policy specifically, it is an interesting assessment of the focus on the rational model and its weaknesses as an analytic tool.

Clavier, C., & de Leeuw, E. (Eds.). (2013). *Health promotion and the policy process*. Oxford: Oxford University Press.
    This contributed volume addresses a gap in the health promotion literature, which has tended to focus on health behaviours and health education. The contributions are concerned with the functioning of the public policy development process and public policies. The contributors present and apply diverse theories on the public policy process in political science and political sociology to explicate health promotion strategies and aims.

Forsey, E.A. (2012). *How Canadians govern themselves* (8th ed.). Ottawa: Library of Parliament. Available online at www.parl.gc.ca.
    This publication is a primer on government in Canada. It is an excellent resource for those who are unfamiliar with the structure of government and the powers of the federal and provincial governments. Eugene Forsey was a constitutional expert in Canada. The Library of Parliament updates his publication and makes it available online.

Hofrichter, R. (Ed.). (2003). *Health and social justice: Politics, ideology, and inequity in the distribution of disease*. San Francisco: Jossey Bass.
    This volume brings together the recent literature on key aspects of health policy, particularly inequalities in health. Each essay examines particular aspects of health inequalities and shows how inequalities are rooted in public policy.

Pal, L.A. (2006). *Beyond policy analysis: Public issue management in turbulent times*. Toronto: Nelson.
    This book is a useful guide to public policy analysis. It defines key concepts and explains the stages of policy formulation, design, implementation, and evaluation. The author factors in the changing political and social environment while focusing on the analytic tools of policy analysis and the conceptual dimension of public policy.

Stone, D. (2012). *Policy paradox: The art of political decision making* (3rd ed.). New York: W.W. Norton & Company.

This timeless text examines the paradox of the polis versus the market. Stone discusses the origins of the current focus on the market and how it depoliticizes politics. Although this is an analysis of American politics, the trends identified pertain to Canadian politics and health policy.

Walt, G. (1994). *Health policy: An introduction to process and power*. London: Zed Books.

This volume is a good basic text on health policy. It is concerned with health policy as process and power. Examples are drawn from health policy in the United Kingdom and Europe.

RELEVANT WEBSITES

Centre for Health Services and Policy Research
chspr.ubc.ca

The Centre for Health Services and Policy Research is based at the University of British Columbia. This website provides useful information and reports on health care and health policy.

European Commission: Public Health
ec.europa.eu/health/index_en.htm

The European Commission addresses a full scope of health policy, including living conditions and health care. The website identifies health policy priorities for the European Union and links to health policy resources.

European Commission Gateway to Health Information and Data
ec.europa.eu/health/programme/portal/index_en.htm

The European Union developed this website as a trustworthy gateway to a broad range of information and data on health-related issues and activities at the European, national, and international levels. The European Commission, the member states of the EU and the European Economic Area (EEA), and EU candidate countries, among others, contributed the content.

Government of Sweden Ministry of Health and Social Affairs
www.government.se/sb/d/2061

This is the website of the Ministry of Health and Social Affairs of the government of Sweden, a world leader in the social determinants of health and exemplar in developing healthy public policy. This website outlines its priorities in public health and provides access to several resources that discuss Swedish health policy.

International Health Impact Assessment Consortium
www.liv.ac.uk/psychology-health-and-society/research/impact/

Based in the Division of Public Health, a WHO Collaborating Centre for Public Policy Research on the Social Determinants of Health at the University of Liverpool in the United Kingdom, this excellent website provides a wide range of information and resources on the impact of policies and programs on the health of a population. It provides access to articles, research, and case studies on health policy issues.

REFERENCES

Albaek, E. (1995). Between knowledge and power: Utilization of social science in public policy-making. *Policy Sciences, 28*(1), 79–100.

Armstrong, H., & Armstrong, P. (2003). *Wasting away: The undermining of Canadian health care.* Toronto: Oxford University Press.

Armstrong, P., Armstrong, H., & Coburn, D. (Eds.). (2001). *Unhealthy times: The political economy of health and care in Canada.* Toronto: Oxford University Press.

Armstrong, P., Boscoe, M., Clow, B., Grant, K., Pederson, A., & Willson, K. (2003). *Reading Romanow.* Ottawa: Canadian Women's Health Network.

Brooks, S., & Miljan, L. (2003). *Public policy in Canada: An introduction.* Toronto: Oxford University Press.

Brunner, R.D. (1991). The policy movement as a policy problem. *Policy Sciences, 24*(1), 65–98.

Bryant, T. (2015). Implications of public policy change models for addressing income-related health inequalities. Special Issue on public policy and health inequalities. *Canadian Public Policy, 39*(4), S10–S16.

Bryant, T., & Raphael, D. (2010). The real epidemic is inequality. *Social Alternatives, 29*(2), 3–7.

Bryant, T., Raphael, D., Schrecker, T., & Labonte, R. (2011). Canada: A land of missed opportunity for addressing the social determinants of health. *Health Policy, 101*(1), 44–58.

Canadian Institute for Health Information & Statistics Canada. (2002). *Health care in Canada 2002.* Retrieved from secure.cihi.ca.

Canadian Population Health Initiative. (2004). *Improving the health of Canadians.* Ottawa: Canadian Population Health Initiative.

Church, J., & Barker, P. (1998). Regionalization of health services in Canada: A critical perspective. *International Journal of Health Services, 28*(3), 467–486.

Coburn, D. (2001). Health, health care, and neo-liberalism. In P. Armstrong, H. Armstrong, & D. Coburn (Eds.), *Unhealthy times: The political economy of health and care in Canada* (pp. 45–65). Toronto: Oxford University Press.

Einhorn, E.S., & Logue, J. (2003). *Modern welfare states: Scandinavian politics and policy in the global age.* Westport, CT: Praeger.

European Policy Health Impact Assessment Project. (2004). *European policy health impact assessment: A guide.* Geneva: European Policy Health Impact Assessment Project.

Government of Canada. (1867/1982). Canadian Constitution. Retrieved from laws.justice.gc.ca.

Government of Canada. (2007). Canada's new government announces patient wait times guarantees. Retrieved from pm.gc.ca.

Grabb, E. (2002). *Theories of social inequality.* Toronto: Harcourt Canada.

Grabb, E. (2007). *Theories of social inequality* (5th ed.). Toronto: Thomson Nelson.

Grieshaber-Otto, J., & Sinclair, S. (2004). *Bad medicine: Trade treaties, privatization, and health care reform in Canada.* Ottawa: Canadian Centre for Policy Alternatives.

Hall, M.A., & Lord, R. (2014). Obamacare: What the Affordable Care Act means for patients and physicians. *British Medical Journal, 349,* g5376.

Hofrichter, R. (2003). The politics of health inequities: Contested terrain. In R. Hofrichter (Ed.), *Health and social justice: Politics, ideology, and inequity in the distribution of disease* (pp. 1–56). San Francisco: Jossey Bass.

Kirby, M.J. (2002). *The health of Canadians: The federal role.* Ottawa: Standing Senate Committee on Social Affairs, Science, and Technology.

Lasswell, H. (1970). The emerging conception of the policy sciences. *Policy Sciences, 1*(1), 3–14.

Mackenbach, J., & Bakker, M. (Eds.). (2002). *Reducing inequalities in health: A European perspective.* London: Routledge.

Mackenbach, J., & Bakker, M. (2003). Tackling socioeconomic inequalities in health: Analysis of European experiences. *Lancet, 362,* 1409–1414.

Marmot, M., & Wilkinson, R. (2006). *Social determinants of health* (2nd ed.). Oxford: Oxford University Press.

Mazankowski, D. (2001). *A framework for reform: Report of the Premier's Advisory Council on Health.* Edmonton: Government of Alberta.

Navarro, V. (1994). *The politics of health policy: The US reforms 1980–1994.* Cambridge: Blackwell Publishers.

Nettleton, S. (1997). Surveillance, health promotion, and the formation of a risk identity. In M. Sidell, L. Jones, J. Katz, & A. Peberdy (Eds.), *Debates and dilemmas in promoting health* (pp. 314–324). London: Open University Press.

Organisation for Economic Co-operation and Development. (2013). *Health at a glance 2013: OECD indicators.* Paris: Organisation for Economic Co-operation and Development.

Pal, L. (2006). *Beyond policy analysis: Public issue management in turbulent times.* Toronto: Nelson.

Rachlis, M. (2004). *Prescription for excellence: How innovation is saving Canada's health care system.* Toronto: HarperCollins.

Rachlis, M. (2005). *Public solutions to health care wait lists.* Ottawa: Canadian Centre for Policy Alternatives.

Raphael, D. (Ed.). (2008). *Social determinants of health: Canadian perspectives* (2nd ed.). Toronto: Canadian Scholars' Press.

Raphael, D. (2015). Beyond policy analysis: The raw politics behind opposition to healthy public policy. *Health Promotion International, 30*(2), 380–396.

Raphael, D., Anstice, S., & Raine, K. (2003). The social determinants of the incidence and management of type 2 diabetes mellitus: Are we prepared to rethink our questions and redirect our research activities? *Leadership in Health Services, 16,* 10–20.

Raphael, D., & Farrell, E.S. (2002). Beyond medicine and lifestyle: Addressing the societal determinants of cardiovascular disease in North America. *Leadership in Health Services*, *15*, 1–5.

Romanow, R.J. (2002). *Building on values: The future of health care in Canada.* Saskatoon: Commission on the Future of Health Care in Canada.

St-Hilaire, F., & Lazar, H. (2003). He said, she said: The debate on vertical fiscal imbalance and federal health-care funding. *Policy Options* (February), 60–67.

Stone, D. (1988). *Policy paradox and political reason.* Glenview, IL: Scott, Foresman.

Stone, D. (2012). *Policy paradox: The art of political decision making* (3rd ed.). New York: W.W. Norton & Company.

Sutcliffe, P., Deber, R., & Pasut, G. (1997). Public health in Canada: A comparative study of six provinces. *Canadian Journal of Public Health*, *88*(4), 246–249.

Teeple, G. (2000). *Globalization and the decline of social reform: Into the twenty-first century.* Aurora, ON: Garamond Press.

Teeple, G. (2006). Foreword. In D. Raphael, T. Bryant, & M. Rioux (Eds.), *Staying alive: Critical perspectives on health, illness, and health care* (pp. 1–4). Toronto: Canadian Scholars' Press.

Teeple, G. (2010). Foreword. In T. Bryant, D. Raphael, & M. Rioux (Eds.), *Staying alive: Critical perspectives on health, illness, and health care* (2nd ed.) (pp. 1–4). Toronto: Canadian Scholars' Press.

Tesh, S.N. (1988). *Hidden arguments: Political ideology and disease prevention policy.* New Brunswick, NJ: Rutgers University Press.

Virchow, R. (1848). Der armenarzt. *Medicinische Reform*, *18*, 125–127.

Walt, G. (1994). *Health policy: An introduction to process and power.* London: Zed Books.

Woolhandler, S., Campbell, T., & Himmelstein, D.U. (2003). Costs of health care administration in the United States and Canada. *New England Journal of Medicine*, *349*(8), 768–775.

Yalnizyan, A. (2006). *Controlling costs: Canada's single-payer system is costly—but least expensive.* Ottawa: Canadian Centre for Policy Alternatives.

Chapter 2

WAYS OF KNOWING: HEALTH POLICY AND HEALTH STUDIES

INTRODUCTION: THE SCOPE OF HEALTH STUDIES AND HEALTH POLICY

The scope of health studies and health policy has traditionally been narrowly focused on clinical health care interventions provided by health care professions such as medicine, nursing, physiotherapy, and occupational therapy. In the early to mid-20th century, health studies focused on treatments carried out by physicians and other health professionals and their effects on the health of individuals. Consistent with this biomedical focus, the emphasis was on the organization and delivery of clinical health care services. Much of these health study activities examined what occurs in hospital settings.

But there is also a tradition of studying health and health care issues in the social sciences that has existed alongside that of the health sciences (Teeple, 2000, 2006). In the mid-19th century, Chadwick, Virchow, and Engels began to link the health of populations to living and working conditions. Sociology of health, illness, and medicine grew out of this tradition, and this is now a standard undergraduate course offered in most sociology programs across Canada. In this approach, social scientists have applied broader social science concepts to elucidate the organization and delivery of medical services, as well as the social—or non-medical—determinants of health and their impact on health. This broader scope has also been concerned with understanding the determinants of health that exist outside of the clinical or hospital setting.

Social scientists have identified critical questions about health concerned with understanding and explicating how economic, political, and social forces influence the organization of the health care system as well as the health of the population (Bryant, Raphael, & Rioux, 2010; Raphael & Bryant, 2015). They have also linked structures such as public policies and political and social institutions with political ideology to explain the organization of health care and health outcomes. They attempt to make explicit that which is implicit and perhaps masked in public policies, such as attitudes or biases that may include racism, sexism, homophobia, and so on. An important focus of this literature is how societal institutions perpetuate political, economic, and social inequalities in power and influence (Grabb, 2002).

As a result of these social science influences, the study of health is no longer limited to strict experimental studies of how one or more factors predict the incidence of a disease or its treatment and outcome. The scope of health studies now includes the determinants of health, the perceptions of health held by individuals, and identifying public policy approaches by which health can be improved and maintained.

As one such example of social science analysis, Figure 2.1 identifies the societal structures that underlie social inequalities (Grabb, 2002). Grabb states: "Social inequality can refer to any of the differences between people (or the socially defined positions they occupy) that are consequential for the lives they lead, more particularly, for the right or opportunities they exercise and the rewards or privileges they enjoy" (p. 2). The model suggests that the components making up the economic structure of a society, consisting of the market (i.e., the systems of production, finance, and exchange), the political structure of the state (i.e., governments and the civil service), and associated ideological structures (comprising religious beliefs, the mass media, educational systems, and others), play important roles in shaping the distribution of resources within a society.

These structures are of such importance in the organization and operation of society that it would also be expected that these societal structures would shape the organization of the health care system and related public policy domains that influence health—in other words, health policy. This indeed appears to be the case. The analysis of how these societal structures—the market and other economic forces, governments, and ideological concepts— influence health policy is a primary goal of this book.

REDEFINING HEALTH

Since the 1970s, growing evidence has supported the belief that health—and its maintenance—is more complex than can be discerned from only examining physical health and treating disease (World Health Organization, 1986). Moreover, the evidence suggests that health can best be understood as a multidimensional concept influenced by a range of factors that fall outside the traditional sphere of

Figure 2.1: The Major Means of Power, Structures of Domination, and Bases for Social Inequality

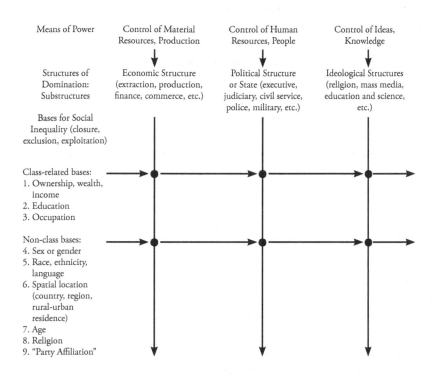

Source: Grabb, E. (2002). *Theories of social inequality* (p. 224). Toronto: Harcourt Canada.

clinical health care (Epp, 1986; Evans, Barer, & Marmor, 1994; Lalonde, 1974). The social sciences contributed to this concept of health as multidimensional and have offered critical insights into the organization and delivery of health care services and the factors that promote health (Teeple, 2006, 2010).

The proliferation of undergraduate and graduate health studies programs at Canadian universities in recent years is testament to the growing interest in health, and in studying health from diverse perspectives. Some of these programs attempt to link traditional health science studies with social science theory in order to raise critical questions about the impact of societal institutions and forces that shape public policies, and thereby influence the health of populations.

The social science disciplines, particularly sociology and political science, have contributed the most compelling insights to the discipline of health studies

(Armstrong, Armstrong, & Coburn, 2001). They have done so by identifying and investigating critical questions about the different meanings of health and the influence of public policy upon the organization and delivery of health care services, and on the other factors that affect health.

In particular, the political economy perspective has been concerned with identifying the economic, political, and social structures (that is, the societal institutions and forces) that influence health (Coburn, 2010). These analyses take two forms. The first focuses on the organization of the health care system. What role do the economic system, the state, and societal ideologies play in shaping the form of the health care system? There are a number of political economy perspectives. To the questions about power and political ideology asked by mainstream political economy, other political economy perspectives add questions concerning the impact of gender, race, and disability, among other attributes, on opportunities for health and health outcomes.

Second, how does the organization of society in general influence the non–health care/non-medical determinants of the health of populations? A political economy analysis of health is very helpful in answering this question. It can capture the political dynamics that shape and interact with economic and social conditions to produce social advantage for some and disadvantage for others. These social determinants include living conditions such as income, housing availability and quality, access to education, nutritious food, and health care, and the influence of gender, among others (Raphael, 2008).

A political economy perspective therefore directs attention to a broad and diverse range of health issues that include how the production and distribution of economic, political, and social resources shape the health care system, as well as the broader determinants of health. These analyses can also help explain how individuals make certain assumptions about their society and their own health, and their expectations of what health care services and health-supporting public policies should be in place (Coburn, 2010).

WAYS OF THINKING ABOUT HEALTH

Both the traditional health sciences and the social sciences have developed various ways of thinking about health. These paradigms range from identifying individual biomedical and behavioural risk factors for specific health conditions, such as the idea that smoking leads to lung cancer, to broader paradigms that emphasize how social environments and public policies shape health (Black & Smith, 1992; Labonte, 1993). More specifically, ways of thinking about health

Figure 2.2: Social Determinants of Health

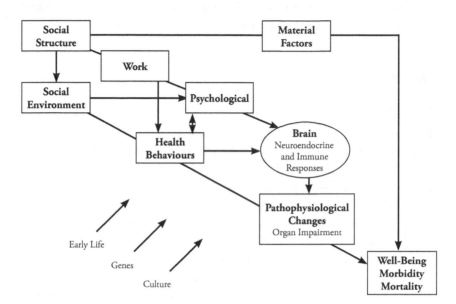

Source: Brunner, E., & Marmot, M.G. (2006). Social organization, stress, and health. In M.G. Marmot & R.G. Wilkinson (Eds.), *Social determinants of health* (p. 9). Oxford: Oxford University Press.

range from traditional concerns about clinical health care to an emphasis on the economic, political, and social forces that shape the organization and delivery of health care services and related public policies that determine the health of a population (Raphael, 2008).

Understanding these different conceptions of health is important because these ideas can strongly influence how health care services are organized and delivered. They can also influence how health-related public policy is defined and implemented.

Four major paradigms for understanding health are available, and these have influenced Canadian health policy to varying degrees. They are the medical, behavioural/lifestyle, socio-environmental, and structural/critical paradigms. Labonte defined the first three, and Raphael defined the structural/ critical paradigm (Labonte, 1993; Raphael, 2007). Each paradigm leads to different definitions of health problems, different strategies for improving health, different target groups, and the delegation of responsibility to different people within society. In some models, health professionals are responsible for maintaining health, while in others, responsibility falls to individual citizens. In still others, the primary responsibility falls to citizens who become organized into political and social movements to advocate on health issues.

The Medical Paradigm

The medical paradigm is the traditional biomedical paradigm that defines health as the absence of disease and disability (Labonte, 1993). The primary health issues are defined in terms of disease categories and physiological risk factors, such as a statistical deviation from the population average. Disease categories are professionally defined and include cardiovascular disease, diabetes, HIV/AIDS, obesity, arthritis, mental disorders, and hypertension, among others. Moreover, the medical paradigm considers disease as having an independent existence from the individual's social environment and ideas (H. Wilson, 2000). It also embodies a cause-and-effect reasoning, such that condition A does something to B, which results in effect C. This paradigm also focuses on the presence of risk factors for these same disease categories. For example, obesity becomes a concern for those working in this approach because it is hypothesized as increasing the risk of developing cardiovascular disease, high blood pressure, and diabetes, among other chronic diseases.

Defining health problems in terms of disease categories and risk factors highlights the need for professionally defined medical interventions to reduce individual risk and manage symptoms and disease. The medical paradigm is focused on physical symptoms and clinical outcomes. The interventions can be surgery, drugs, and other therapies that usually require a referral from a physician. They also include medically managed behavioural change through patient compliance with diet and exercise regimens, and ongoing patient education related to these factors.

The targets of such interventions are individuals identified as afflicted with a disease or those at higher risk for a disease. The general intervention approach is highly individualized. Physicians, nurses, and other allied health professionals are responsible for delivering these interventions to individuals one at a time. The monitoring of individuals and their biomedical indicators is an important part of this process.

The organization and delivery of health care services are clearly organized within the parameters of the medical paradigm. Emphasis is on the detection of disease and treatment by health care professionals. It is not surprising, given the vast expenditure on health care services, that governmental and public attention is focused upon these activities. Additionally, the medical paradigm is clearly the dominant manner by which the media, policy-makers, and the public think about the meaning of determinants of health and the means by which health can be promoted (Gasher et al., 2007; Hayes et al., 2007).

The Behavioural/Lifestyle Paradigm

The behavioural or lifestyle paradigm also provides an individualized concept of health (Labonte, 1993). Health is defined primarily in terms of individual energy, functional ability, and disease-preventing lifestyles. The primary health problems are seen as behavioural risk factors such as smoking, poor dietary habits, and lack of exercise. Drug or alcohol abuse, poor coping skills, and lack of life skills are also identified as important health problems in this paradigm.

The principal strategies or interventions for changing these risk behaviours are health education, social marketing, and advocacy for public policies that support and promote lifestyle changes. These activities can include smoking bans, prohibition on the use of trans fats in food products, and construction of bicycle paths to promote active lifestyles (Labonte, 1993). The targets for such interventions are groups of individuals deemed to be at high risk for health problems, usually children and youth.

Those responsible for delivering these interventions are employees of municipal and regional public health departments; chronic disease advocacy groups such as the Canadian Cancer Society and the Lung Association; and municipal, provincial, territorial, and federal governments. Ultimately, however, individuals are seen as responsible for maintaining their health by taking these risk-reduction measures.

All three levels of government in Canada engage in social marketing that promotes individual responsibility for maintaining health. For example, public health departments develop anti-smoking campaigns that target youth, particularly adolescent girls. These campaigns exhort adolescents not to smoke, and focus on strategies to resist peer pressure to smoke. Many health authorities engage in such lifestyle campaigns; an example of such a campaign is provided in the first part of Box 2.1.

Surveys indicate that the Canadian public clearly subscribes to many tenets of the behavioural/lifestyle paradigm. When asked what may be the best ways to promote health, the overwhelming tendency is to provide behavioural/lifestyle responses concerned with diet, exercise, and tobacco

Box 2.1: Different Approaches to 10 Tips for Better Health

#1: The Traditional 10 Tips for Better Health

1. Don't smoke. If you can, stop. If you can't, cut down.
2. Follow a balanced diet with plenty of fruit and vegetables.
3. Keep physically active.
4. Manage stress by, for example, talking things through and making time to relax.
5. If you drink alcohol, do so in moderation.
6. Cover up in the sun, and protect children from sunburn.
7. Practice safer sex.
8. Take up cancer-screening opportunities.
9. Be safe on the roads: follow the Highway Code.
10. Learn the First Aid ABCs: airways, breathing, circulation.

#2: The Social Determinants 10 Tips for Better Health

1. Don't be poor. If you can, stop. If you can't, try not to be poor for long.
2. Don't have poor parents.
3. Own a car.
4. Don't work in a stressful, low-paid manual job.
5. Don't live in damp, low-quality housing.
6. Be able to afford to go on a foreign holiday and sunbathe.
7. Practice not losing your job and don't become unemployed.
8. Take up all benefits you are entitled to, if you are unemployed, retired, or sick or disabled.
9. Don't live next to a busy major road or near a polluting factory.
10. Learn how to fill in the complex housing benefit/asylum application forms before you become homeless and destitute.

Sources: Donaldson, L. (2003). *Ten Tips for Better Health*. London: Stationary Office; Gordon, D., *Ten Tips for Better Health*, 1999 (message posted on the Spirit of 1848 Listserv).

use (Canadian Population Health Initiative, 2004). The experts respond with an emphasis on obesity. The current focus on obesity exemplifies an individualist approach to health. The focus on mapping the extent of obesity in a population (Gotay et al., 2013), for example, may detract from broader issues that influence health, such as income-related health inequalities.

Although the behavioural/lifestyle paradigm shares some similarities with the traditional medical paradigm, it emphasizes the prevention rather than the treatment of existing health conditions. Its advocates may argue that they are empowering people to take control of and improve their health. As noted above, they do so primarily within an individualist approach (Labonte, 1996, 1997). Individuals are considered responsible for adopting healthy behaviours to promote good health, thereby reducing their risk of disease. While there is some effort to provide environmental supports to "make the healthy choice, the easy choice" (Koelen & Lindström, 2005) (e.g., the imposition of sin taxes, changing food offerings in school cafeterias, and providing other incentives to "healthy living"), government interventions aim to improve individual behaviours by emphasizing personal responsibility for health.

The Socio-environmental Paradigm

The socio-environmental paradigm—also termed the materialist paradigm—is concerned with risk conditions such as poverty or low income rather than individual risk factors such as cholesterol or blood pressure (Labonte, 1993). Health is defined as a positive concept in terms of connectedness to family, friends, and one's community. It is concerned with people having control over their lives and having the ability to engage in activities that are important or have meaning for them. It directs attention to community and societal factors that support health. Health problems are defined in terms of psychosocial and socio-environmental risk factors such as poverty, residing in a district with high industrial pollution, isolation, stressful environments, and hazardous living and working conditions, among others. This approach can be seen as consistent with the second part of Box 2.1.

While attention is directed to the larger environments in which individuals live, some aspects of an individualized paradigm are present. The paradigm emphasizes building social supports for individuals to cope with problems in their lives. Joining organizations such as community centres or being with family and friends provide means for coping. The primary interventions promoted by this paradigm include small group development, community development, coalition building, political action and advocacy, and societal change (Labonte, 1993).

The target of these interventions is ultimately high-risk environments. The socio-environmental paradigm recognizes that the organization of communities and societies shapes health and the importance of developing political and economic policies in support of health. Key agents of change are considered to be citizens, social development and welfare organizations, political movements such as the environmental and social justice movements, and political parties. This paradigm, however, does not explicitly direct attention to the influence of larger economic, political, and social forces that shape the local environments that influence health.

The Structural/Critical Paradigm

The structural/critical paradigm—also termed neo-materialism—is distinguished by its explicit concern with the organization of society, and how it organizes and distributes social and economic resources within a population (Raphael, 2007). The structural/critical paradigm defines health in terms of an unequal distribution and control of economic and social power and resources within a society. The sources of this unequal distribution are attributed to the political ideology held by governing parties and an unequal distribution of political power (Armstrong, Armstrong, & Coburn, 2001; Coburn, 2006). An important focus of this approach is challenging the dominance of certain groups, such as the corporate sector.

There are two features of this paradigm that have relevance for understanding health policy. These features are the roles of political ideology and political power in shaping the organization and delivery of health care services in a society. How does political ideology and the unequal distribution of resources and power determine the form of health care? Who gets to control how these institutions operate?

The second focus of the critical/structural paradigm is on examining how a society organizes the production and distribution of social and economic resources (i.e., income, employment, housing, and education) that shape health (Armstrong, Armstrong, & Coburn, 2001). The paradigm most closely related to this paradigm is the political economy approach.

In this paradigm, there is a focus on the collective or whole society, not the individual, as the instrument for change. Particular attention is paid to the policy change process. Interventions or strategies for change involve mobilizing the population for political action to bring about desired public policy changes. Labour and other social movements (e.g., anti-poverty, feminist, labour, and cultural/racial) and social democratic political parties are seen as the catalysts for such mobilization and promoting public policies in support of health.

Implications for Health Policy

When one considers the decisions governments make about health, one has to consider which dominant paradigm of health is at play. One way to ascertain the dominant paradigm of a jurisdiction is to consider what attention governments give to various ways of promoting health. It should come as no surprise that in Canada, primary attention is given to the medical and behavioural/lifestyle paradigms. Why this is the case and the implications for understanding the scope of health policy constitutes much of the content of this book.

Ways of understanding the world are essential for understanding how knowledge exists in different forms, how these forms shape ways of thinking about health, and how knowledge can be used by those attempting to influence health research and the health policy process. How these actors perceive or understand knowledge also influences how they use it in their activities. Moreover, the dominant knowledge approach influences how policy-makers and elected representatives decide which forms of knowledge—or evidence— are appropriate areas for health policy activity.

Box 2.2: A Larger Focus: Ways of Understanding the World

Understanding world views and how they shape public policy development raises some important questions: How do certain assumptions influence governments' health policy? What processes lead to privileging certain types of understanding over others in the health policy change process? How does the research and policy development process in the health area reflect these differing approaches?

These considerations lead to the question: How do epistemological and political assumptions influence the creation and dissemination of knowledge to influence governments' health policies? What processes lead to privileging certain types of knowledge over others in the health policy change process? How does the research and policy development process in the health area reflect these differing epistemological approaches?

Perspectives on what constitutes knowledge about the world are also known as world views or paradigms. A knowledge paradigm can be defined as a set of basic beliefs or assumptions about knowledge and how it is created (Guba & Lincoln, 1994). More importantly, a paradigm sets parameters on what can be known. A paradigm consists of three components: ontology, epistemology, and methodology.

Ontology: Ontology refers to the form in which reality and its objects are said to exist. There are widely different views of what constitutes the nature of the world, and this is particularly the case when issues such as health and health policy are considered. Ontology defines what can be known (Guba, 1990). For example, the ontology of the medical paradigm described above is that reality consists of biomedical and physiological indicators of cell, organ, and body systems functioning. Patterns of bodily functioning are driven by natural laws and mechanisms. In the health sciences, this view is clearly dominant and reflects the understandings held by most health care professionals. The notion of reality—what health is and how to promote it—held by the other health paradigms (behavioural/lifestyle, socio-environmental, and structural/critical) are very different.

Epistemology: Epistemology refers to how the inquirer—that is, the one (doctor, nurse, or social scientist) who wishes to understand the world—creates knowledge about health or other phenomena through research and experience. What are the appropriate research approaches that can be used to learn about the world or health? Should one use the methodology of objective observation and experimentation developed in the natural sciences? Or, should knowledge be gained though understanding the personal experiences of individuals who are most affected by health issues? Perhaps knowledge can be gained by understanding the societal structures that shape the distribution of economic, political, and social resources among the population. What role do values play in shaping our inquiries and determining what is worthy of attention? Epistemology, therefore, represents a key aspect of the knowledge creation process, since it shapes how knowledge is believed to be acquired and understood.

Methodology: Methodology is about the tool kit employed to acquire knowledge. The tool kit can contain experimental methodologies that focus on observation of the world, interactive approaches that examine the lived experiences of people, or critical analyses that consider the ways in which social institutions shape the distribution of resources.

All of these ways of understanding the world—through ontology, epistemology, and methodology—will shape our health care and profoundly affect health-related public policy action and public policy efforts to improve and maintain health.

It is important to identify the epistemological assumptions of these various theories and what they have to say about health and health care. Since these theories reflect a view of how the world, including health care and health-related public policy, should be, it is essential to explicitly consider their underpinnings and implications (Burrell & Morgan, 1979).

SOCIAL THEORY UNDERLYING THE APPROACHES TO HEALTH

Social theory can support the various approaches to health. The following sections will examine three social theories that are particularly insightful. Each offers a different perspective, some with individualist orientations to health, or micro-analysis, and some socially based, or macro-analysis. The three main theories are:

- Positivism (as well as structural functionalism)
- Interpretivism (with a short discussion of symbolic interactionism)
- Critical social science (including political economy)

Positivism/Rationalism

Positivism is a philosophy that states that the only authentic knowledge is scientific knowledge, and that such knowledge can come only from positive affirmation of theories through strict adherence to the scientific method. It begins with immediate and concrete shifts to general laws or axioms (Davoudi, 2012). The cornerstone of positivism is hypothesis-testing and identifying relationships, especially causal relationships. Traditional positivism holds that both natural phenomena and human behaviour can best be explained through universal laws. In physics, for example, Newton's laws of motion explain the action of inanimate objects such as planets or falling apples (Brunner, 1991). The positivist approach emphasizes rational and linear concepts to explain the world with a focus on the observable and concrete.

The aim of positivist science is to predict and control conditions (Park, 1993; Guba, 1990). Knowledge is conceived as "bottom-up experience" (a posteriori) (Davoudi, 2012, p. 3). The physical and biological sciences and much of the health sciences are organized within this approach. There is an emphasis on the criteria of reliability, validity, and objectivity. The goal of inquiry is to search for truth, logic, generalizability, originality, and relevance (Albaek, 1995).

Box 2.3: The Beliefs of Positivism

The essential beliefs of positivism as applied to knowledge and inquiry are: (1) there is an external world that exists independent of human interpretation; and (2) objective knowledge about the world can be acquired through direct sensory experience. Usually these experiences are identified and interpreted within the framework of the experimental scientific method (Fishman, 1991). Phenomena that cannot be observed directly through either experience or observation are excluded from this definition of credible knowledge.

Positivism has been the dominant paradigm in social sciences and public policy studies, and this has especially been the case in health policy–related studies. It informs quantitative research. Positivism, applied to public policy analysis, depends on empirical testing of quantitative predictions that are logically inferred from hypotheses. It involves a quest for universal truths through the identification of patterns, trends, and conditions (Burawoy, 2011). Thus, knowledge creation involves developing a set of general principles that can explain and predict events. Why shouldn't these scientific methods, argue positivists, be applied to understanding health and health care, and the public policy processes that shape their form?

One reason they should not is that positivism holds that science is neutral and denies the influence of values—and politics—on inquiry (Wilson, 1983b). It also neglects the study of power and fails to consider how inequalities in power shape the definition of what constitutes credible knowledge and the means by which such knowledge can be obtained and applied. Positivism, to state it bluntly, implicitly accepts the status quo (Woodill, 1992). In this way, it is thought to reinforce economic, political, and social inequalities. Interpretations of the link between knowledge, health, and health policy have traditionally been informed by the positivist knowledge paradigm (Wilson, 1983b). The positivist paradigm grew out of the physical and natural sciences. This makes examining economic, political, and social forces and how they influence knowledge development and application somewhat difficult (Albaek, 1995; Gagnon, 1990).

Linear assumptions about reality—and the assumption of a single reality as the only truth—may blind the analyst to the many complex factors that shape social phenomena (Feilzer, 2010; Mills, 1959). In addition, the paradigm usually does not consider the importance of power relations in shaping social reality and policy development. In the health policy field, it limits the focus and understanding to biomedical and physiological indicators and behavioural risk factors. The focus is usually at the individual level. These understandings fit in with individualist interpretations. Positivism depoliticizes issues with its value-free claims.

Linking back to the earlier discussion, the medical and behavioural/ lifestyle paradigms discussed earlier, which emphasize individual risk factors and regimens that shape individual behaviours, are informed primarily by the positivist approach. These approaches prefer to understand disease and its treatment and prevention in terms of individual risk factors (Labonte, 1993). They seek to discover predictable, usually narrow, cause-and-effect relationships. The concern with measuring and quantifying individual risk factors and specifying the impact of medical interventions on medical conditions reflect many assumptions of the positivist paradigm. These approaches further minimize and detract from efforts to address broader determinants of health and health inequalities.

Attractiveness of Positivism for the Health Sciences and Health Policy Sectors

Despite the limitations of the positivist approach, researchers, health science professionals, and many health policy analysts value the research carried out in the positivist tradition because it emphasizes relationships between observable biomedical and behavioural risk factors and health outcomes. Positivist research made significant discoveries and continues to be important in identifying causes and treatments for a range of serious acute and chronic medical conditions.

But this is a distinctively depoliticized approach, as it emphasizes objectivity. It is also expert-driven, as exemplified by top-down authoritative research paradigms. In the health sciences, it is assumed that health can be maintained through medical interventions and by individuals following the recommendations of physicians, public health educators, and others who are deemed to be "experts" on appropriate medical and lifestyle regimens. Similarly, health policy activities focus on the capacity to quantify or measure impacts of various medical interventions.

Box 2.4: Positivism and Policy Analysis

The introduction of positivism into the policymaking process was an attempt to make it more like traditional science. In the positivist-rationalist policy paradigm, politics is perceived as incongruent and competing with rational action (Albaek, 1995; Gagnon, 1990; Jones & McBeth, 2010). Whereas science can be seen as driven by devotion to objective and open inquiry, reason, and truth, politics is concerned with power and interests, and therefore does not adhere to the claims of scientific rationality and objective inquiry. Thus, the methods and process of science are considered by some as essential to making public policy analysis and development a purely rational process.

Limitations of Positivism

Positivism tends to examine phenomena separately from the context in which they naturally exist or occur, a process that can be described as "context-stripping" (Lincoln & Guba, 1985). Indeed, the primary weaknesses of positivism stem from its linear assumptions about social reality and its need to remove all context that shapes the phenomenon being investigated (Bryant, 2001; Burawoy, 2011; Feilzer, 2010). Research is primarily about determining the form these fixed and constant processes take. Few studies consider the impact of the broader economic, political, and social context on the phenomenon chosen to be of interest. This is evident in the clinical health sciences and the lifestyle-related behavioural approach to disease prevention. Positivism supports and reinforces the individualism embedded in the biomedical and behavioural paradigms. There is little consideration of the implications for health in general and health inequalities in particular.

Another important aspect of positivism is the emphasis on a restrictive understanding of evidence as referring to experimental evidence, and also deductive quantitative research design to obtain this evidence (Bambra, 2009; Phoenix et al., 2013). This has restricted what can be said about what works, for example, to reduce health inequalities or improve the health of a population. It shifts the focus to *downstream* factors, such as pharmaceutical, medical, or other individual-level interventions, rather than structural or societal factors that lead to these inequalities in health outcomes.

Policy-makers also tend to be oriented to a positivist approach to knowledge. They tend not to examine people's lived experiences or the root causes of social inequality and can be dismissive of knowledge derived from critical analyses of structural social relations. Policy analysts may emphasize their ability to observe impartially and develop theory about health policy issues while holding their values at bay (Rathbun, 2012). This means appraising relevant data and other evidence without prejudice. The traditional approach, therefore, may privilege some forms of knowledge above others, a process known as the legitimization of knowledge. At the same time, it delegitimizes other forms of knowledge, such as personal stories and lived experience, thereby shutting out some alternative perspectives from health policy debates. The more traditional positivist approach has also been criticized for excluding vulnerable populations, thereby exacerbating their social and economic marginalization.

Box 2.5: Poverty and Heart Disease

Poverty Is Main Predictor of Heart Disease, Says Canadian Report
By W. Kondro
The Lancet

Poverty is a greater predictor of heart disease than risk factors such as smoking, obesity, stress, or blood cholesterol concentrations, a Canadian sociologist says. In a review of more than 100 studies on the causes of heart disease, associate professor of health policy Dennis Raphael (York University, Toronto, Canada) suggests: "The economic and social conditions under which people live their lives, rather than medical treatments and lifestyle choices, are the major factors determining whether they develop cardiovascular disease." The report was published on May 3 by the Centre for Social Justice, a Toronto-based advocacy group. Lifestyle approaches to improvement of cardiovascular health, such as programmes to curb smoking or obesity, are counterproductive, Raphael said in an interview. They have the negative effect of pushing issues like income distribution, community services, and public transportation off the health-policy table. Poor people end up blaming themselves for their heart disease and "that's harmful because it diverts people from these main contributors to their heart disease, which [are] material deprivation, psychosocial stress, and the adoption of unhealthy behaviours (like using drugs) as a result of that stress."

Raphael's report, "Social Justice Is Good for Our Hearts," which is yet to be published in a peer-reviewed journal, suggests some 22% of life years lost before age 75 years (according to a Statistics Canada extrapolation) are because of income differences. "Were all Canadians' rates of death from cardiovascular disease equal to those living in the wealthiest quintile of neighbourhoods, there would be 6366 fewer deaths each year from cardiovascular disease," says Raphael.

The poor are at greater risk of developing heart disease because of "social exclusion," Raphael argues. "Individuals who suffer from material deprivation have greater exposures to negative events such as hunger and lack of quality food, poor quality of housing, inadequate clothing, and poor environmental conditions at home and work. In addition, individuals suffering from material deprivation also have less exposures to positive resources such as education, books, newspapers, and other stimulating resources, attendance at cultural events, opportunities for recreation and other leisure activities," he says.

Some of the political remedies Raphael advocates are: higher welfare and unemployment insurance outlays; improved pay equity; establishment of a national guaranteed minimum income; stronger antidiscrimination legislation; higher taxes on the wealthy, including an inheritance tax; a national housing strategy; and creation of national day care and pharmacare programmes. He also suggests "directing attention to the health needs of immigrants and paying attention to the unfavourable socioeconomic position of many groups and the particular difficulties many new Canadians face in accessing health and other care services."

The report "Social Justice is Good for Our Hearts" is available online at www.socialjustice.org/pdfs/JusticeGoodHearts.pdf.

Source: Kondro, W. (2002, May 11). Poverty is main predictor of heart disease, says Canadian report. *The Lancet*, p. 1679.

Positivist Policy Analysis and Alternative Frameworks

Public policy analysts have long debated the value of alternative analytic frameworks and paradigms for examining and improving public policy decisions. During the 1990s, a debate on positivism and post-positivism (i.e., narrative deconstruction) examined the merits of each approach (Jones & McBeth, 2010). Weimer (1998) identifies prediction as an asset of positivism and quantitative research. In contrast, Fischer (2003), a proponent of alternative approaches to policy analysis, considers qualitative research as critical because "facts" are social constructions. Weimer and Fischer recognize the value of the opposing paradigm, but the debate only considers the positivist versus interpretivist/constructivist dualism.

Post-positivism—sometimes termed *critical realism*—represents a rejection of a number of the key tenets of positivism, but they also share a number of features. Ontologically, both post-positivism and positivism consider reality that is external and can be studied (Phoenix et al., 2013). Epistemologically, knowledge is considered to be objective. Post-positivism, however, considers that human measurement and instruments are inherently faulty, and researchers cannot execute research outside of their own biases about social and health phenomena. This tenet highlights that no single method or perspective can capture the full essence of external reality. While post-positivism, like positivism, stresses empirical evidence to support hypotheses, objectivity is an ideal rather than an imperative of research. Multi- or mixed-method research design is a feature of post-positivist research.

Post-positivist and critical policy analysts criticize positivist policy analysis for being focused on the use of systematic methods, developing testable hypotheses, and relying on statistical analysis. Sabatier (1988), a proponent of positivist policy analysis, calls for rigorous criteria, including clearly defined concepts, verifiable hypotheses, and falsification. It is important to note that not all post-positivist research is critical, as it may not address issues of power and other structural issues. Critical theory is examined in more depth in a later section of this chapter.

Discussion has turned to the use of narrative analysis as a potential alternative to positivist policy analysis, if not a complementary method to positivist policy analysis (Feilzer, 2010; Jones & McBeth, 2010). Some seek to devise a theory-driven approach to narrative that satisfies Sabatier's criteria that such an approach is both empirical and falsifiable (Jones & McBeth, 2010).

STRUCTURAL FUNCTIONALISM

In practice, many inquiries that are grounded in structural-functionalist approaches tend to apply positivist notions of knowledge and methodology. Structural functionalism is a social theory developed by early sociologists after positivism (Babble & Benaquisto, 2010). Like positivism, it can also support the medical approach to health. This theory views society as an organism, a system of parts, all of which serve a function together for the overall effectiveness and efficiency of society. It views society as a system of checks and balances. Structural functionalism is, at its core, a consensus theory. It is therefore a theory that sees society as built upon order, interrelation, and balance among parts as a means to maintain the smooth functioning of the whole.

Structural functionalism views shared norms and values as the basis of society, focuses on social order based on tacit agreements between groups and organizations, and views social change as occurring in a slow and orderly fashion. Functionalists acknowledge that change is sometimes necessary to correct social dysfunctions (the opposite of functions), but that it must occur slowly so that people and institutions can adapt without rapid disorder.

To sum up, structural functionalism makes specific assumptions about society:

- Societies are held together by co-operation and orderliness.
- Societies work best when they function smoothly as organisms, with all parts working toward the "natural" or smooth working of the system.
- Allocation and integration are two fundamental processes necessary for a state of equilibrium within a system.
- Each part interrelates to create efficiency and harmony; the most capable individuals must be motivated to fill the most important roles/positions.
- Systems tend toward self-maintenance involving control of boundaries and relationships of parts to the whole, control of the environment, and control of tendencies to change the system from within.

Limitations of Structural Functionalism

When applied to health and health policy, structural functionalism would have limited use. It would view health issues as "fixable" through medical intervention, as each part of society would be successfully fulfilling a function. Effective change, in other words, is difficult to explain with this model.

INTERPRETIVISM

Interpretivism emerged from a critique of positivism (Bryman, Bell, & Teevan, 2012). As such, it offers an alternative to positivist social science. Interpretivism, or hermeneutics, is an approach that highlights how individuals understand themselves and others through shared systems of meaning (Wilson, 1983a). Interpretivism begins from the premise that people create meaning to make sense of their actions and the conditions in which they live and work. Meaning manifests itself through shared categories that help make sense of interpersonal relationships and social institutions (Park, 1993).

The intellectual partners in this paradigm include symbolic interactionism, ethnography, participant observation, and grounded theory, among others (Lincoln, 1994; Lincoln, Lynham, & Guba, 2011). This perspective clearly moves beyond many limitations of positivism, but may not explicitly address issues of unequal power relations created by societal institutions and economic, political, and social forces. One of the interesting aspects of this approach is that all views are considered equally valid. Individuals' understandings of how and why something occurs are accepted without critique. This may be a problem when there are clear issues of injustice and inequality that may not be perceived or understood by the individual being studied or the policy issue being considered. Thus, interpretive approaches can also lead to removing important contexts that help explain individual understandings and experiences.

The interpretive approach is typical of health studies that examine the experience of an individual with various health conditions. The focus is on describing and understanding the condition from the standpoint of the individual. Such studies provide important insights into the lived experiences of individuals and their interactions with the health care system. The results may help other individuals who have similar experiences and their families in providing support. Such studies also have their place in the body of knowledge on various medical conditions and their implications for coping and support. It is a fair conclusion, however, that these kinds of studies are clearly subordinate to positivist-oriented health sciences studies and rarely inform health policy decisions (Raphael et al., 2004).

Linking again to the earlier discussion, the socio-environmental approach to health presented earlier is related to interpretivism because it emphasizes the lived experiences of individuals. The socio-environmental approach also encourages the individual to engage in activities that enable him or her to find meaning in his or her life. Social context becomes important as community structures, such as community centres or organizations, help to promote a sense of connectedness. Clearly understanding individuals' lived experiences would be a valuable addition when carrying out health sciences and health policy studies that aim to maintain and promote health.

Symbolic Interactionism

As noted, symbolic interactionism dovetails with the interpretive approach. Symbolic interactionism is based on qualitative research, not quantitative figures and tables, and it is primarily concerned with individual experience and subjective analysis. Perception is everything. Meaning derives from social interaction. In other words, it is possible to understand a person's actions in relation to other (surrounding) people. Body language is a perfect example.

Limitations of Interpretive Approaches

The primary weakness of this way of knowing is its treatment of all perspectives as equally valid. It fails to take into account the impact of social relations. In particular, the approach does not consider social and other inequalities and how these shape the experiences and understandings of individuals concerning health issues and their experience of the health care system. Few of these kinds of analyses explicitly link the immediate experience of a health issue to the influence of larger systems on individual health outcomes and the experience of the health care system.

In addition, the interpretive approach fails to consider how differences in power and influence often define what may even come to be considered a health issue. Why do some health and health care issues arise at certain times while others do not? Who shapes the form that health care institutions take and the kinds of day-to-day aspects of life that individuals experience? Who decides what is a health issue and how it is ultimately defined?

CRITICAL THEORY

An alternative approach is critical theory. This perspective is concerned with the structures and processes that are usually hidden and ignored by positivists and idealists/interpretivists. Critical theory is social theory oriented toward critiquing and transforming society as a whole, in contrast to traditional theory, which is concerned primarily with understanding or explaining society as it is. Critical theory refers to a cluster of perspectives that challenge the bases of both the positivist/rationalist and interpretive/hermeneutics paradigms. These approaches inform the health sciences and health policy areas by locating actors (those involved in developing research and policy) within discourses (ways of talking about and understanding issues of concern) (Torgerson, 1996). Critical theory, also termed critical realism, differentiates between the world and people's actual experience of it, and also between the real, the actual, and the empirical (Sayers, 2000; see Box 2.6).

Box 2.6: Key Features of Critical Realism

Critical realism distinguishes not only between the world and our experience of it, but between the real, the actual and the empirical, defining these in a special way (Bhaskar, 1975). When critical realists refer to "the real" this is not in order to claim privileged knowledge of it but to note two things. First, the real is whatever exists, be it natural or social, regardless of whether it is an empirical object for us, and whether we happen to have an adequate understanding of its nature. Secondly, the real is the real of objects, their structures and powers. Whether they be physical, like minerals, or social, like bureaucracies, they have certain structures and causal powers, that is, capacities to behave in particular ways, and causal liabilities or passive powers, that is specific susceptibilities to certain kinds of change.

Sources: Sayers, A. (2000). *Realism and social science.* London: Sage Publications; Bhaskar, R. (1975). *A realist theory of science.* Leeds: Leeds Books.

Critical approaches include critical realism, critique and deconstruction, and political economy (Torgerson, 1996). These perspectives vary in the degree to which they examine the interplay between power and public policy development.

Unlike the other approaches, critical theory considers the "haves" and "have-nots" of society. It also considers power relationships and social inequality. It frequently focuses on the socio-economic context in which institutions are shaped and individuals' lives are lived (Torgerson, 1996). Critical theorists focus on the nature and distribution of power among social institutions such as the state, the economic system, and citizens in their ability to bring about social and political change.

Critical theory explicitly links forms of knowledge to the existence and application of various degrees of power as a central organizing concept (Fay, 1987). By dealing explicitly with issues of power and domination in the social context of society, critical theory provides some of these categories of understanding. The approach considers the constructions of reality made by differentially positioned actors as resulting from the form that their social relations take. In its concern with issues of power and domination, it frequently focuses on the social, economic, and political context in which institutions are shaped and individuals' lives are lived (Torgerson, 1996).

The means by which these social relations can be understood is through analyses of the distribution of resources and the lived experience of individuals. Interpretivist or hermeneutic analyses can describe some of these relations, but conventional hermeneutic categories of meaning may not expose important categories related to the distribution of power and resources that are themselves shaped by societal institutions and systems.

By dealing explicitly with issues of power and domination within the social context of society, critical theory provides some of these categories of understanding. In the form of critical theory presented in this volume, insights from political economy inform the concern with power and suggest that societal transformation may be necessary. The social order is characterized as having inherent political and social contradictions that reproduce themselves, thereby perpetuating social inequalities (Fay, 1987).

Political Economy Approach

Political economy falls under the umbrella of critical theory. It focuses on the broader social, political, and economic context to analyze how objective living conditions help inform a variety of health-related issues (Coburn, 2006, 2010). For example, political economy considers how political and economic structures shape the form the health care system takes. It also examines how the distribution of economic, political, and social resources shapes mortality and morbidity rates within a population. It carries out these analyses independent of the perceptions that citizens may have of these issues.

As will be discussed in chapter 3, there are different types of political economy, including feminist political economy, which is concerned with how gender interacts with public policy, political ideology, and other societal structures and how it shapes opportunities for women. It is beyond dispute that critical theory, in particular critical analytic frameworks such as political economy, has identified important questions about societies and how the organization of societies shapes the form of the health care system and the health of the population.

Limitations of Critical Theory

With their emphasis on power and domination, critical perspectives may neglect other important factors in their attempts to highlight inequalities in influence and power. It is important to highlight, however, that critical theory can have a social action agenda that aims to democratize policy analysis. Its proponents argue that it provides the best opportunity for collaborative policy analysis between professional policy analysts, such as those employed by professional think tanks and citizen activists (Fischer, 2000, 2003; Hawkesworth, 1988; Torgerson, 1996). It challenges the basic terms of conventional discussion and demands that authority and decision making be rooted in democratic principles. It also enables the combination of different forms of evidence for political advocacy.

Despite its limitations, the critical approach provides insights about power and domination in analyses of public policy and health issues, which provides a critical lens for framing and evaluating theories of public policy and policy change. This lens may be particularly relevant for analyzing knowledge issues and how they are deployed by particular groups to influence health policy in the provincial and federal policy arenas in Canada, and in the international political arena.

Table 2.1: Matching Approaches to Health with Research Paradigms

Approach to Health		Social Theory That Endorses the Approach
Medical Approach	→→→	Positivism
- individual-based or micro		- objective, rational
Behavioural/Lifestyle Approach	→→→	Positivism (structural functionalism)
- individual-based or micro		- objective, rational
Socio-environmental Approach	→→→	Interpretive
- both individual and environmentally based		- subjective
Structural/Critical Approach	→→→	Critical (and Political Economy)
- socially based, structural, macro		- both objective and subjective

APPLICATION OF THESE CONCEPTS TO THE SOCIAL DETERMINANTS OF HEALTH

As an example of how these concepts help explicate important health issues, consider the issue of the social determinants of health. An important development in understanding the sources of health has been the recognition that living conditions are the primary determinants of health in nations such as Canada (Marmot & Wilkinson, 2006: Raphael, 2008).

The social determinants of health field is primarily about describing and understanding how living conditions—as indicated by such factors as social class, income level, employment security, quality of working conditions, adequacy of housing, levels of education, access to nutritious food, and availability of health and social services, among others—shape health. Informing these analyses is a concern with how the organization, production, and distribution of social and economic resources influence health. As a result, various researchers and organizations have developed sets of social determinants that show marked similarities, as well as some differences.

Table 2.2 shows four of the dominant conceptualizations of the social determinants of health. The Ottawa Charter in 1986, for example, identified various "prerequisites for health" (World Health Organization, 1986). For the first time, health was conceptualized as a resource for living rather than simply the absence of disease. People were identified as change agents who had the power to act on their social environments to improve their conditions of living.

The Canadian Institute for Advanced Research (CIAR) drew up its own list of health determinants, some of which are social determinants of health, which Health Canada has largely adopted. While on the surface these determinants have similarities with the World Health Organization's "prerequisites of health," some argue that this list of health determinants represents a "re-medicalization of health promotion" (Labonte, 1996), as some of its terms, such as physical and social environments, derive from an epidemiological (that is, positivist) approach to health. In addition, there is frequently a refocusing on biomedical risk factors and a neglect of issues concerned with the organization of society and the unequal distribution of economic, political, and social resources (Raphael & Bryant, 2002).

The CIAR population health approach considers population-based health status indicators such as infant mortality, morbidity, and mortality rates. It also recognizes the importance of available resources and various social determinants of health, but it betrays a tendency to apply a concern with the concrete and observable, typical of positivist notions, at the cost of considering

Table 2.2: Various Conceptualizations of the Social Determinants of Health

Ottawa Charter[1]	Health Canada (CIAR)[2]	World Health Organization[3]	SDOH National Conference[4]
peace	income and social status	social gradient	Aboriginal status
shelter	social support networks	stress	early life
education	education	early life	education
food	employment and working conditions	social exclusion	employment and working conditions
income	physical environments	work	food security
stable ecosystem	social environments	unemployment	health care services
sustainable resources	healthy child development	social support	housing
social justice	health services	addictions	income and its distribution
equity	culture	food	social safety net
	gender	transport	social exclusion
			unemployment and employment security

1. World Health Organization. (1986). *Ottawa Charter for health promotion*. Retrieved from www.who.dk.
2. Health Canada. (1998). *Taking action on population health: A position paper for Health Promotion and Programs Branch staff*. Ottawa: Health Canada.
3. Wilkinson, R.G., & Marmot, M. (2003). *Social determinants of health: The solid facts*. Copenhagen: World Health Organization European Office.
4. Raphael, D. (2004). *Social determinants of health: Canadian perspectives*. Toronto: Canadian Scholars' Press.

broader societal issues concerned with the unequal distribution of resources and the political and economic systems.

The CIAR approach frequently employs statistical tables of traditional biomedical and epidemiological indicators. One such example is provided by Labonte (1997), in which a CIAR publication argues for promoting "slight shifts in the overall distribution of serum cholesterol" to influence CVD (cardiovascular disease) rate (Labonte, 1997). They say little, however, about the forces that shape these distributions and the reason for inequalities in health outcomes among different groups. Trevor Hancock discusses how the population health approach typified by the CIAR has dominated health discussion since the early 1990s. He attributes its dominance to its consistency with growing neoliberalism in advanced capitalist economies such as Canada and the United States, among others (Hancock, 2011). He notes that while population health clearly identifies the social determinants of health, it offers little on how to address them. It was therefore deemed more acceptable to governments determined to reduce public spending, and reluctant to address the social determinants. Focusing on social determinants would require addressing the underlying assumptions about the organization of society (Hancock, 2011). This is in stark contrast to health promotion, which challenged the existence of social and health inequalities and called for social, political, and economic change.

Social science research shows these indicators do not occur in a vacuum. They are influenced by the broader economic, political, and social contexts within which people live. These health indicators—and the living conditions that spawn them—are amenable to public policy action.

In this book, the opportunities provided by the political economy approach are taken to understand the forms that health policy takes in Canada. It is assumed that economic, political, and social forces shape the parameters within which health policy is defined and health policy action is taken. While each health and epistemological framework has an important role to play in this exercise, the organization and delivery of health care and health-related public policies can best be understood within a political economy framework.

CONCLUSIONS

This chapter has examined different approaches to understanding health and the means of influencing it. Differing paradigms represent differing world views concerning the nature of health and define the "appropriate" realms for health care policy action. These approaches are themselves informed by different ways of knowing. Such epistemological analyses make explicit their assumptions about knowledge and how it is created.

By focusing on biomedical and behavioural/lifestyle factors, most of these health paradigms fail to consider how the distribution of economic, political, and social resources shapes the form that health care services take and the health status of citizens. These paradigms also emphasize individual responsibility for health and fail to articulate how political power and public policy influence the health of a population. Arguably, the medical and lifestyle/behavioural approaches to health, by not making explicit the nature of societal structures and their influence, lead to an acceptance of society as it is.

In contrast, the socio-environmental and structural/critical approaches provide a basis for societal change. The political economy approach especially recognizes how unequal distributions of resources and power influence policymaking and calls for the redistribution of such power in the service of health. These analyses suggest that improved health policy—both in the form of health care services and in the social determinants of health—requires policy approaches that address inequalities and provide means for their remediation.

CRITICAL THINKING QUESTIONS

1. Which of the approaches to health is consistent with your own view of what health is and how it can be maintained? What approach do the media present in reports on health and health care issues?
2. What epistemological approach underlies Canadian health policy? What aspects of health do policy-makers emphasize?
3. How do the epistemology approaches of public policy-makers influence their receptivity to diverse approaches to health policy issues?
4. Which health approach provides an opportunity for marginalized populations to influence health policy?
5. How can shifts in health policy occur? Do we need a shift in health policy?

FURTHER READINGS

Brunner, E., & Marmot, M. (2006). Social organization, stress, and health. In M. Marmot & R.G. Wilkinson (Eds.), *Social determinants of health* (2nd ed.) (pp. 6–30). Oxford: Oxford University Press.

This chapter is one of a collection that examines different aspects of the social determinants of health. While there is an emphasis on quantitative studies, these all highlight the influence of social structures on health outcomes.

Bryant, T., Raphael, D., & Rioux, M. (Eds.). (2010). *Staying alive: Critical perspectives on health, illness, and health care* (2nd ed.). Toronto: Canadian Scholars' Press.

Staying Alive provides a fresh perspective on the issues regarding health, health care, and illness. In addition to the traditional approaches of health sciences and the sociology of health, this book shows the impact that human rights issues and political economy have on health.

Evans, R.G., & Stoddart, G. (1990). Producing health, consuming health care. *Social Science & Medicine, 31*(12), 1347–1363.

This article is an example of the population health approach of the Canadian Institute for Advanced Research (CIAR), an organization dedicated to research on population health. They present a framework to understand the evidence on population health and the various factors that influence health outcomes.

Hancock, T. (2011). Health promotion in Canada: 25 years of unfulfilled promise. *Health Promotion International, 26*(S2), ii263–ii267.

This article traces the history of health promotion in Canada and the influence/dominance of population health. Hancock documents how the emergence of population health was consistent with neoliberalism and the determinant of governments in Canada to reduce public expenditures and deficits.

Labonte, R. (1993). *Health promotion and empowerment: Practice frameworks.* Toronto: Centre for Health Promotion and ParticipAction.

This landmark report helpfully outlines and explains the dominant approaches to health. It provides a critical assessment of each of the approaches.

Poland, B., Coburn, D., Robertson, A., & Eakin, J. (1998). Wealth, equity, and health care: A critique of a population health perspective on the determinants of health. *Social Science & Medicine, 46*(7), 785–798.

The authors critique Evans and Stoddart's population health perspective. They provide a political economy analysis of key issues in Evans and Stoddart's "Producing Health, Consuming Health Care." This is a good example of a critical social science approach to health issues.

Shaw, M., Dorling, D., Gordon, D., & Smith, G.D. (1999). *The widening gap: Health inequalities and policy in Britain.* Bristol: The Policy Press.

This volume is an excellent examination of the growing gap between low- and high-income groups in the United Kingdom and other advanced Western economies. The important message from this volume is that disadvantage clusters among a range of determinants, such that some groups experience social and economic marginalization.

RELEVANT WEBSITES

Centre for Public Policy and Health, Durham University
www.dur.ac.uk/public.health
   Based in the United Kingdom, the Centre for Public Policy and Health conducts research on public health policy and management: evidence, decision making and policy implementation, inequalities in health, health effects of public policy, and work and unemployment.

Politics of Health Group
www.pohg.org.uk
   This Politics of Health website is based at the University of Liverpool in the United Kingdom. The Politics of Health Group consists of people who believe that power exercised through politics and its impact on public policy is of critical importance for health. The group is based in the UK, but has a clear international perspective and members throughout the world.

Politics of Health Knowledge Network
www.politicsofhealth.org
   The Politics of Health Knowledge Network is a forum for the exploration of the impact of political decisions on health. The network is concerned with how politics affect health on all levels, from individual organisms, to social groups, to the earth as a total ecological system.

Wellesley Institute
www.wellesleyinstitute.com
   The Wellesley Institute is a Toronto-based non-profit and non-partisan research and policy institute. The institute is the former Wellesley Hospital. Its focus is on developing research and community-based policy solutions to the problems of urban health, including poverty and inequalities in health.

REFERENCES

Albaek, E. (1995). Between knowledge and power: Utilization of social science in public policy-making. *Policy Sciences, 28*(1), 79–100.

Armstrong, P., Armstrong, H., & Coburn, D. (Eds.). (2001). *Unhealthy times: The political economy of health and care in Canada.* Toronto: Oxford University Press.

Babble, E., & Benaquisto, L. (2010). *Fundamentals of social research* (2nd Canadian ed.). Toronto: Nelson Education.

Bambra, C. (2009). Changing the world? Reflections on the interface between social science, epidemiology and public health. *Journal of Epidemiology and Community Health, 63*(11), 867–868.

Bhaskar, R. (1975). *A realist theory of science.* New York: Routledge.

Black, D., & Smith, C. (1992). The Black Report. In P. Townsend, N. Davidson, & M. Whitehead (Eds.), *Inequalities in health: The Black Report and the health divide.* New York: Penguin.

Brunner, R.D. (1991). The policy movement as a policy problem. *Policy Sciences, 24*(1), 65–98.

Bryant, T. (2001). *The social welfare policy change process: Civil society actors and the role of knowledge* (Unpublished PhD thesis). University of Toronto.

Bryant, T., Raphael, D., & Rioux, M. (Eds.). (2010). *Staying alive: Critical perspectives on health, illness, and health care* (2nd ed.). Toronto: Canadian Scholars' Press.

Bryman, A., Bell, E., & Teevan, J.J. (2012). *Social research methods* (3rd Canadian ed.). Don Mills: Oxford University Press.

Burawoy, M. (2011). The last positivist. *Contemporary Sociology, 40*(4), 396–404.

Burrell, G., & Morgan, G. (1979). *Sociological paradigms and organisational analysis: Elements of the sociology of corporate life.* Portsmouth, NH: Heineman Arena.

Canadian Population Health Initiative. (2004). *Select highlights on public views of the determinants of health.* Ottawa: CPHI.

Coburn, D. (2006). Health and health care: A political economy perspective. In D. Raphael, T. Bryant, & M. Rioux (Eds.), *Staying alive: Critical perspectives on health, illness, and health care* (pp. 59–84). Toronto: Canadian Scholars' Press.

Coburn, D. (2010). Health and health care: A political economy perspective. In T. Bryant, D. Raphael, & M. Rioux (Eds.), *Staying alive: Critical perspectives on health, illness, and health care* (2nd ed.) (pp. 65–91). Toronto: Canadian Scholars' Press.

Davoudi, S. (2012). The legacy of positivism and the emergence of interpretive tradition in spatial planning. *Regional Studies, 46*(4), 429–441.

Epp, J. (1986). *Achieving health for all: A framework for health promotion.* Ottawa: Health and Welfare Canada.

Evans, R.G., Barer, M.L., & Marmor, T.R. (Eds.). (1994). *Why are some people healthy and others not? The determinants of health of populations.* Hawthorne, NY: Aldine DeGruyter.

Fay, B. (1987). *Critical social science: Liberation and its limits.* Ithaca, NY: Cornell University Press.

Feilzer, M.Y. (2010). Doing mix methods research pragmatically: Implications for the rediscovery of pragmatism as a research paradigm. *Journal of Mixed Methods Research, 4*(1), 6–16.

Fischer, F. (2000). *Citizens, experts, and the environment: The politics of local knowledge.* Durham, NC: Duke University Press.

Fischer, F. (2003). *Reframing public policy: Discursive politics and deliberative practices*. New York: Oxford University Press.

Fishman, D.B. (1991). Epistemological paradigms in evaluation: Implications for practice. *Evaluation and Program Planning, 18*(1), 351–363.

Gagnon, A.-G. (1990). The influence of social scientists in public policy. In S. Brooks & A.-G. Gagnon (Eds.), *Social scientists, policy, and the state* (pp. 1–20). New York: Praeger.

Gasher, M., Hayes, M., Ross, I., Hackett, R., Gutstein, D., & Dunn, J. (2007). Spreading the news: Social determinants of health reportage in Canadian daily newspapers. *Canadian Journal of Communication, 32*(3), 557–574.

Gotay, C.C., Katzmarzyk, P.T., Janssen, I., Dawson, M.Y., Aminoltejari, K., & Bartley, N. (2013). Updating the Canadian obesity maps: An epidemic in progress. *Canadian Journal of Public Health, 104*(1), e64–e68.

Grabb, E. (2002). *Theories of social inequality*. Toronto: Harcourt Canada.

Grabb, E. (2007). *Theories of social inequality* (5th ed.). Toronto: Harcourt Canada.

Guba, E. (Ed.). (1990). *The paradigm dialog*. Newbury Park, CA: Sage.

Guba, E.G., & Lincoln, Y.S. (1994). Competing paradigms in qualitative research. In N.K. Denzin & Y.S. Lincoln (Eds.), *Handbook of qualitative research* (pp. 105–117). Thousand Oaks, CA: Sage Publications.

Hancock, T. (2011). Health promotion in Canada: 25 years of unfulfilled promise. *Health Promotion International, 26*(suppl. 2), ii263–ii267.

Hawkesworth, M.E. (1988). *Theoretical issues in policy analysis*. Albany: State University of New York.

Hayes, M., Ross, I., Gasher, M., Gutstein, D., Dunn, J., & Hackett, R. (2007). Telling stories: News media, health literacy, and public policy in Canada. *Social Science & Medicine, 54*, 445–457.

Jones, M.D., & McBeth, M.K. (2010). A narrative policy framework: Clear enough to be wrong? *Policy Studies Journal, 38*(2), 329–352.

Koelen, M.A., & Lindström, B. (2005). Making healthy choices easy choices: The role of empowerment. *European Journal of Clinical Nutrition, 59*(Suppl. 1), S10–S16.

Labonte, R. (1993). *Health promotion and empowerment: Practice frameworks*. Toronto: Centre for Health Promotion and ParticipAction.

Labonte, R. (1996). *The population health/health promotion debate in Canada: The politics of explanation, economics, and action*. Toronto: University of Toronto Press.

Labonte, R. (1997). The population health/health promotion debate in Canada: The politics of explanation, economics, and action. *Critical Public Health, 7*(1 & 2), 7–27.

Lalonde, M. (1974). *A new perspective on the health of Canadians: A working document*. Retrieved from www.hc-sc.gc.ca.

Lincoln, Y. (1994). Sympathetic connections between qualitative research methods and health research. *Qualitative Health Research, 2*, 375–391.

Lincoln, Y., & Guba, E. (1985). *Naturalist inquiry*. Newbury Park, CA: Sage.

Lincoln, Y.S., Lynham, S.A., & Guba, E.G. (2011). Paradigmatic controversies, contradictions, and emerging confluences, revisited. *The Sage handbook of qualitative research, 4*, 97–128.

Marmot, M., & Wilkinson, R. (2006). *Social determinants of health* (2nd ed.). Oxford: Oxford University Press.

Mills, C.W. (1959). *The sociological imagination*. New York: Oxford University Press.

Park, P. (1993). What is participatory research? A theoretical and methodological perspective. In P. Park, M. Brydon-Miller, B. Hall, & T. Jackson (Eds.), *Voices of change: Participatory research in the United States and Canada* (pp. 1–19). Toronto: Ontario Institute for Studies in Education Press.

Phoenix, C., Osborne, N.J., Redshaw, C., Moran, R., Stahl-Timmins, W., Depledge, M.H., & Wheeler, B.W. (2013). Paradigmatic approaches to studying environment and human health: (Forgotten) implications for interdisciplinary research. *Environmental Science & Policy, 25*, 218–228.

Raphael, D. (2007). Poverty and health. In D. Raphael (Ed.), *Poverty and policy in Canada: Implications for health and quality of life* (pp. 205–238). Toronto: Canadian Scholars' Press.

Raphael, D. (Ed.). (2008). *Social determinants of health: Canadian perspectives* (2nd ed.). Toronto: Canadian Scholars' Press.

Raphael, D. (Ed.). (2016). *Social determinants of health: Canadian perspectives* (3rd ed.). Toronto: Canadian Scholars' Press.

Raphael, D., & Bryant, T. (2002). The limitations of population health as a model for a new public health. *Health Promotion International, 17*, 189–199.

Raphael, D., & Bryant, T. (2015). Power, intersectionality and the life-course: Identifying the political and economic structures of welfare states that support or threaten health. *Social Theory & Health, 13*(3/4), 245–266.

Raphael, D., Macdonald, J., Labonte, R., Colman, R., Hayward, K. & Torgerson, R. (2004). Researching income and income distribution as a determinant of health in Canada: Gaps between theoretical knowledge, research practice, and policy implementation. *Health Policy, 72*, 217–232.

Rathbun, B. (2012). Politics and paradigm preferences: The implicit ideology of international relations scholars. *International Studies Quarterly, 56*(3), 607–622.

Sabatier, P. (1988). An advocacy coalition framework of policy change and the role of policy learning therein. *Political Sciences, 21*, 128–168.

Sayers, A. (2000). *Realism and social science.* London: Sage Publications.

Teeple, G. (2000). *Globalization and the decline of social reform: Into the twenty-first century.* Aurora, ON: Garamond Press.

Teeple, G. (2006). Foreword. In D. Raphael, T. Bryant, & M. Rioux (Eds.), *Staying alive: Critical perspectives on health, illness, and health care* (pp. 1–4). Toronto: Canadian Scholars' Press.

Teeple, G. (2010). Foreword. In T. Bryant, D. Raphael, & M. Rioux (Eds.), *Staying alive: Critical perspectives on health, illness, and health care* (pp. 1–4). Toronto: Canadian Scholars' Press.

Torgerson, D. (1996). Power and insight in policy discourse: Post-positivism and problem definition. In L. Dobuzinskis, M. Howlett, & D. Laycock (Eds.), *Policy studies in Canada: The state of the art* (pp. 226–298). Toronto: University of Toronto Press.

Weimer, D.L. (1998). Policy analysis and evidence: A craft perspective. *Policy Studies Journal, 26*(1), 114–128.

Wilson, H. (2000). The myth of objectivity: Is medicine moving toward a social constructivist medical paradigm? *Family Practice, 17*(2), 203–209.

Wilson, J. (1983a). Idealism. In J. Wilson (Ed.), *Social theory* (pp. 106–121). Englewood Cliffs, NJ: Prentice Hall.

Wilson, J. (1983b). Positivism. In J. Wilson (Ed.), *Social theory* (pp. 11–18). Englewood Cliffs, NJ: Prentice Hall.

Woodill, G. (1992). *Independent living and participation in research: A critical analysis.* Toronto: Centre for Independent Living in Toronto.

World Health Organization. (1986). *Ottawa charter for health promotion.* Retrieved from www.who.dk.

Chapter 3

THEORIES OF PUBLIC POLICY

INTRODUCTION: THE CONTRIBUTION OF PUBLIC POLICY THEORY TO UNDERSTANDING HEALTH POLICY

Health policy is a subset of public policy. As defined in chapter 1, public policy is a course of action chosen by government to address what has come to be identified as a public issue (Pal, 2006). The political science literature provides a wide range of theories of public policy. Understanding the assumptions of these theories and how they are hypothesized to influence the development and implementation of public policy is important for understanding a range of health policy issues.

A theory is a framework for understanding and explaining how a set of facts or phenomena comes to be. It consists of a set of statements or principles developed to explain these facts or phenomena (Walt, 1994). Public policy theories are devised to help explain the nature of decision making in the public policy process (Brooks & Miljan, 2003). A variety of such theories exist. Each theory emphasizes different features of the public policy process in an attempt to explain how governments make decisions and develop public policy. They can also help identify opportunities to influence the public policy process to bring about desired policy change.

These theories have different approaches to understanding the influence of power and how it is exercised in the public policy process (Brooks & Miljan, 2003). Not surprisingly, each theory has a particular set of values that inform their approaches. Each is also informed by a general model of society and how society is considered to function.

DEFINING THE CHARACTERISTICS OF DIFFERENT TYPES OF THEORIES

Theories of public policy may take a predominantly macro-, meso-, or micro-view of the public policy process. In addition, theories can be distinguished as being either consensus or conflict models of public policy, as noted in chapter 1 (Signal, 1998; Walt, 1994). Consensus theories tend to be concerned with the technical, day-to-day activities of public policy-makers and the various groups in civil society that are involved in a specific policy area. They do not consider the political, economic, and social forces that shape public policy decisions, nor do they consider that not all groups have equal influence on the public policy process.

In contrast, critical models consider the unequal distribution of social and economic resources and political power in a society. As their designation suggests, they critique government and public policy decisions. They are concerned with the unseen structures of society and how these can lead to inequality and poverty. They also consider the role of political ideology and the market in shaping public policy outcomes. The ultimate goal of such models is policy change and social and political transformation.

Macro-view theories consider broad issues of the general shape of political systems and how power is exercised in these political systems. In relation to health policy, it has been argued that health policy consists of two types of public policy. The first is concerned with the organization and delivery of health care services. The second is concerned with the development and implementation of various health-related public policies.

Regarding the first type, health policy may be concerned with whether health care services are publicly or privately financed—that is, provided as entitlements through the rights of citizenship or made available as commodities to be bought and sold on the open market. When governments are involved in providing the financing and direction for the delivery of health care services to the population, the system is said to be publicly financed and managed. This reflects the polis, defined in chapter 1. The value that underlies a public approach is that health risk should be shared across the population. The value that underlies a private approach is that of free enterprise and the commodification (or selling) of goods and services, including health care. When government—or the state—is not involved in financing and delivering health care services, it is said to be a private system. This is consistent with a market model of society. Analysis of such profound differences in health policy is the focus of macro-level theories. In these analyses, it is essential to understand how economic, political, and social forces both influence and reflect the predominant values within a society.

The second type of health policy is that of health-related public policy. Societies that value—and have economic, political, and social structures concerned with promoting—equity and human rights usually create policies that assure economic and social security. Societies that have rather less concern with such values—and have less responsive societal institutions—may favour market-oriented approaches to the provision of goods and services. In both cases, understanding the form these systems and related public policies take requires analyses of these macro-level forces.

Meso-view theories focus on the influence of advisory boards and departments within governments, government ministries, and other "middle-level" institutions upon public policy (Signal, 1998). Middle-level institutions can be organizations within governments charged with particular responsibilities or independent agencies that, while established by governments, operate at arm's length. Ultimately, both types of agencies are still accountable to government for their decisions and public recommendations. These kinds of organizations may make recommendations of both types of health policy: health care–related and health-related public policy. The kinds of changes recommended may be profound or incremental.

Micro-view theories are concerned with administrative routine and the day-to-day government apparatus that shapes policymaking. These concerns may include minor tinkering of public policy, but the focus is primarily on monitoring the operation of government operations, including allocating spending, monitoring operations, and revising guidelines for practice. Table 3.1 provides some examples of each type of policymaking activity in these two health policy spheres.

Three prominent theories of public policy with value for understanding the definition, development, and implementation of health policy are pluralism, new institutionalism, and political economy. These theories provide a lens through which the features of a health care system and health-related public policy come about and how they can be changed. Each theory has particular assumptions about the nature of society and how public policy is made. In addition, each theory tends to focus on a specific aspect of the public policy development process as it attempts to explain public policy outcomes.

PLURALISM

Pluralism, or pluralist interest group theory, identifies interest groups as the most important unit of analysis (Latham, 1952; Signal, 1998; Walt, 1994;

Table 3.1: Examples of Health Policy Issues at Differing Levels of Analysis

	Macro-Level	Meso-Level	Micro-Level
Health care policy	Creation of public-private partnerships	Creating a Telehealth line	Increasing funding to community health centres
Health-related public policy	Creation of national day care program	Changing eligibility requirements for social assistance	Increasing housing subsidy amounts for tenants

Dahl, 1961). These groups vie for power and access to the state to achieve their goals and objectives. This viewpoint is consistent with the idea that democratic societies are generally organized in the interests of the citizenry, and that citizens have agency to influence governmental directions. Policy emerges from competition among these different groups in developing and advancing ideas.

Since pluralism considers that all groups have equal opportunity to influence the policy change process, the resulting policy output reflects a rational balancing of costs and benefits. Pluralist policy analysis identifies the different interest groups and how they are organized. It also identifies the resources and strategies they apply to achieve their objectives. In the end, it documents the nature and success of their attempts to influence the public policy change process.

Pluralism and the Liberal Conception of Society

Pluralism is consistent with a liberal conception of society in which all citizens are considered to participate in numerous ways in the political process (Walt, 1994). The state is considered to consist of a neutral set of institutions that mediate diverse social and economic interests. Pluralist theory developed alongside theories of Western democracy, specifically later theories of democracy that emphasize the importance of regular elections as part of the democratic process (Ham & Hill, 1984). Schumpeter (1947) defines democracy as "that institutional arrangement for arriving at political decisions in which individuals acquire the power to decide by means of a competitive struggle for the people's

Box 3.1: The Pluralist View

1.   Basic political rights to vote and free speech safeguard political equality and individualism. Citizens have access to government through regular competitive elections, trying to influence government through advocacy for particular policy changes and other activities.

2.   Citizens gain power and influence by joining organizations and other groups to participate in the political process. Citizen engagement provides a means to challenge government decisions and influence public policy.

3.   The State in a pluralist society is defined as a complex of institutions that mediates diverse social and economic interests. The State is neutral and does not align itself with any one class or group, nor does it privilege particular interests over others.

4.   The State is described as a "plurality" of elites. In other words, no single elite dominates at all times.

Source: Smith, B. (1977). *Policymaking in British government.* London: Martin Robertson. Cited in Walt, G. (1994). *Health policy: An introduction to process and power* (p. 36). London: Zed Books.

vote" (p. 269). In democracies, interest groups are believed to compete to influence public policy decisions. Thus, pluralism was based on key features that characterize liberal democracy: political rights, citizens' access to political power, and the responsiveness of the political system to provide rational public policy outcomes (Smith, 1977).

For example, Easton's model of the political system shows the different inputs into the political system, with government institutions at the centre. It presents the government as neutral and therefore receptive to all interests in society, including the business community, market forces, and civil society organizations such as social movements, unions, and other organizations.

Kingdon's (2003) agenda-setting model also reflects pluralist principles. His model depicts the public policy development process as comprising three streams: problem identification, policy, and political. Each stream is governed by its own set of rules. How these streams converge to generate windows of opportunity shape policy change outcomes. The problem identification stream is where government considers which problems require action. The political stream is the sphere in which political ideology and beliefs influence which

Figure 3.1: Easton's Model of the Political System

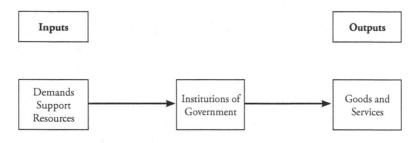

Source: Easton, D. (1965). *A framework for political analysis.* Englewood Cliffs, NJ: Prentice-Hall.

issues and indeed which public policy proposals will gain acceptance by government (Kingdon, 2003). This stream comprises the dynamics that occur independently of the other two streams, such as changes in public opinion or global events like the 2008 economic collapse.

Kingdon conceived the model in the American political context, but it can be applied to case studies of Canadian public policy. Kingdon stresses that the orientation of a government and its receptivity to addressing an issue fundamentally influence the movement of an issue onto the public policy agenda.

Figure 3.2: Kingdon's Policy Stream Convergence

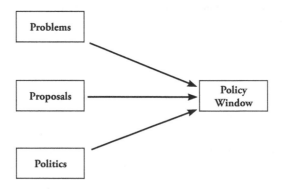

Source: Coffman, J. (2007 Spring). Evaluation-based theories of the policy process. *Harvard Family Research Project. The Evaluation Exchange, XIII*(1), 6–7.

Limitations of Pluralism

Critics argue that pluralism fails to consider the role that political power or political ideology plays in the policymaking process (Signal, 1998; Walt, 1994; Howlett, Ramesh, & Perl, 2009). Pluralism seems to explain away these concepts, viewing the political process as essentially consensual and conflict-free. It presents governments as neutral arbiters of diverse interests considered to be equal in their capacity to influence the political system. Pluralism does not consider power relations and the existence of economic, political, and social inequalities. It says little about structural and societal factors that influence political power and how it is exercised.

Studies of policy change have demonstrated how governing parties can privilege particular interests that are consistent with their own perspectives at the expense of other groups and interests (Rochon & Mazmanian, 1993). In other words, governments can deliberately shut out groups whose perspectives and solutions differ from their own. Such decisions are ideologically driven. Governments operate under the control of political parties that run in competitive elections on public policy platforms. Political parties always have a political ideology, but may not make their ideological commitments explicit in their electoral platforms. These platforms promise to address issues in particular ways, but political ideology guides their selection of priorities and issues, and the types of public policies they enact to address issues they define as important and requiring public policy action.

Yet, in spite of these limitations, pluralism has remained the dominant understanding and approach of advocacy groups trying to influence politics and public policy in Western nations, particularly in North America. As a consensus approach to politics and governance, its avoidance of political conflict and neglect of social cleavages makes it an attractive approach for advocacy groups trying to change public policies.

For example, groups will work for years—with rather little effect—to convince government to enact particular policy solutions to address poverty or poor health outcomes. Since these groups have no other way of understanding the policy development and change process, they are limited to activities of advocating, educating, and attempting to influence governments to change policy. This may mean advocating for changes to the health care system, rather than considering other potential sources of poor health outcomes, such as poverty. One way of thinking about this is that groups strive to draw in government by making it "part of the solution," rather than recognizing that these governments and their policies may actually be the problem. In the end, pluralism's consensual approach to public policy change disguises the sources of groups' differences with the government and may stymie the development of the public policy outcomes they seek.

Much has been written about the limitations of pluralism. Some critics consider pluralism to offer a simplistic presentation of how the public policy process works (Howlett et al., 2009). Indeed, McLennan's insights are apt: "It is impossible to read the standard works without getting the sense that resources, information and the means of political communication are openly available to all citizens, that groups form an array of equivalent power centres in society, and that all legitimate voices can and will be heard" (McLennan cited in Howlett et al., 2009, pp. 38–39).

Pluralism has little to say about health or income inequalities, for example, or how they come about (Bryant, 2015). Rising income inequality in the United States prompted Dahl and Lindblom (1976), leading pluralist theorists, to reconsider pluralism and its capacity to explain this issue. This led to the development of neo- or post-pluralism (Manley, 1983). This new school of pluralism inserted influence and power and seemed to permeate pluralist theory with left-leaning politics. In short, neo-pluralism seemed to redefine pluralism to consider the unequal distribution of political power in conjunction with the traditional pluralist emphasis on competition among interest groups in the political process (McFarland, 2007).

As suggested in chapter 1, the pluralist dominance may reflect a preference, particularly in North American politics, to depoliticize issues and to emphasize individualized approaches to health care and health-related policy formulations. This would explain the preoccupation with health care and the neglect of issues that lead to unequal health outcomes.

In the UK and western Europe, policymaking and politics tend to be less pluralist and more conflict-oriented. This can at times contribute to social cleavages along racial or income lines. It recognizes, however, that health care and health-related public policy are heavily politicized and require public solutions. While governments' responses do not always result in the implementation of progressive policies, governments may be more likely to recognize citizens' needs and respond to these needs proactively within such an explanatory framework.

NEW INSTITUTIONALISM

Many political science models of public policy adopt a consensus-driven political process. One influential model has been what is termed the new institutionalism. The new institutionalism has some pluralist features, but adds an interest in how institutions structure the nature of politics and political debate and the policy change process. New institutionalism approaches to understanding public policy change have been prominently applied to explain the evolution of the health care system in Canada (see Tuohy, 1999).

The focus of the new institutionalism is how societal institutions influence and structure public policymaking and policy change outcomes (Signal, 1998; Thelen & Steinmo, 1992; Hall & Taylor, 1996). These institutions structure and manage the politics associated with policy change by determining the conditions and nature of political discourse (March & Olsen, 1984; Coleman & Skogstad, 1990). That is, institutions define the terms of engagement: What are the appropriate public policy domains that can serve as targets of political action? The new institutionalism is seen as a reaction to the behavioural approaches that dominated during the 1960s and 1970s (Hall & Taylor, 1996). In particular, institutionalists identified a lack of theory to explain the manner by which institutions can foster or impede policy change.

The new institutionalism consists of three frequently integrated theoretical approaches: (1) historical institutionalism, which traces how the past shapes the future; (2) rational choice institutionalism, which highlights the economic position of political actors; and (3) sociological institutionalism, which emphasizes culture and norms as determining influences (Hall & Taylor, 1996; Fischer, 2003). What they all share is a belief that institutions are primary in shaping or structuring the value and policy preferences of those working in the public policy realm (Coleman & Skogstad, 1990; March & Olsen, 1984).

Defining Political Institutions

Political institutions are state and governmental structures that develop over time and persist in their effects. These institutions can be formal rules of operation, organizational structures, and standard operating procedures as exemplified by the rules and regulations established by government institutions for obtaining services. The new institutionalism conceives these institutions as independent forces that promote particular ideologies and restrict the choices available to policy-makers. These political institutions therefore "structure" political reality and define the terms and nature of political debate. Institutionalist analysis can also examine the activities of advisory boards to government, government departments, and political institutions such as Parliament in order to understand how they influence the public policy process.

New institutionalists have contributed significantly to the understanding of the complexity of social and political change in modern societies. Their contribution is in analyzing the interaction between political elites, interest groups' demands, institutional processes, and ideas in political and policy analysis (Hall & Taylor, 1996; King, 1973, 1974). The focus for historical institutionalists is both macro-level (higher-level) and meso-level (middle-level) processes. By analyzing both macro- (i.e., politics and political parties) and meso-level (i.e., agencies and departments) processes, they provide analyses of some of the most important influences on the public policy process (Signal, 1998).

Historical Institutionalism: The Development of Public Health Care

Historical institutionalism provides one theoretical framework for examining health and health care policy issues by highlighting how the institutions of a political system structure policy discourse (Tuohy, 1992, 1999). One objective of the framework is to understand the uniqueness of national political outcomes. Another is to understand how the inequalities that characterize these outcomes come about (Eckstein & Apter, 1963).

Historical institutionalism identifies conflict among competing groups for scarce resources as key to understanding politics. An important focus is on how political and economic structures may interact with each other and with current situations to produce outcomes where some interests are privileged while others are demobilized or ignored.

For example, Carolyn Tuohy draws on historical institutionalism and rational choice approaches to explain health care decision making and varying policy outcomes in the United Kingdom, Canada, and the United States (Tuohy, 1999). Tuohy examines the logics of particular decision-making systems within which actors are considered to respond rationally to incentives and resources available to them. In other words, political goals and objectives, as well as the strategies to achieve these objectives, result from the incentives and resources available to policy-makers. She argues that the dynamics of change in decision-making systems must consider the temporal context. That is, policy change occurs when choices become available as a result of particular historical contexts. Structure allows change, but also sets limits to change:

> The structural dimension relates to the balance of influence across key
> categories of actors: in the case of health care, the balance across the State,

the medical profession, and private finance. The institutional dimension refers to the mix of various instruments of social control—hierarchy, market, and collegiality. Change in the policy parameters establishing the structural balance and the institutional mix of the health care system requires an extraordinary mobilization of political authority and will. (Tuohy, 1999, p. 7)

Further, she argues that a key feature of the three health care systems and the logics or political dynamics that shaped them is how they have structured the relationship between the medical profession and the state. These systems are

> shaped by the climate of ideas and the constellation of interests that exist at the time that such a confluence occurs. Once established, the institutional mix and structural balance of these systems intersect to generate a distinctive logic that governs the behavior of participants and the ongoing dynamic of change. (Tuohy, 1999, p. 7)

By way of illustration, Tuohy argues that the single-payer system, which has become synonymous with the Canadian approach to health care, operates according to the logic or dynamics of an accommodation between the medical profession and the state (Tuohy, 1999). The provincial and territorial governments are the "single payers" for a comprehensive range of medical and hospital services that are provided on the basis of need to those living in the province or territory. In the United Kingdom, the National Health Services involves an agency relationship between the government and the British medical profession (Tuohy, 1999). An agency relationship is one in which a prospective recipient of health care services assigns decision-making authority to particular health care providers. Providers in such relationships have wide discretion to decide the nature of and how much medical care an individual will receive. Mechanisms are put in place to protect against potential abuse that may stem from allowing wide discretion for providers.

In the United States, although proposals for national health insurance were unsuccessful, the immediate postwar era gave way to initiatives such as hospital construction grants from the federal government (Tuohy, 1999). Tuohy thus considers the institutional mix and the structural balance established in each country to understand how each arrived at their particular policy response to the provision of health care services (Tuohy, 1999).

As is evident, Tuohy focuses primarily on the roles of government and the medical profession in the development of the health care systems. Tuohy's focus on institutions seems to exclude other important factors and groups, such as citizens and the labour movements, in these countries that helped to bring about a public health care system in Canada and the United Kingdom.

As noted, in this analysis, institutions are central to understanding policy outcomes. Some argue that while institutions can be important units of analysis to explain different aspects of public policy development, in reality such an analysis says little about how public policies develop or change over time (Thelen & Steinmo, 1992). It may be that institutionalism as a policy framework minimizes the degree of policy change that is possible (Clemens & Cook, 1999). It does so by emphasizing that institutions can constrain and limit opportunities for change because they are enduring, and embody the social, political, and economic values of a society. These, in turn, are influenced by structures and interests in a society over time.

Since they seem to constrain change, institutions may not be a useful analytic tool for explaining change. There is a need to consider institutions in relation to other factors that influence public policy outcomes. These may include various social, political, and economic forces than can be mobilized in the service of public policy change.

The new institutionalism is considered a middle-level theory about the evolution of health care systems. Ideas and knowledge are seen as driving policy responses. The new institutionalism can therefore be understood as a rational approach to public policy analysis. In contrast to the new institutionalism, political economy is a materialist perspective that considers living conditions as giving rise to ideas for social and policy change (Coburn, 2010).

The Political Economy Critique

Contrast Tuohy's view of the development of the Canadian health care system with the political economy perspective. The latter sees the creation of the public health care system as a victory for the working class, which made demands on the state to provide social security to citizens in the immediate postwar era (Teeple, 2000; Armstrong & Armstrong, 2003).

In this analysis, the public health care system, as well as many aspects of the welfare state in Canada, came about during the 1960s and 1970s, when the economy was thriving. Political and economic forces were able to pressure governments to provide a modicum of economic and social security to their citizens (Armstrong & Armstrong, 2003).

The seeds of these movements were planted at the end of the Second World War, when citizens developed expectations that their efforts during the war required some responses. It took many years following the war to build on this momentum, however, and this was especially the case for the public health care system. Ruling politicians, the media, and the medical profession were wary of public health care and what they perceived to be a socialist idea.

Nevertheless, the government of Tommy Douglas in Saskatchewan established the first publicly funded health care system in 1947, which was well received. It wasn't until the 1960s that the federal government decided to model a national health care system on the successful health care program established in Saskatchewan. How can we explain the role played by economic, political, and social forces such as these in the policy development process?

OVERVIEW OF THE POLITICAL ECONOMY APPROACH

It is the premise of this book that the political economy approach offers the most useful means of understanding how public policy, including health policy, is created and implemented. To provide a means of applying these concepts to the study of health policy, the remainder of this chapter introduces a variety of political economy concepts and illustrations.

The political economy approach to understanding policy development and change is explicitly concerned with the economic, political, and social structures that influence the distribution of power and resources in a society (Armstrong, Armstrong, & Coburn, 2001; Armstrong & Armstrong, 2003; Coburn, 2006). How a society organizes the production and distribution of economic and social resources is essential to understanding policy outcomes. Political economists carry out these inquiries by looking at states, markets, power, ideas, discourses, and civil society and their impact on policy development.

There are a number of political economy perspectives (Coburn, 2006). One important political economy perspective is materialist. In contrast to the new institutionalist emphasis on the primacy of ideas, materialist political economists consider that how a society organizes the production and distribution of social and economic resources shapes ideas and institutions. Political economists use concepts such as the mode of production and social class to explain political events and phenomena (Grabb, 2002). The mode of production refers to the manner in which societal goods and services are produced and distributed. In Canada and most other countries, the current social formation is the capitalist mode of production. Political economy considers that this capitalist mode of production shapes all aspects of economic, political, and social life, including relations among different groups in society.

Groups that are especially important include those that differ by social class, gender, and race, among others (Grabb, 2002).

Feminist political economy is also concerned with the complex of institutions and social relations that operate through the political and economic systems to shape ideological and cultural systems (Drache & Clement, 1985). Feminist political economy focuses on gender and how it structures women's access to health care services and their opportunities for good health as compared to men (Armstrong & Armstrong, 2010). There is also interest in the power dynamic that shapes these relations and the conditions of life for men and women such that men appear to have more—and better—opportunities than women.

Box 3.2: Focus of a Feminist Political Economy

Feminist political economy considers how the political, economic, and social organization of health structures opportunities for health for women. This focus is concerned with the role of political ideology in shaping health policy, indeed all public policies, with an attendant analysis of implications for women and other vulnerable populations. Thus, it is assumed that gender, race, and other social attributes such as class can increase vulnerability. Especially important is the increased likelihood of experiencing social and economic marginalization.

Political Economy as Critical Social Science Applied to Public Policy

Materialist and other political economy perspectives represent a critical social science perspective (Coburn, 2004, 2000, 2001; Armstrong et al., 2001). Political economy focuses on issues of power. As critical social theory, it embodies a transformative component. This means that people are considered to have the power and the ability to change their environment, such as improving living conditions and health in the community in which they live. In addition, an important outcome component of a political economy analysis is how power shapes policy change, which then influences the health of populations. The context in which events such as the development of public policies or emerging conflict among groups in society occur is considered important. Relations and power are considered to shape this context and the social, political, and economic institutions that develop in a society.

The Role of the State: Accumulation and Legitimation

Central to the political economy perspective is recognition of the role of the state. O'Connor (1973) argues that the capitalist state plays critical roles of accumulation and legitimation. Accumulation refers to state provision of the conditions that enable building private profits. States help foster these conditions by providing infrastructure such as roads, highways, and communication services, and an educated workforce. States also ensure social cohesion and mediate conflict among social classes by providing a justice system and services. Legitimation refers to the state's socially sanctioned right to use force in order to ensure social order and cohesion. Accumulation and legitimation are contradictory roles that require the state to vary its support between business and labour in order to maintain social cohesion and reduce the possibility of class conflict.

O'Connor argues that by the 1970s, states were paying for more of the costs of accumulation than they had in the past, yet at the same time allowed for the collection and control of profits by private interests. O'Connor attributes the oil crisis that developed in the 1970s to the private appropriation of state power to protect private interests (O'Connor, 1973; Armstrong & Armstrong, 2003). Within a political economy perspective, the processes of legitimation and accumulation have particularly adverse impacts on women and racial minorities in the formal economy. They foster large "surplus populations outside the market" (Armstrong & Armstrong, 2010, p. 8; O'Connor, 1973).

Armstrong and Armstrong and others argue that O'Connor neglects the special impacts these processes have on households, particularly for women, who bear the larger burden of caregiving (Armstrong & Armstrong, 2003). For example, changes in the state's role that resulted in increasing market approaches to health care have affected women as primary caregivers within families. Women frequently carry out health care responsibilities normally provided by trained health care professionals, such as nurses, in their families.

The Armstrongs argue that O'Connor's theory requires a third role for the state in addition to accumulation and legitimation: distribution. This is because the state has a critical role "in structuring what is provided for publicly in the market and privately in households, in determining who does the work in these spheres and how it is done" (Armstrong & Armstrong, 2010, p. 8). Indeed, health care and health are integral components of the welfare state. Pressure from the labour movement and citizens contributed to the development of public health care programs in Western countries, except the United States.

The Impact of Political Ideology on Health Policy

Of particular interest to political economists is the influence of the ascent of neoliberalism as a governing political ideology. Neoliberalism is a political ideology that favours the market as the vehicle for fostering economic growth and innovation (Coburn, 2000). Specifically, free enterprise policies are seen as key to economic growth and the basis for the well-being of the population. Political economists trace the advent of neoliberalism to events in the 1970s, such as the oil crisis in 1973 (Teeple, 2000; Coburn, 2006). Morever, they consider deregulation, efforts to reduce the power of labour, and contracting the role of the state as not inevitable or accidental, but as deliberate attempts to shift political and economic power (Harvey, 2007).

In later chapters, the specific influence of neoliberalism on the organization and delivery of health care will be examined. In these sections, the focus is on how neoliberalism has been associated with growing inequalities in health between different groups in developed political economies such as Canada, the US, and the UK. Inequalities in health refer to unequal health outcomes that are based on some group characteristic of individuals.

HEALTH INEQUALITIES, SOCIAL INEQUALITIES, AND HEALTH CARE

In Europe, the focus has been on health inequalities as a function of social class or occupational status (Townsend, Davidson, & Whitehead, 1992; Mackenbach & Bakker, 2002). In Canada, the primary focus has been on issues of income and poverty (Raphael, 2007b). A vast literature has established the link between low income and poverty with poor health status and outcomes (Phipps, 2002; Auger, Raynault, Lessard, & Choinière, 2004; Raphael, 2007a).

Their belief in markets means that supporters of neoliberalism tend to accept whatever the market produces, including social and health inequalities. These inequalities are seen as somewhat natural and stemming from personal failure to succeed in the market. They do not usually consider these inequalities

Box 3.3: The Main Tenets of Neoliberalism

David Coburn considers that neoliberalism refers to the dominance of markets and the market model. He identifies the three main assumptions of neoliberalism and the new right:

1. Markets are perceived as most efficient in the production and distribution of resources in a society.
2. Societies are comprised of autonomous individuals (producers and consumers) who are driven primarily by material or economic gain.
3. Competition is the primary source of innovation.

Coburn distinguishes between neoliberalism and neoconservatism because the latter is concerned with a particular social component supportive of traditional family values and certain religious traditions, among other issues, and is not only concerned with a laissez-faire economic doctrine. The essence of neoliberalism is a commitment to the virtues of a market economy.

Moreover, neoliberals tend not to be troubled by inequality, nor do they consider it as either positive or inevitable. If the market is "the best or most efficient allocator of goods and resources, neoliberals are inclined to accept whatever markets bring" (Coburn, 2000, p. 138).

Source: Coburn, D. (2000). Income inequality, social cohesion, and the health status of populations: The role of neo-liberalism. *Social Science & Medicine, 51*(1), 135–146.

to be related to public policies that allow increased skewing of the distribution of economic resources or to the social exclusion of some groups. Social exclusion is closely associated with social inequalities. Social exclusion is a process of marginalization of some groups, such as indigenous populations and populations of colour, among others, resulting in these groups being denied access to basic resources, such as sufficient income and affordable housing. This process is strongly influenced by a wide range of forces, as illustrated in Figure 3.3.

Coburn (2000) considers the relationship between income inequality and health within and among nations. He argues that there is a need to consider the "basic social causes of inequality and health" (p. 136) by analyzing the social, political, and economic context within which income and health inequalities

Figure 3.3: Social Exclusion in Context

Globalization and Associated Structural Changes

National Context: Particularities of
Economic Policy, Welfare Regimes, Rights of
Citizenship, and Responses to Globalization

Local Context: Particularities
of Place, Population, and Local
Governance

Social Exclusion

Source: Percy-Smith, J. (2000). Introduction: The contours of social exclusion. In J. Percy-Smith (Ed.), *Policy responses to social exclusion: Toward inclusion* (p. 5). Buckingham: Open University Press.

emerge. Coburn and others have linked inequalities to the welfare state and the class origins of different types of welfare state regimes. Such a focus enables a consideration of the relationships among markets, states, and civil society. Coburn argues that it also presents a different causal configuration about national and international differences in income inequality and in longevity than are usually acknowledged in the literature.

Neoliberalism has undermined the welfare state, as reflected by Western governments such as Canada and the United Kingdom, by dismantling social programs that form these welfare states. As noted earlier in this chapter, the formation of the welfare state was intended as a way of sharing risk across the population, and as means to redistribute income and access to programs from higher-income groups to lower-income groups.

Considerable research evidence shows that low-income groups especially benefit from these programs. Indeed, reduced poverty rates among different groups, particularly seniors, have been attributed to welfare state programs (Raphael, 2007b). Coburn and others have argued that the welfare state contributed to social cohesion or solidarity among social classes because it mitigated class differences. Coburn shows that the basic assumptions of neoliberalism are consistent with higher levels of inequality and lowered social cohesion or increased class conflict attributable to accentuated differences among classes (Coburn, 2000).

Armstrong and Armstrong have shown how neoliberal policies have led to reforms that have undermined health care through cutbacks in public financing and new approaches to managing health care services (Armstrong & Armstrong, 2003). They argue that hospital CEOs in particular have adopted new management strategies with a view to making hospitals more efficient. This approach results in reducing nursing and other hospital staff and providing care at the lowest unit cost (Bourgeault, 2006, 2010). This means that hospital staff who tend to be the least skilled in patient care usually end up providing greater amounts of patient care.

Some observers describe the deskilling of care, whereby families are trained to perform activities usually performed by registered nurses, such as inserting catheters and other health equipment (Armstrong & Armstrong, 2003). Some hospitals trained cleaning staff to do the work of registered nurses as a way of reducing the cost of patient care. These processes have contributed to a decline

Box 3.4: Political Economy Analysis: Social Exclusion, Gender, Race, and Health

A political economy approach can be applied to examine how social positions such as gender and race structure opportunities for health and the determinants of health such as income, employment, and access to a range of other resources. Political economy examines how race, gender, and other factors lead to social exclusion. Social exclusion is defined as both a process and an outcome, whereby people experience social and economic marginalization on the basis of gender, race, or another characteristic (Galabuzi, 2006).

Political economists reject the view that the capitalist formation and the social relations that develop within society are inevitable (Coburn, 2006; Teeple, 2000). Rather, they consider capitalism and the social relations that emerge from the organization of society, such as inequalities between women and men, White populations and populations of colour, among others, to be social constructions. That is, society creates these processes and categories to make sense of differences within a population. These processes and categories tend to reflect the dominant attitudes of a culture toward people of colour or other marginalized populations. Often, these differences are treated as pathologies or unattractive attributes and can become the basis of discrimination against various groups.

in patient care, increased risk of infections in hospitals, and other problems that are preventable through proper cleaning of patients' rooms and other facilities in hospitals. These developments have been attributed to the under-resourcing of hospitals and the health care system as a whole.

CONCLUSIONS

This chapter has examined the assumptions of three theories of public policy that represent the dominant political perspectives in the social science literature. These theories can be arranged along a continuum from consensus models to conflict models of the policy process. Consensus models tend to focus on group behaviours in the political process, whereas conflict theories are concerned with the influence of politics and economics on public policy outcomes. Institutionalist models take a middle course.

Pluralism has become one of the most influential theories of public policy and politics in Western societies such as Canada. It contends that politics consists of a "plurality" of interest groups that compete to influence public policy. No single interest group or political elite dominates the political process. Pluralism fails to recognize the inequality of access to the political system or the role of political power. The state is portrayed as a neutral arbitrator of interests that contributes to policy decisions arrived at by consensus. Neo-pluralism attempted to inculcate concerns about income inequality, but it is unclear to what extent pluralists are concerned with income inequality or health inequalities.

The new institutionalism focuses on institutions as shaping policy behaviours and policy change outcomes. It is a structural approach that considers institutions to be primary in shaping the preferences and values of political actors. Institutions "structure" political reality and define the terms and nature of political debate. The focus on institutions tends to preclude a consideration of other forces that may be time-specific and important variables for understanding policy change outcomes.

Political economy is concerned with the relationship between politics and economics and how this structures policy change. Material conditions of societies are seen as primary in influencing ideas and institutions. Political economy considers political power and the influence of political ideology on policy change outcomes and health outcomes. It focuses on the broader political and economic contexts as being causal factors in influencing health outcomes. These theories also represent different levels of analysis. The application of theories reflects different perspectives on which factors can help explain political outcomes.

CRITICAL THINKING QUESTIONS

1. Which of the public policy theories best explains recent developments occurring in health policy in Canada?
2. What are the specific issues of interest of each of the three main public policy theories?
3. What kinds of evidence do you think guide current health policymaking in Canada?
4. How do theories of public policy contribute to our understanding of health policies and their impact on the health of populations?
5. What considerations should be brought to bear on health policy discussions in order to improve health policy decisions?

FURTHER READINGS

Coburn, D. (2000). Income inequality, social cohesion, and the health status of populations: The role of neo-liberalism. *Social Science & Medicine, 51*(1), 135–146.
    Coburn is one of the foremost political economy analysts in Canada. In this article, Coburn examines the impact of neoliberalism on health policy, specifically the increase in inequalities in health in Canada and elsewhere.

Coleman, W., & Skogstad, G. (Eds.). (1990). *Policy communities and public policy in Canada: A structural approach.* Toronto: Copp Clark Pittman.
    This text is a collection of essays on Canadian public policy examined from a new institutionalist perspective. The essays help to explicate the key areas of interest in the new institutionalism.

Hall, P.A., & Taylor, R.C.R. (1996). Political science and the three institutionalisms. *Political Studies, 44*, 936–957.
    This article was among the first to explain the three variants of the new institutionalism and continues to be an important work on this policy approach. It defines rational choice, historical, and sociological institutionalism and key areas of interest of each with reference to American public policy.

Signal, L. (1998). The politics of health promotion: Insights from political theory. *Health Promotion International, 13*(3), 257–263.

This article examines three theories of pluralism, the new institutionalism, and political economy and their contributions to understanding and explaining health promotion.

Walt, G. (1994). *Health policy: An introduction to process and power*. London: Zed Books.

The book provides an overview of the health policy process and examines different theories of public policy. Walt examines international health policy issues. The author's interests are in power and politics in health policy.

RELEVANT WEBSITES

Canadian Centre for Policy Alternatives
www.policyalternatives.ca

The Canadian Centre for Policy Alternatives is a think tank that publishes research papers and articles on current public policy issues in Canada. Its theoretical orientation on Canadian health policy and other public policies is political economy. Reports can be downloaded from this website.

Centre for Health Services and Policy Research, University of British Columbia
www.chspr.ubc.ca

This site provides research on current Canadian health care issues. It focuses on scientific inquiry into health care and population health policy research.

The Institute for Research on Public Policy
www.irpp.org

The Institute for Research on Public Policy was founded by Hugh Segal, former political aide to Ontario premiers and Canadian prime ministers. The institute publishes books on current Canadian public policy issues and the journal *Policy Options*. Current and back issues of *Policy Options* can be downloaded from its website.

School for Policy Studies, University of Bristol
www.bristol.ac.uk/sps/index.html

The school is renowned for its studies on public policies in the United Kingdom. Although not specifically focused on "health" policy, it addresses many issues related to health policy, such as social exclusion and poverty.

World Health Organization
www.who.int/en

The World Health Organization addresses a wide range of health policy and health care policy issues. It is the directing and coordinating authority for health in the United Nations and provides leadership on global health issues. Its website provides information on current global health issues and public policy.

REFERENCES

Armstrong, H., & Armstrong, P. (2003). *Wasting away: The undermining of Canadian health care*. Toronto: Oxford University Press.

Armstrong, P., & Armstrong, H. (2010). *Wasting away: The undermining of Canadian health care* (2nd ed.). Toronto: Oxford University Press.

Armstrong, P., Armstrong, H., & Coburn, D. (Eds.). (2001). *Unhealthy times: The political economy of health and care in Canada*. Toronto: Oxford University Press.

Auger, N., Raynault, M., Lessard, R., & Choinière, R. (2004). Income and health in Canada. In D. Raphael (Ed.), *Social determinants of health: Canadian perspectives* (pp. 39–52). Toronto: Canadian Scholars' Press.

Bourgeault, I. (2006). The provision of care: Professions, politics, and profit. In D. Raphael, T. Bryant, & M. Rioux (Eds.), *Staying alive: Critical perspectives on health, illness, and health care* (pp. 263–286). Toronto: Canadian Scholars' Press.

Bourgeault, I. (2010). The provision of care: Professions, politics, and profit. In T. Bryant, D. Raphael, & M. Rioux (Eds.), *Staying alive: Critical perspectives on health, illness, and health care* (2nd ed.) (pp. 41-63). Toronto: Canadian Scholars' Press.

Brooks, S., & Miljan, L. (2003). *Public policy in Canada: An introduction*. Toronto: Oxford University Press.

Bryant, T. (2015). Implications of public policy change models for addressing income-related health inequalities. *Canadian Public Policy, 42*(2), 510–516.

Clemens, E.S., & Cook, J.M. (1999). Politics and institutionalism: Explaining durability and change. *Annual Review of Sociology, 25*, 441–466.

Coburn, D. (2000). Income inequality, social cohesion, and the health status of populations: The role of neo-liberalism. *Social Science & Medicine, 51*(1), 135–146.

Coburn, D. (2001). Health, health care, and neo-liberalism. In P. Armstrong, H. Armstrong, & D. Coburn (Eds.), *Unhealthy times: The political economy of health and care in Canada* (pp. 45–65). Toronto: Oxford University Press.

Coburn, D. (2004). Beyond the income inequality hypothesis: Globalization, neo-liberalism, and health inequalities. *Social Science & Medicine, 58*, 41–56.

Coburn, D. (2006). Health and health care: A political economy perspective. In D. Raphael, T. Bryant, & M. Rioux (Eds.), *Staying alive: Critical perspectives on health, illness, and health care* (pp. 59–84). Toronto: Canadian Scholars' Press.

Coburn, D. (2010). Health and health care: A political economy perspective. In T. Bryant, D. Raphael, & M. Rioux (Eds.), *Staying alive: Critical perspectives on health, illness, and health care* (2nd ed.) (pp. 65–91). Toronto: Canadian Scholars' Press.

Coleman, W., & Skogstad, G. (Eds.). (1990). *Policy communities and public policy in Canada: A structural approach*. Toronto: Copp Clark Pittman.

Dahl, R.A. (1961). *Who governs?* New Haven: Yale University Press.

Dahl, R.A., & Lindblom, C.E. (1976). *Politics, economics and welfare: Planning and politico-economic systems resolved into basic social processes* (2nd ed). Chicago: University of Chicago Press.

Drache, D., & Clement, W. (1985). *The new practical guide to Canadian political economy.* Toronto: James Lorimer.

Eckstein, H., & Apter, D. (1963). *Comparative politics.* Glencoe: Free Press.

Fischer, F. (2003). *Reframing public policy: Discursive politics and deliberative practices.* New York: Oxford University Press.

Galabuzi, G.E. (2006). *Canada's economic apartheid: The social exclusion of racialized groups in the new century.* Toronto: Canadian Scholars' Press.

Grabb, E. (2002). *Theories of social inequality.* Toronto: Harcourt Canada.

Hall, P.A., & Taylor, R.C.R. (1996). Political science and the three institutionalisms. *Political Studies, 44,* 936–957.

Ham, C., & Hill, M. (1984). *The policy process in the modern capitalist state.* Brighton: Wheatsheaf Books.

Harvey, D. (2007). *A brief history of neoliberalism.* Oxford: Oxford University Press.

Howlett, M., Ramesh, M., & Perl, A. (2009). *Studying public policy: Policy cycles and policy subsystems.* Don Mills: Oxford University Press.

King, A. (1973). Ideas, institutions and the policies of governments: A comparative analysis, I. *British Journal of Political Science, 3*(3), 291–313.

King, A. (1974). Ideas, institutions and the policies of governments: A comparative analysis, II. *British Journal of Political Science, 3,* 409–423.

Kingdon, J.W. (2003). *Agendas, alternatives, and public policies* (2nd ed.). New York: Longman Publishing.

Latham, E. (1952). *The group basis of politics.* Ithaca, NY: Cornell University Press.

Mackenbach, J., & Bakker, M. (Eds.). (2002). *Reducing inequalities in health: A European perspective.* London: Routledge.

Manley, J. (1983). Neo-pluralism: A class analysis of pluralism I and pluralism II. *American Political Science Review, 77*(2), 368–383.

March, J.G., & Olsen, J.P. (1984). The new institutionalism: Organizational factors in political life. *American Political Science Review, 78,* 734–749.

McFarland, A.S. (2007). Neopluralism. *Annual Review of Political Science, 10,* 45–66.

O'Connor, J. (1973). *The fiscal crisis of the state.* New York: St. Martin's Press.

Pal, L. (2006). *Beyond policy analysis: Public issue management in turbulent times.* Toronto: Nelson.

Phipps, S. (2002). *The impact of poverty on health.* Ottawa: Canadian Population Health Initiative.

Raphael, D. (2007a). Addressing health inequalities in Canada: Little attention, inadequate action, limited success. In A. Pederson, I. Rootman, M. O'Neill, & S. Dupéré (Eds.), *Health promotion in Canada: Critical perspectives* (pp. 106–122). Toronto: Canadian Scholars' Press.

Raphael, D. (2007b). *Poverty and policy in Canada: Implications for health and quality of life.* Toronto: Canadian Scholars' Press.

Rochon, T., & Mazmanian, D. (1993). Social movements and the policy process. *The Annals of the American Academy of Political and Social Science, 528,* 75–85.

Schumpeter, J. (1947). *Capitalism, socialism, and democracy.* London: Allen & Unwin.

Signal, L. (1998). The politics of health promotion: Insights from political theory. *Health Promotion International, 13*(3), 257–263.

Smith, B. (1977). *Policymaking in British government.* London: Martin Robertson.

Teeple, G. (2000). *Globalization and the decline of social reform: Into the twenty-first century.* Aurora, ON: Garamond Press.

Thelen, K., & Steinmo, S. (1992). Historical institutionalism in comparative politics. In S. Steinmo, K. Thelen, & F. Longstreth (Eds.), *Structuring politics: Historical institutionalism in comparative analysis* (pp. 1–32). New York: Cambridge University Press.

Townsend, P., Davidson, N., & Whitehead, M. (Eds.). (1992). *Inequalities in health: The Black Report and the health divide.* New York: Penguin.

Tuohy, C. (1992). *Policy and politics in Canada: Institutionalized ambivalence.* Philadelphia: Temple University Press.

Tuohy, C. (1999). *Accidental logics: The dynamics of change in the health care arena in the United States, Britain, and Canada.* New York: Oxford University Press.

Walt, G. (1994). *Health policy: An introduction to process and power.* London: Zed Books.

Chapter 4

UNDERSTANDING POLICY CHANGE

INTRODUCTION

Policy change is an adjustment to an existing public policy or set of related public policies. These adjustments can be incremental, leading to small changes in policy, such as increasing the fee schedule for physicians or adjusting the amounts of financial transfers to community health centres and hospitals. Adjustments can also be radical changes that lead to a fundamental shift in the underlying philosophy of a public policy area, such as a shift from institutional care to community-based care, or a shift from a biomedical understanding of health to a social determinants perspective that emphasizes living conditions as the primary influences on health.

While most theories of the public policy process, such as those examined in chapter 3, address policy change, they vary in their specificity about policy change, the roles different actors play, and the role of the state in the process (Mintrom & Vergari, 1996). A set of models termed *learning models of policy change* has been very influential in the policy studies area. These models show many conceptual similarities with the pluralism and new institutionalism approaches to understanding public policy presented in chapter 3.

These models tend to de-emphasize the influence of conflict between interest groups and differences in the amount of, and exercise of, power in policy change. They focus instead on how the acquisition and application of knowledge influences policy-makers. The adherents of this view argue that such an emphasis produces better explanations of how public policies are developed and implemented than do conflict-based theories (Bennett & Howlett, 1992; Heclo, 1974).

Learning models, therefore, focus on learning as a potential source of policy change (Bennett & Howlett, 1992). Adherents of these views also argue that conflict-oriented theories neglect the role that information or knowledge plays in this process. Illustrating the focus on process over analyses of economic, political, and social forces, Heclo argues that policy change can arise from uncertainty: "men collectively wondering what to do" (Heclo, 1974, p. 305). The learning approaches, therefore, focus on learning and assert that the state—and policy-makers—learn from experience and change public policies on the basis of their interpretations of how well previous policies have performed.

THE SCOPE OF LEARNING MODELS

The political science literature identifies several learning models of policy change (Bryant, 2001, 2002a, 2003, 2004b). This chapter is not intended to provide a definitive examination of all of these. Instead, it focuses on two representative models: the policy paradigms (Hall, 1993) and the knowledge paradigms policy change models (Bryant, 2004b).

Building on the insights of historical institutionalism presented in chapter 3, Hall's model emphasizes the role that institutions and social learning play in policy change. He defines change as intentional efforts to adjust the goals or instruments of policy, given the experience of past policies and new information (Hall, 1993). The knowledge paradigms policy change conceptual framework builds on Hall's insights on knowledge and adds political economy concerns about how power, conflict, and political ideology influence policy change. Apart from Tuohy's (1999) excellent analysis using historical institutionalism to explain the development of public health care, this approach is rarely applied to health policy issues. The knowledge paradigms policy change model has been used in analyses of both health care policy and health-related public policy. This chapter explores the usefulness of the policy paradigms model and the knowledge paradigms policy change conceptual framework for understanding how health policy develops and changes.

POLICY PARADIGMS

The new institutionalism, discussed in chapter 3, is an important contribution to understanding the role that institutions play in the policy change process. As enduring bodies in society with clear policy influence, they have the potential to shape policy changes. But of equal or more importance, they have the potential to constrain the policy change process and impede social and political change.

Hall integrated aspects of historical institutionalism and the literature on scientific paradigms to explicate the roles played by ideas and knowledge in public decision making (Kuhn, 1970). Public policy discussion occurs within specific realms of discourse (Anderson, 1978). Policy-makers work within specific frameworks of ideas and standards that specify policy goals and the instruments or means by which these goals can be attained. These frameworks are grounded in the kind of language through which policy-makers convey and do their work.

There exist, therefore, influential systems of ideas that guide both policy development and the policy-makers themselves. This may be problematic "because so much of it is taken for granted and is not amenable to scrutiny as a whole" (Hall, 1993, p. 279). These systems of ideas specify what types of problems will be defined as legitimate public problems requiring government action. These systems also specify the tools that government may apply to address these problems (Hall, 1993). Hall refers to these interpretive frameworks as *policy paradigms*, which help to explain different patterns of policy change by linking these paradigms to specific instances of social learning.

Box 4.1: The Process of Social Learning

Hall draws on Heclo's work to formulate the concept of social learning. He argues that a key factor affecting policy at time-1 is policy at time-0. Previous policy is an important influence on current policy. In fact, Hall suggests that policy responds "less directly to social and economic conditions than it does to the consequences of past policy" (Hall, 1993, p. 277). Moreover, consistent with Weir and Skocpol (1985), he argues that the interests and ideals that policy-makers choose to follow are influenced largely by what are termed *policy legacies* (i.e., previous policy shapes future policy). In addition, experts in a policy field in which policy change is being considered tend to be very influential in the learning process. They may advise the state from a privileged and critical position at high-level meetings between the bureaucracy and intellectual leaders.

Hall's portrayal of the policy change process suggests a highly elitist activity from which some groups may be shut out. This suggests that policy changes reflect the interests of those attending such high-level meetings more than those who are likely to be adversely affected by policy changes.

Social learning refers to policy change that results from both new information about an issue and learning from past policy experience (Hall, 1993). Social learning, therefore, is primarily concerned with the role ideas play in policymaking. The social learning process is dominated by government officials and highly placed experts whose power is likely to be particularly influential. For Hall, this influence is especially the case in technical policy fields such as environmental or energy policy. The health policy area can be added to these technical policy fields where the views of experts are especially valued. Hall's interest is also to examine how knowledge created by scientists and social scientists influences the policymaking process (Hall, 1993).

Different Types of Policy Change

A further aim of Hall's model is to analyze how policy-makers apply knowledge to effect different types of policy changes. Two such kinds of changes are routine (first- and second-order) and radical (third-order) policy changes (Hall, 1993). Hall terms these two kinds of policy change as *normal* and *paradigmatic* patterns of policy change (Hall, 1993).

First-order change has many elements of incrementalism, such as "satisficing" and "routinized" decision making (Hall, 1993). Such changes are usually minor adjustments to policy, such as increasing physicians' fees for various medical procedures, or increasing or lowering monthly social assistance payments. This constitutes much of the day-to-day activities of governments and agencies.

Second-order change usually involves developing new policy instruments and moving toward strategic action (Hall, 1993). An example of second-order change would be a provincial government's decision to develop a Telehealth line for the public to call for health advice from registered nurses to reduce inappropriate use of hospital emergency departments. Another instance might be modifying the means by which individuals could apply for social assistance and the means by which such applications would be processed. In both these first- and second-order policy change processes, the overall goals of a policy area basically remain the same.

Third-order change is characterized by radical (paradigmatic) change in the overall terms of policy discourse. This change would result in diverging from the "received" or dominant paradigm (Hall, 1993). As defined in chapter 2, a paradigm is a set of beliefs concerning the nature of an issue and the problems or set of issues associated with it. For example, one paradigm of health care is that it be seen as a commodity subject to being bought or sold on the market. A competing paradigm would be that health care is a basic human right and therefore should be an entitlement of citizenship. Not all paradigmatic issues are as profound in their implications as this particular one, but paradigm disagreements usually involve a fairly significant discrepancy between sets of ideas and values.

Hall suggests that paradigmatic shifts involve simultaneous changes in all three components of policy: (1) the instrument settings; (2) the instruments themselves; and (3) the policy goals and objectives. For example, the creation of a national public health care system in Canada in 1961 represented a shift from a system based on ability to pay for health services to a system based on service provision in response to need (Romanow, 2002). Rather than health care being funded by individuals on an out-of-pocket basis, the government now pays for health care from general revenues. The policy goal of ensuring that all Canadian citizens receive care on the basis of need rather than ability to pay represents a paradigmatic policy change.

In the health-related policy area, government decisions to withdraw from providing affordable housing for those in need, which occurred federally during the 1990s, would represent a paradigmatic shift (Bryant, 2004a; Shapcott, 2004). Frequently, these kinds of profound shifts are made with little warning and little, if any, public consultation.

The Importance of Politics in Paradigmatic Policy Change

Noting the relative lack of attention in the policy change literature to the role politics plays in understanding third-order policy change, Hall argues that policy paradigms are never completely understandable solely in scientific or technical terms (Hall, 1993). Instead, the change from one paradigm to another is more likely to result from political influences rather than the accumulation of scientific knowledge.

Indeed, the policy change outcome may also depend on the arguments of competing groups in a policy arena and from the advantages or disadvantages these various interest groups possess within this broader policy arena. In addition, resources available to competing political actors for advocacy activities may determine the shape of policy change. Sometimes external factors such as changes in the economy (the onset of a recession or surging economic growth) can affect the capacity of a group of actors to impose its ideas or policy paradigm on others.

Since each paradigm has its own explanation of how the world of policy-makers works, it is often difficult, if not impossible, for advocates of different paradigms to agree on a common body of knowledge on which to favour one paradigm over another. Yet sometimes paradigmatic change is a gradual process shaped by experiences accrued from policy experimentation and policy failure.

Box 4.2: Advocacy Coalition Framework

Like Hall's policy paradigms, Sabatier's advocacy coalition framework is a learning model of policy change. The advocacy coalition framework of policy change is a conceptual framework for examining policy change of a decade or more (Sabatier, 1993). This model attempts to explain the strategic interaction of political elites and policy experts in a policy community or subsystem. The policy subsystem consists of ideologically based advocacy coalitions that are involved in a particular policy area. Coalitions can include actors from both the public and private sectors, such as social scientists, senior civil servants, the media, politicians, and interest groups. The coalition can also include actors from local and regional governments involved in policy formulation and implementation. These actors can all play a role in the generation, dissemination, and evaluation of policy ideas (Dunleavy, 1981; Heclo, 1978; Milward & Wamsley, 1984).

Consistent with Heclo, Sabatier argues that policy change occurs within a social, economic, and political context (Heclo, 1974). Policy change can also involve competition for power and conflicting activities within the community that emerge to address a policy problem. Sabatier is particularly interested in the role of technical information—or expert knowledge—and ideology throughout the policy process. Some key concepts require examination.

Belief system: Subsystem members can come from different advocacy coalitions, and this shapes their activities (Sabatier, 1993). All share a set of normative and causal beliefs (ideology). Beliefs shape policy positions, instrumental decisions, and the information selected to support specific policy positions. The belief system consists of three structural categories. These categories are termed the *deep (normative) core*, which comprises fundamental normative and ontological beliefs; the *near (policy) core*, which are the coalition's policy positions; and *secondary aspects*, which are instrumental decisions and information inquiries enlisted to support the policy core. The coalition's strategies (policy core) and secondary aspects respond to perceptions about the adequacy of governmental decisions in relation to the perceived problem. Changes in strategy can include lobbying for major institutional revisions at the broad policy level, or minor revisions at the operational level. The differences among the components of the belief systems are not always clear.

Change in the larger environment: Sabatier identifies a range of factors that can influence an advocacy coalition and its activities as well as its success in effecting policy change (Sabatier, 1993). Stable parameters and dynamic external events are identified as sources of new information that can affect perceptions of policy issues and lead to alterations in the belief systems of advocacy coalitions. Stable influences, such as established policy parameters and the social, legal, and resource features of the society, persist over a period of several decades. These influences frame and constrain the activities of advocacy coalitions. Dynamic influences, such as changes in global socio-economic conditions (e.g., the 1973 Arab oil embargo or the election of Ronald Reagan in 1980), can alter the composition and resources of various coalitions. These influences also affect how public policy is carried out within the subsystem. Personnel changes at senior levels within government ministries can also affect the political resources of various coalitions and the decisions that are made at the collective and operational levels.

Policy-oriented learning: A key component of the framework is policy-oriented learning. This refers to relatively enduring changes in thought or behavioural intentions that are based on previous policy experience (Sabatier, 1993). Learning occurs through internal feedback mechanisms and includes perceptions of external dynamics and increased knowledge of problem parameters. Such learning is instrumental, since it is assumed that members of the various coalitions seek to improve their understanding of the world in order to further the achievement of their policy objectives. This is termed the *enlightenment function* of public policymaking, which implies that political actors are more committed to improving the quality of public policy decisions than to furthering their own political interests.

Paradigmatic shift can also occur as a result of an accumulation of inconsistencies in the old paradigm through testing new forms of policy. The accumulation of problems associated with existing policy can weaken its dominance if its adherents are unable to explain new developments. For example, the outbreak of severe acute respiratory syndrome (SARS) in Toronto in 2003 was recognized as resulting from the lack of a central institution to monitor disease outbreaks in various jurisdictions (National

Advisory Committee on SARS and Public Health, 2003). In response to the SARS outbreak, the Public Health Agency was established, with one centre given responsibility for monitoring infection outbreaks in Canada and elsewhere.

Another example is that the spread of SARS in Toronto from hospital to hospital was identified as resulting from many nurses working part-time and having to move from one hospital to another on any given day (National Advisory Committee on SARS and Public Health, 2003). One response was to review the employment situation of nurses and develop public policy to address the part-time employment situation of nurses.

Therefore, policy failures such as the SARS outbreak or an explosion of homelessness or food bank use can bring about a shift in paradigmatic authority. These changes in policy can heighten conflict between competing paradigms (Hall, 1993). Efforts to explain these new and potentially problematic phenomena by persisting in using an old paradigm can further undermine its intellectual coherence. Politicians may be especially instrumental in deciding whose knowledge claim—and whose paradigm—becomes authoritative and will prevail in a policy arena.

Hall's most widely quoted application of his model was his explanation of the shift from Keynesian welfare state economic policy in Britain to a monetarist approach during the 1970–1989 period (Hall, 1993). Keynesianism had led to the development of the welfare state and hence significant government intervention to provide publicly funded health care. However, economic stresses led to a questioning of the value of such a paradigm.

British politicians intervened when social scientists were unable to resolve the dispute between these Keynesian and monetarist paradigms (Hall, 1993). The politicians, who happened to be Conservative, favoured monetarism because it was consistent with their neoliberal ideology of wanting to advance the role the market played in allocating resources at the expense of the state.

The British government thus launched a new era in economic policymaking that, while drawing on social science, did so in a selective manner to support the very right-wing inclinations of Margaret Thatcher, the leader of the Conservative Party. Monetarists successfully attributed rising unemployment and other economic problems to perceived failures of Keynesianism. Hall concludes that social science ideas in this case and others enter policy debates through the broader political system rather than through the traditional knowledge contributions of a narrow network of experts and officials.

Hall therefore shows how understanding changes, such as shifting economic policy from Keynesianism to monetarism, requires analysis of the influence institutions have to impede new ideas or help bring them into the policy discourse and public policy decisions (Fischer, 2003). Changes in the British economy, specifically an unemployment crisis and high levels of inflation, challenging the principles of Keynesianism, contributed to the paradigm shift to monetarism. These changes therefore provided an opportunity for the application of new paradigmatic ideas from the Conservative Party (Fischer, 2003).

Limitations of Policy Paradigms

Hall provides a compelling explanation of the shift to monetarism and shows how institutions can structure outcomes. The focus on institutions, however, precludes other considerations. For example, his model fails to consider how structures and interests influence political, economic, and social change. He seems unconcerned about the close association between certain interests, such as social scientists and the political system.

Moreover, Hall does not consider how the Thatcher government deliberately excluded particular groups from the political process. For example, after her election as prime minister, Thatcher undermined trade unions in the United Kingdom, thereby increasing class conflict (Krieger, 1987; Towers, 1989). This increase in class conflict distorted the policy change process by weakening the ability of information and knowledge supportive of the working class to influence policy change. More overtly, she also abolished the Greater London City Council, since it appeared to oppose her policies. These actions represented clear exercise of raw political power that deliberately limited the ability of opposition groups to challenge these policy changes (Raphael, 2014).

Hall identifies the influence of political elites on the policy change process, but does so in a manner that implies that this relationship and its impact on the policy change process is unproblematic. This close relationship between elites and policy-makers may be construed as policy development in the service of particular segments or interests of the population to the detriment of others.

In addition, Hall articulates a single path to paradigmatic change. Paradigmatic change occurs in response to a series of policy failures, a shift in political power, or external shocks. But there is another trajectory for paradigmatic policy change. Paradigmatic policy change can also result from a series of incremental policy changes over several years (Coleman, Skogstad, & Atkinson, 1997).

Hall recognizes political considerations as having a significant role in bringing about change (Hall, 1993). He demonstrates how Thatcher's contingent within the Conservative Party contributed to shifting state machinery toward monetarism. The model provides some useful analytic tools for classifying different types of policy change. However, it depicts the public policy arena as being almost exclusively the purview of senior civil servants, policy analysts, and academics—or knowledge experts.

While much policy debate occurs at this level, other interests mobilize to try to influence policy change outcomes. Hall describes state and societal actors as the chief agents of learning, but does not consider the relationship between the civil service and the general public, or the relationship between the state and civil society.

Identifying these concerns is important to draw attention to inequalities in the distribution of power and opportunities to influence policy change outcomes. In Hall's model, the shift from one policy paradigm to another emerges as a largely academic debate in which politicians seem to arbitrate over whose paradigm will dominate in a given policy arena. There is a need for a model that considers the impact of an unequal distribution of political power and a broader range of political actors, and defines the role of the state in public policy debates.

In a more recent publication, Hall considers the prospects for the emergence of a new paradigm in the wake of the economic crisis of 2008, changing the dominant economic paradigms over the last 60 years (Hall, 2013). He suggests that the conditions for a major shift in policy—growing income inequality, discontentment with austerity programs intended to reduce government debt—may lead to a new era. He adds that a shift to a new paradigm is often precipitated by a new economic paradigm that gathers strong political appeal. This does not appear to bode well for the potential of a new paradigm to address income inequality and poverty.

KNOWLEDGE PARADIGMS POLICY CHANGE FRAMEWORK

The knowledge paradigms policy change framework builds on Hall's insights into policy change and the role of political ideology by incorporating a concern with inequality, conflict, political ideology, and power in the political process (Bryant, 2002a, 2002b). It also explicitly considers how various forms of knowledge can influence the different types of changes contained in Hall's models. Figure 4.1 shows the framework and its key components.

Figure 4.1: Model Informing the Policy Change Process

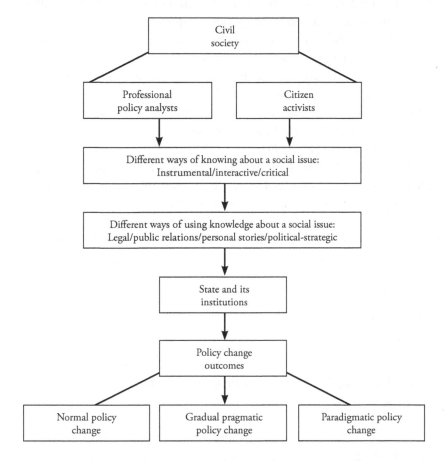

Source: Bryant, T. (2009). Housing and health. In D. Raphael (Ed.), *Social determinants of health* (2nd ed.) (p. 246). Toronto: Canadian Scholars' Press.

Policy Actors

The first component of the model considers the various actors in the policy change process. While Hall focused on technical experts, policy-makers, and elected officials, other segments of the population can be involved in the policy change process.

Civil society: Beginning at the top of the figure, civil society encapsulates the values and beliefs of the citizenry, as well as its institutions and traditions, thereby providing a context for the policy change process.

Professional policy analysts and *citizen activists*: Civil society consists of many groups, including the market, trade unions, professional associations such as medical and nursing associations, other health professions' associations, and faith communities, among others. The groups of interests identified in the figure are professional policy analysts, the experts in Hall's policy paradigms, and citizen activists, because these are the groups that try to act on the political system to influence public policy.

Some political actors constitute a hybrid. That is, they usually possess post-secondary degrees and specialized knowledge in a particular policy field. They may work as policy analysts for trade unions or social and health policy think tanks. These aggregates are politically engaged groups of civil society and are not necessarily mutually exclusive, nor are they intended to be representative of all groups in civil society. They represent different political entities in the public policy process.

An important element here is the inequality in the capacity of each group to influence the political process in terms of finances and other resources such as education. Both kinds of groups engage in knowledge creation and advocacy activities (see Box 4.3).

Box 4.3: Editorial: Better Health, Lower Costs
Toronto Star

The case for a national pharmacare program, covering prescription drug costs for all Canadians, is now noticeably stronger. A persuasive new study analyzing the cost of such coverage has found it would save a great deal of money, especially for the private sector, with relatively little expense to government.

"In many of the scenarios that we modelled, universal pharmacare was cost-neutral for governments," said Dr. Danielle Martin, one of the study's authors and a vice-president at Women's College Hospital in Toronto. "This goes against current thinking that a universal program will cost more."

These findings, published on Monday in the *Canadian Medical Association Journal,* should be required reading for provincial and territorial politicians and especially in Ottawa, where federal determination to make pharmacare happen has been noticeably lacking.

Universal public drug coverage could lower annual spending on prescription medicine in Canada by $7.3 billion, conclude the study's authors. Several scenarios were developed on what such a program might cost government, with the worst-case estimate pegging additional costs at $5.4 billion and the best-case scenario producing a net saving of $2.9 billion.

Under a mid-range "base scenario," total cost to governments would be $958 million. But that would generate an $8.2-billion drop in private-sector spending on prescription drugs. It's an investment well worth making. Savings of this magnitude would put Canadian per capita prescription drug spending on par with levels in countries such as Switzerland, Austria and Spain, note the authors. (Nations such as the United Kingdom, New Zealand and Sweden spend even less.)

Canadians currently shell out an average of 50 per cent more, per capita, than people in other developed countries. And it's no coincidence that Canada is alone in having a universal health insurance system that does not include the cost of prescription drugs.

Instead, what we have in this country is a mishmash of private drug plans— with access typically depending on where a person works—and a patchwork of federal and provincial systems, typically serving groups deemed to be in need, such as the elderly and welfare recipients. Their prescriptions are already funded by taxpayers.

It's a woefully inadequate system that leaves many Canadians with no drug coverage at all, especially the young, the self-employed and people working for small businesses that can't afford to provide a drug plan. As a result, millions of Canadians lack money to buy the medicines they need.

A national pharmacare program would unite the country's purchasing power and use economies of scale to help negotiate lower prices for both generic and brand-name drugs. That's the main way other countries have managed to control expenditure.

There would be a modest increase in one cost category: uninsured people who can't afford medicine will finally fill the prescriptions they've been given. But there would be additional savings, too, by eliminating the duplication of legal, technical and administrative work inherent in Canada's existing, disjointed approach. The net result would be a far more cost-effective system.

But the goal of national pharmacare isn't just to save money. Prescription medication can keep people healthy, ease pain, avoid trips to the hospital, and even save lives.

Pharmacare is ultimately about giving all Canadians access to the medicines they need—regardless of where they work, the province where they live, their age, their medical condition or whether they're on welfare. It's about closing a disgraceful gap in our universal health-care system.

Source: Better Health, Lower Costs [Editorial]. (2015, March 17). *Toronto Star*, p. A12.

Professional policy analysts are perceived as having specialized knowledge that gives them an aura of objectivity and authority, which can enhance their credibility in the public domain. In contrast, citizen activists may be seen as lay experts. The wider public may perceive citizen activists as addressing issues that affect them personally and therefore as self-interested. For example, a university professor or policy analyst speaking out against barriers to accessing health care for marginalized communities may be considered to have more credibility in the public domain than someone who is actually experiencing barriers to accessing health care services. Citizen activists may also advocate on behalf of communities that experience barriers in their access to health care services, yet not actually experience such barriers themselves.

Different ways of knowing about a social issue—instrumental/interactive/ critical: One typology of knowledge—the Habermas-Park typology—represents different ways of knowing about or understanding an issue. According to this typology, there are three types of knowledge: instrumental, interactive, and critical knowledge (Habermas, 1968; Park, 1993). The different types of knowledge represent different approaches to understanding the nature of knowledge and how it is created.

Box 4.4: Habermas's Typology of Knowledge

Habermas devised three categories of knowledge that Park has refined as instrumental knowledge, interactive knowledge, and critical knowledge. Park's interest in these categories is to understand the role of lay knowledge to engage in participatory research that helps to empower marginalized populations and give them a voice in the political process.

Instrumental knowledge is knowledge produced by the traditional sciences through systematic research and hypothesis testing. It involves detachment and objectivity on the part of the researcher. This knowledge aims to control external events and create explanatory theories of causal relationships. An example is carrying out an experiment on a new pharmaceutical product or medication to test its efficacy in treating a health condition. The experiment would consist of an experimental group with the health condition who would receive the drug, and a control group that also has the health condition as well as similar characteristics as the experimental group, such as age, income level, education, and so on. The control group does not receive the drug. The researcher carries out statistical analysis to compare the results for the two groups. Did the experimental group improve their symptoms as a result of taking the medication? Or did the control group experience similar improvements in their symptoms?

Interactive knowledge is created through exchanges or conversations with other people. People exchange information and actions supported by common experience, tradition, history, and culture. This knowledge builds connections among members of a community and enables the formation of community. An example of interactive knowledge would be a lived experience such as asking people what they would do for their children if they were unable to find a child care space, or understanding the culture of nurses working in a particular ward of a hospital. What is the nurses' informal understanding of their work, and their relationships with each other, physicians, other health professions, and patients?

Critical knowledge is derived from reflection and action. Citizens acquire critical knowledge by questioning or challenging their life conditions and identifying what they wish to achieve as self-determining social beings. Through critical knowledge, they can mobilize others to challenge existing public policies and programs that govern their lives. Thus, critical knowledge has a transformative element. An example of critical knowledge would be the relative power of nurses and doctors and how this developed. Nurses would acquire a critical understanding of why they are subordinate to doctors and hence undervalued for their contribution to patient care.

Source: Park, P. (1993). What is participatory research? A theoretical and methodological perspective. In P. Park, M. Brydon-Miller, B. Hall, & T. Jackson (Eds.), *Voices of change: Participatory research in the United States and Canada* (pp. 1–19). Toronto: Ontario Institute for Studies in Education.

Instrumental knowledge represents a positivist-rationalist approach to problem solving, as exemplified by the biomedical approach defined in chapter 2. It is usually associated with experts such as epidemiologists, social scientists, physicians, or others in the health field, for example, with specialized knowledge perceived as objective and value-free.

Interactive knowledge develops from people's daily interactions with one another or their perceptions and understandings of a health condition, for example. This type of knowledge can be stories or concepts that people create in order to make sense of an event or experience. For example, nurses in a hospital may discuss with one another how doctors treat them poorly and do not respect their professionalism. They may, however, lack insight into why doctors treat them disrespectfully. Another example might be someone trying to make sense of why they have a particular disease or health condition. They may attribute their affliction to exposures to toxins, but may not consider that it could have something to do with government public or housing policy, or to conditions in their community. They would not see their disease or condition as a problem of low income, which means they can afford only housing with poor conditions that impair their health.

Both instrumental and interactive knowledge may tend to depoliticize issues. Interactive knowledge is consistent with the interpretive research paradigm discussed in chapter 2, in which all perceptions and understandings are treated as having equal validity. There is little recognition of the societal tendency to privilege certain types of knowledge and understanding over others.

Critical knowledge reflects an awareness of power and its influences on society, and an explicit interest in initiating political action to change life conditions. Thus, unlike instrumental or interactive knowledge, critical knowledge has a transformative component. Critical knowledge is consistent with the structural-critical and political economy perspectives defined in chapters 2 and 3.

For example, members of the Chalk River community in Ontario opposed the reopening of the nuclear plant for fear of increasing the incidence of cancer diagnoses among residents. They saw a potential relationship between the incidence of cancer and the presence of a nuclear plant. They lobbied the state, which they saw as authorizing the reopening of the plant with little concern about the potential impact on the health of the local community.

Another example is the recovery process in the aftermath of Hurricane Katrina in New Orleans. This process revealed that poverty in the United States is highly racialized and gendered. A CNN reporter remarked at the time that residents were "so poor and ... so black" (Blitzer, 2005).

Both aggregates of policy actors—expert actors and citizen activists—may draw upon all three ways of knowing in their political activities. They all engage in processes to decide what kind of evidence they need to convince the government of their position.

Different ways of using knowledge to lobby—legal, public relations, political-strategic, personal stories approaches: Professional policy analysts and citizens use different activities and strategies to convince policy-makers to make policy changes. Lobbying is political pressure that aims to achieve a particular

Box 4.5: Feminist Policy Analysis: A Form of Critical Knowledge

Rational policy analysis, heir to positivism, attempts to imbue political action and policy activity with the attributes of science (Albaek, 1995). Science is concerned with a methodical, detached approach to data collection and analysis of policy options. Rational policy analysis has been the dominant approach to policy analysis.

From a feminist perspective, Hawkesworth (1988) criticizes positivism as having a "misplaced concern with objectivity" about the influence of personal experiences. The biases and perceptions of the observer are seen as hampering understanding of the phenomenon under study. Hawkesworth argues that this concern with objectivity masks reality. An important aim of feminism is to make apparent how social values such as racism and sexism "filter perception, mediate arguments, and structure research investigations" (Hawkesworth, 1994, p. 21). Positivism separates social phenomena from their social and political context, a process known as *context-stripping*. Feminism is a form of critical knowledge that attempts to explain the power dynamic between women and men and inequality between men and women. The economic and political structures are considered to reinforce gender inequality.

In an era of economic globalization, these issues—that is, differences between groups in a society—become especially salient and accentuated, and the basis for increased social and economic inequality. As Grabb (2007) notes, differences between groups are accentuated as political power becomes more concentrated and the state divests on issues that it once regulated.

policy change. These approaches—legal, public relations, political/strategic, and personal stories—are strategies. They all have elements of the three ways of knowing and involve processes of knowledge dissemination to promote a policy position.

The legal approach is the use of legal knowledge, cases, and analysis. Public relations refers to how advocates market or present their ideas to government. The political-strategic approach uses knowledge about the political process and how to work one's way through it to lobby government and present policy ideas. Finally, personal stories refer to the use of narratives about experiences as a result of public policies. For example, former patients may present information to a legislative committee about how laying off registered nurses affected the quality of care they received when they were in hospital. Fewer nurses means that patients may not have their needs addressed as quickly as may be necessary.

All of these approaches are about how to present information to government in order to influence public policy decisions. They are therefore informed by political considerations and questions of how advocates can effectively make their case on proposed policy changes and draw media attention to their efforts. Knowledge dissemination and issue promotion are also inherently political activities. Civil society actors present their policy ideas to government officials and opposition parties to achieve particular policy change outcomes. They also attempt to influence other civil society actors. They may form new alliances to enhance their political power. Media presence can help groups enhance their political power by increasing their visibility. This may help increase their visibility and generate public sympathy for their cause.

The state: The state consists of the government of the day and state institutions responsible for a policy domain. In Canada, state institutions consist of legislative bodies, including Parliament, the Senate, legislative committees, law-making institutions such as the courts, and ministries or government departments run by civil servants (Ham & Hill, 1984). These different components of the state exist at different levels. In Canada, for example, there are municipal, provincial/territorial, and federal levels of government, with varying degrees of responsibility for enacting and enforcing laws in public policy. The state represents the legitimate use of force to achieve certain objectives and outcomes (Ham & Hill, 1984). In most jurisdictions, the state is led by a political party that is elected by citizens every four years.

The state is not always well conceptualized in models of public policy. It is often presented as one-dimensional—as an essentially neutral or apolitical organization that mediates among competing interests. In this way, it is consistent with the pluralist view of policymaking presented in chapter 3.

The state has numerous roles within the many areas that constitute health policy in modern capitalist societies such as Canada, the United States, and the United Kingdom. The economic system is integrally related to the political system, and state roles are often contradictory. The state must promote economic development while at the same time ensuring social order and solidarity among different social classes and other groups in society (Teeple, 2000). Thus, in addition to identifying the institutions that make up the state, the links between the state and the social system—including hierarchies of class, gender, ability/disability, immigrant status, and race, among others—must be clearly articulated.

With the creation of medicare, the federal and provincial/territorial governments assumed significant roles in health policy. The federal government developed legislation to use its spending power to help finance health care programs in each province and territory. As discussed in chapter 1, the British North America Act and the Canadian Constitution assign responsibility for the administration of health care to the provincial and territorial governments.

Since the 1980s, the federal and many provincial governments have attempted to reduce the role of government in health care and related health policy areas. Few governments appear willing to address inequalities in health outcomes in the Canadian population. This retreat of government has also occurred in other areas of health policy. For example, Lexchin (2006, 2013) shows how government has ceded its responsibility for regulating the pharmaceutical industry by allowing the industry to regulate itself and test its own products for consumer safety, and by not conducting its own independent tests of new drug products. Many consider this approach as providing inadequate protection for consumers, and believe it is a conflict of interest for the industry to regulate itself.

Civil servants, such as deputy ministers and senior policy analysts, interact with both groups of civil society actors in policy discussions. An assumption of this framework is that the state or government of the day is not neutral, but has its own political agenda. The government as a political actor can try to exclude civil society actors from the process by selecting or filtering out knowledge provided by specific civil society actors.

Policy outcomes: The knowledge paradigms framework incorporates Hall's (1993) typology of policy change: first- and second-order change as normal policy change, and third-order change as paradigmatic change that involves a fundamental shift in overall policy goals. The framework identifies two potential paths to paradigmatic change. The first is a series of incremental changes that results in a paradigm shift. The second is an accumulation of policy failure and anomalies in the received paradigm that results in a sharp paradigmatic shift (Coleman et al., 1997). Deciding not to change policy is also a policy decision. The government always makes these decisions on the basis of what they perceive as valid reasons.

This framework can serve as a template for analyzing the policy change process on a case-by-case basis. It can also be used to understand a government's general approach to policy change over time. The framework was applied to a case study of Women's College Hospital during the hospital restructuring process in Ontario, Canada, in 1996. It was also applied to a study of government changes to a health-related public policy—rent control in Ontario—around that same period.

THE CASE OF WOMEN'S COLLEGE HOSPITAL AND THE HEALTH SERVICES RESTRUCTURING COMMISSION

This case study focused on the experience of Women's College Hospital during the hospital restructuring process from 1995 to 1998 in Toronto (Bryant, 2003). The purpose of the study was to learn about the knowledge activities used by individuals attempting to influence the health policy change process to see whether and how knowledge influenced the outcome. The specific policy goal of the hospital was to forestall its proposed closure by the Hospital Services Restructuring Commission during a period of economic retrenchment and health care service rationalization.

Box 4.6: Case Study of Women's College Hospital: Methodology and Data Analysis

Document review and in-depth interviews with key informants explored the relationship between knowledge and the influence of civil society actors on the policy change process through the exemplar of the Health Services Restructuring Commission. The document review identified key issues in health policy and the motivations of state and civil society actors and their epistemological assumptions. Friends of Women's College Hospital provided copies of all of their own and the hospital's submissions to the Health Services Restructuring Commission and access to materials on the campaign against the proposed merger with Toronto Hospital in 1989–1990. This information supplemented the data provided by in-depth interviews. The in-depth interviews provided insights about participants' perceptions of knowledge, and how they selected the information and evidence to use in their briefs. Interviews were recorded and transcribed. Themes and issues contained within the data were identified.

The data were organized using concepts and categories identified in the policy change model. For example, civil society actors were organized into the categories of professional policy analysts and citizens. Additional categories were created for activists who were paid employees of interest groups. The knowledge used by these actors was classified into categories of interactive, rational/scientific, and critical. Policy change patterns were identified and coded using the typology in the policy change framework: normal, paradigmatic, and gradual paradigmatic change. These initial concepts and categories were tested on emergent understandings. New categories were developed to fit the data.

Analysis involved identification of key ideas associated with the use of knowledge in political advocacy and policy change. Inductive analysis was used to analyze notes taken during the document review. Comments from the interviews were used to devise additional categories to accurately reflect emerging themes and patterns in the data. This approach allowed for consideration of alternative explanations and understandings. Participants identified a range of issues on knowledge and its uses in political advocacy. The focus was on issues relating to the types of knowledge brought to bear on the hospital restructuring process by Women's College Hospital.

Of all the Toronto hospitals facing closure, Women's College Hospital presents an interesting case. Women's College Hospital grew out of the Ontario Women's Medical College, established in 1911 (Kendrick & Slade, 1993). The founding of the college was a response to the refusal of the University of Toronto to accept women as medical students in the late 19th century. The college provided an opportunity for women to study and practise medicine. The hospital retained the word *College* in its name as a reminder of this history. In 1960, Women's College Hospital sought affiliation with the University of Toronto and became a teaching hospital.

Starting in the late 1980s, Ontario governments grew increasingly concerned about controlling hospital expenditures. One of several hospitals running a deficit during this period, Women's College Hospital received one-time-only bridge grants of $2 million for the 1988/89 and 1989/90 fiscal years on the condition that it eliminate its deficit (Lownsbrough, 1990). In October 1989, the hospital board voted in favour of pursuing a merger with the larger Toronto Hospital, which had already merged with its western division, Toronto Western Hospital.

Women's College Hospital's medical staff association and other staff opposed the proposed merger. Friends of Women's College Hospital was formed to oppose the merger and worked with the medical staff association on this aim. By reframing the issue as a stakeholder debate, these combined forces defeated the merger at a public meeting, where 648 of 700 hospital shareholders voted against the merger.

In November 1995, the newly elected provincial Conservative government introduced legislation—Bill 26, the Savings and Restructuring Act (also referred to as the Omnibus Bill)—that created the Health Services Restructuring Commission (HSRC) (The Caledon Institute, 2001). The bill empowered the commission to close and merge hospitals across Ontario in order to eliminate $1.3 billion from the hospital budget within two years. In

Metropolitan Toronto, the goal was to close 12 of 44 hospitals. The commission recommended closing Women's College Hospital and merging its in-patient services with Sunnybrook Health Sciences Centre.

In the end, Women's College Hospital applied sufficient pressure to force the HSRC to reverse its decision to close the hospital. Specifically, it threatened to sue the commission, which helped to secure the outcome the hospital sought. Not only did the hospital avert closure, it legally secured its existence in legislation—a first in any jurisdiction—and was reconfigured as an ambulatory care centre for women's health programs. It has since reclaimed its independent status, as the Ontario Liberal government severed the merger in 2006.

Through document review and interviews with key strategists for the hospital and policy analysts, among others, the case study considered how the board of Women's College Hospital influenced the health policy change outcome (Bryant, 2001, 2003). Of key interest was whether knowledge presented by Women's College Hospital was the decisive factor in the final decision of the commission.

Box 4.7: Case of Women's College Hospital during the Hospital Restructuring Process in Ontario, 1995

"Without the word being used, it was defined as woman-driven and woman-centred and woman-positive at its founding ... in direct response to discrimination from the University of Toronto ... you wouldn't necessarily use the term 'feminist' ... if you look at what was said and you look at the values and whatever the defining term was, it was about equal opportunity."

—Participant Interview

Source: Bryant, T. (2003). A critical examination of the hospital restructuring process in Ontario, Canada. *Health Policy, 64,* 193–205.

Among the findings was that Women's College Hospital advocates used various forms of evidence to avert closure in its dealings with the HSRC. By doing so, it mobilized women across the province to help fight the closure.

Yet, while there was careful selection and deployment of various forms of knowledge in its submissions to the commission and in informing its supporters, it was the combination of political skills and access to the government that may have clinched the outcome for the hospital. The hospital's strategists arranged meetings with Cabinet ministers in the Ontario government through contacts of board members. Some of the themes that emerged from this analysis have direct implications for understanding the policy change process.

FINDINGS FROM THE WOMEN'S COLLEGE HOSPITAL STUDY

The detailed findings from this case study are available (Bryant, 2003). Generally, it was found that advocates for Women's College Hospital used various forms of evidence to avert closure in their dealings with the Health Services Restructuring Commission. By doing so, they mobilized women across the province to help fight the closure.

HSRC's Emphasis on Quantitative Evidence

The commission was identified as being focused on objective, quantitative indicators such as the condition of the physical plant of a hospital, the number of patients receiving care, and the number of procedures carried out at a given hospital, rather than information about the experiences that women had when they were patients at the hospital. This focus led to the exclusion of quality of care issues and the neglect of women's health issues.

Feminist Issues and Feminist Policy Analysis

The strategists used gender and gender issues to market the hospital. They viewed the hospital as committed to feminist principles, a pioneer in women's health research, and as having a history of providing quality health services to women. The uniqueness of the hospital was also expressed in terms of its organization of power and its collaborative approach to care.

Use of Legal Arguments and Analysis

Legal arguments and analysis were applied in both the 1989 and 1995 anti-merger campaigns. During the 1989 campaign, the issue was defined as a shareholder fight. Advocates sought legal advice on litigation options, although litigation was not pursued. Participants perceived legal arguments and analysis as strengthening the case of the hospital in the restructuring process.

Knowledge Is Political

It was concluded that knowledge and its use were profoundly political in this case. Both the government and the advocates saw each piece of information provided through the lens of political ideology. When considering the hospital's outcome, some advocates considered the hospital unsuccessful, since it lost its independence, while others saw it as being successful, since it secured its existence in legislation. As one interview participant argued, it may have been not lack of knowledge but lack of power that determined the outcome in the restructuring process.

In summary, the use of various forms of knowledge was consistent with the conceptual framework presented. The findings add to an understanding of how different forms of knowledge can influence the health policy development process. Particularly important was not only the gender and abilities of the hospital strategists, but also their close association with the governing Conservative Party at Queen's Park. Many were lawyers and highly skilled, and therefore knew how to strategize to meet their political objectives. In other words, specific interests drove the process. The elite did not achieve the outcome it sought, which was retaining the independence of Women's College Hospital. Thus, in the end, the outcome can be attributed not so much to knowledge and its uses during the restructuring process, but rather to the dominance of specific interests and structures that ensured particular policy outcomes.

Women represented an important constituency that the Ontario Conservative government did not wish to offend. Women's College Hospital represented the health interests of predominantly white, middle-class, professional women. There was little concern with the health issues of marginalized women, such as women of colour, women who are homeless, and other communities of women who may use the health care system, but lack a political voice to assert their interests in the political arena.

Different Ways of Knowing about a Social Issue

Different ways of knowing were used to influence policy change in this case. The approach of Women's College Hospital to the selection of knowledge and evidence was affected by the priorities of the Health Services Restructuring Commission and the commitments of the hospital's board.

Since the commission emphasized instrumental knowledge in its use of objective indicators, such as volume of care issues, program levels, clinical activity, and the state of the physical plants of hospitals, the strategists provided these kinds of information, as well as interactive and critical information. This evidence and other information were developed through legal cases. Legal arguments are made using verifiable evidence and judicial rulings. Rulings arising from legal cases are considered authoritative and demand discipline in the construction of cases.

The differences in approaches to knowledge used by the commission and Women's College Hospital can be understood as a clash of world views. The hospital emphasized quality of care and women's perspectives on health care issues, while the commission emphasized objective indicators such as the number of procedures carried out at a hospital to justify hospital closures. The impact of this framing was to limit debate and depoliticize the process, and potentially silence opposition to the restructuring process and how it was carried out.

The case of Women's College Hospital demonstrates the use of instrumental, interactive, and critical ways of knowing in political advocacy. While knowledge was important and helped to establish the credibility of the hospital, it did not emerge as the decisive factor in the case. Political considerations were more important in shaping the outcome.

The relative success of the hospital can be attributed to a number of factors. Among these is its use of gender, its status as an institution, its capacity to initiate legal action to force a policy change to achieve its objectives, and the political connections of some board members to the Ontario Conservative government. Some board members were card-holding members of the Ontario Conservative Party. The hospital and women represented constituencies that the government did not wish to offend and identified as important to its future electoral success.

THE CASE OF THE TENANT PROTECTION ACT

The second case provides an example of analysis of a health-related public policy change. The case study on housing policy change focused on the Tenant Protection Act (Government of Ontario, 1997). This study systematically examined the context within which the new provincial regime changed rental housing policy from 1995 to 1998. It focused on how tenant advocates in Toronto, the largest urban centre in Ontario, attempted to influence the policy change process. A particular focus was how oral presentations that challenged the provisions of the legislation were constructed through the selection of specific forms of knowledge and evidence. These oral briefs were means by which tenant advocates constructed their arguments and selected evidence, and the epistemological commitments within these briefs shaped how decisions were made in their attempts to influence the government.

A number of other activities occurred at this time: media campaigns, speeches, material distribution by advocates, and Opposition party activities. The use of briefs provided a selected sample of information-rich exemplars of the processes used to influence government policy by civil society actors.

Canadian provincial governments have constitutional responsibility for providing social housing and rent control. Most provide some form of housing subsidy, but fiscal conservatism in recent years has reduced these subsidies. In Ontario from the 1970s until 1995, successive provincial governments were committed to rent regulation to protect an affordable rental housing stock in the private rental housing market, and to increase the number of social housing units.

In 1975, the Conservative government introduced rent-control legislation as an anti-inflation strategy. In 1995, the Conservative Party won a majority government on a Common Sense Revolution platform (Progressive Conservative Party of Ontario, 1995). This platform reversed many long-held commitments to social housing and rent control. For example, it emphasized cutting taxes and increasing efficiencies to reduce the provincial deficit. The document proposed shelter allowances for low-income populations, but did not identify the government's intention to eliminate rent control.

The 1996 Tenant Protection Act replaced all existing legislation related to rental housing and introduced vacancy decontrol to remove rent control one unit at a time (Government of Ontario, 1997). Vacancy decontrol allows landlords to increase rent without restriction when a tenant vacates a rental unit. The tenant is protected from large rent increases provided she or he does not move.

The act also amended the Ontario Human Rights Code to allow landlords to use income criteria to screen potential tenants. This amendment sharply reduced the access of low-income groups to housing. In addition, the government imposed a moratorium on social housing construction, ending the prospect of 18,000 planned social housing units. Shortly after its election, the government also reduced social assistance by 22 percent. These changes had severe implications for low-income populations who were dependent on these programs for shelter and income.

FINDINGS FROM THE CASE OF THE TENANT PROTECTION ACT

Detailed findings from this case are available (Bryant, 2004b). The findings were very similar to those of the Women's College Hospital case study. The advocates were all professional policy analysts, yet described a participatory process in which they drew upon their professional work as lawyers and community workers. They emphasized the use of a variety of forms of knowledge. Some collected primary data through systematic research processes consistent with positivist assumptions about knowledge and evidence. They also provided evidence that considered the lived experiences of low-income tenants and provided a critical analysis of how the proposed legislation would affect an especially vulnerable group of people.

Uses of Evidence

Empirical evidence applied in the briefs was grounded in the lived experience of tenants. Advocates emphasized the need for empirical data to support their claims and to persuade politicians and the public of the validity of their positions. Advocates also used legal analysis and arguments that contained elements of instrumental, interactive, and critical ways of knowing.

Getting on the Public Record

Participants did not believe that their presentations would change the legislation to address their issues. Participating in the public hearings, however, provided a means to mobilize tenants and plan for future changes in government to elect officials who would be more likely to address the concerns of low-income tenants.

Different Ways of Using Knowledge about a Social Issue

Participants used various strategies, including legal knowledge and interpretation of the provisions of the act. They also used personal stories drawn from their professional and clients' experiences with landlord and tenant issues, and political-strategic approaches to navigate the political system by meeting with senior civil servants in the Ministry of Housing to influence the government.

Finally, they met with Opposition parties to help them develop amendments to the proposed legislation. While the knowledge and evidence they presented did not influence the government, it helped Opposition parties in developing their positions. In the end, participants described the government as interested only in evidence that reinforced its ideological commitments.

The Role of Political Ideology

Participants identified how government ideology was a barrier to their effectiveness in the policy change process. Political ideology drove the legislation and therefore hampered their ability to protect the interests of their constituencies. Advocates considered the current regime in Ontario to be unreceptive to perspectives that did not agree with its own, and motivated solely by ideological considerations.

CONCLUSIONS FROM BOTH CASE STUDIES

Political ideology and influence play a particular role in both health care and health-related public policy change. The political ideology of the state shapes perspectives on health care and health-related issues and determines, in large part, the policy responses developed to address these issues. Political influence shapes government receptivity to information. Although knowledge came to the government from diverse sources inside and outside government, political influence and ideology emerged in the housing case study as one of the most important dynamics influencing housing policy change during the Harris Conservative regime in Ontario under Premier Mike Harris.

The case studies identified the complex of actors who can work to influence policy. They exemplified the existence and application of various forms of knowledge in the policy change process identified in the knowledge paradigms policy change framework. They also allow for specifying the kinds of change that eventually occur. In both case studies, political and economic structures and interests shaped the outcomes.

CONCLUSIONS

This chapter examined two approaches to understanding and explaining the policy change process. Hall's policy paradigms is primarily a rational model concerned with the role of ideas in shaping public policy change outcomes. Policy paradigms refer to the system of ideas in which policy-makers work. They determine the policy instruments and goals of policy, and define the issues that will be recognized as public issues requiring government action.

Policy paradigms focus on the role of social learning, whereby policy-makers make decisions based on experience with previous public policies and new information on a given issue in a policy field. As such, the policy paradigms model is concerned with the role of experts such as social scientists in the public policy process. Hall applied the model to understand the ascendance of neoliberalism led by Margaret Thatcher in the United Kingdom in the late 1970s. The model builds on the insights of historical institutionalism, which emphasizes how institutions structure politics and thereby influence political outcomes. Above all, it demonstrates how institutions can obstruct policy change.

The model considers a limited range of participants in the public policy process and seems to consider the close association between experts and policy-makers as unproblematic. The model does not seem to recognize inequality in access to the political system and in the distribution of political power as being important factors shaping the policy change process.

The knowledge paradigms policy change framework builds on Hall's insights into knowledge, but considers a broader range of knowledge and approaches to influencing the public policy process. The framework is also concerned with the role of political and economic structures such as political ideology, inequality, political power, and the privileging of information and groups in the political process. Applied to the cases of Women's College Hospital during the hospital restructuring process and changes to the Tenant Protection Act in Ontario, the framework highlights the influence of political issues upon knowledge development, state receptivity, and its eventual application.

Policy change, especially in health care and health-related public policy, can be politically charged. Many areas of health policy are contentious. Dominant health interests attempt to hide behind a veil of objectivity and intellectual detachment from issues. The aura of scientific inquiry can sometimes draw attention away from the highly conflictual nature of the health policy field. In the next chapter, the various actors who attempt to influence health policy are examined.

CRITICAL THINKING QUESTIONS

1. What do you think are critical determinants of recent health policy changes?

2. Which of the two policy change models presented in this chapter explain recent health policy changes that have occurred in Canada or elsewhere?
3. How can we understand the role of institutions, gender, or social class in health policy change outcomes?
4. How does political ideology influence public policy change?
5. How can civil society actors have greater influence on the health policy change process?

FURTHER READINGS

Bennett, C., & Howlett, M. (1992). The lessons of learning: Reconciling theories of policy learning and policy change. *Policy Sciences*, *25*(3), 275–294.

The authors provide an excellent assessment of the learning models of policy change and compare conflict-based theories with new institutionalist approaches. In particular, they highlight some of the limitations of these approaches to understanding policy change.

Bryant, T. (2003). A critical examination of the hospital restructuring process in Ontario, Canada. *Health Policy*, *64*, 193–205.

Building on some of the insights of Hall's policy paradigms, Bryant presents the knowledge paradigms policy change framework to examine the case of Women's College Hospital during the hospital restructuring process in Ontario in 1996. One of the key findings was that although knowledge was important, political considerations were more decisive in the final outcome for the hospital.

Fischer, F. (2003). *Reframing public policy: Discursive politics and deliberative practices*. New York: Oxford University Press.

Frank Fischer appraises Hall's policy paradigms model. While he extols Hall's efforts to demonstrate the influence of institutions on the public policy change process, he provides a post-positivist alternative that focuses on policy discourse and argumentation.

Hall, P.A. (2013). Brother, can you paradigm? *Governance*, *26*(2), 189–192.

Hall re-examines paradigm shifts. He considers the potential for a paradigm shift from neoliberalism to a policy paradigm that promotes major shifts in economic and social policy.

Hawkesworth, M.E. (1988). *Theoretical issues in policy analysis*. Albany: State University of New York.

This book provides an excellent discussion about gender in public policy analysis. Hawkesworth articulates a convincing case for feminist policy analysis and its key elements.

RELEVANT WEBSITES

Canadian Research Institute for the Advancement of Women (CRIAW)
www.criaw-icref.ca/en

CRIAW is the only women's organization in Canada focused exclusively on nurturing feminist research and making it accessible for public advocacy and education. All CRIAW activities flow from an overarching goal to provide tools to help organizations taking action to advance social justice and equality for all women. It carries out research on a wide range of public policy areas, including health.

Center for Health Policy
www.brookings.edu/about/centers/health

This website provides tools for policy change, as well as definitions of policy and how communities can engage to change health policies. Although based in the United States, the site focuses on civil society as a key actor in the health policy change process.

The Change Foundation
www.changefoundation.ca

The Change Foundation was founded and endowed by the Ontario Hospital Association. It is a health policy think tank that focuses on research and information on health care policy issues to promote health care policy change.

The Health Communications Unit
https://www.publichealthontario.ca/en/ServicesAndTools/HealthPromo
tionServices/Pages/default.aspx

The Health Communications Unit is part of the Health Promotion Capacity Building Team of Public Health Ontario. Its mandate was recently expanded to include health policy change. The site provides tools and workshops to help communities and public health authorities work for health policy change.

The Policy Project

www.policyproject.com

The Policy Project is based in the United States and provides another approach to health policy. Its focus is on helping governments and civil society organizations in developing countries to advance policies on family planning and HIV/AIDS, and promote human rights and gender equality through multisectoral activity.

REFERENCES

Albaek, E. (1995). Between knowledge and power: Utilization of social science in public policymaking. *Policy Sciences, 28*(1), 79–100.

Anderson, C. (1978). The logic of public problems: Evaluation in comparative policy research. In D. Ashford (Ed.), *Comparing public policies* (pp. 19–41). Beverly Hills, CA: Sage.

Bennett, C., & Howlett, M. (1992). The lessons of learning: Reconciling theories of policy learning and policy change. *Policy Sciences, 25*(3), 275–294.

Blitzer, W. (2005, September 11). Aftermath of Hurricane Katrina: New Orleans mayor pleads for help; Race and class affecting the crisis? *CNN.com.* Retrieved from http://transcripts.cnn.com/TRANSCRIPT/05/09/01/sitroom.02.html.

Bryant, T. (2001). *The social welfare policy change process: Civil society actors and the role of knowledge* (Unpublished PhD thesis). University of Toronto.

Bryant, T. (2002a). The role of knowledge in progressive social policy development and implementation. *Canadian Review of Social Policy, 49*(50), 5–24.

Bryant, T. (2002b). Role of knowledge in public health and health promotion policy change. *Health Promotion International, 17*(1), 89–98.

Bryant, T. (2003). A critical examination of the hospital restructuring process in Ontario, Canada. *Health Policy, 64*, 193–205.

Bryant, T. (2004a). Housing and health. In D. Raphael (Ed.), *Social determinants of health: Canadian perspectives* (pp. 217–232). Toronto: Canadian Scholars' Press.

Bryant, T. (2004b). The role of political ideology in rental housing policy in Ontario. *Housing Studies, 19*, 635–651.

Bryant, T. (2009). Housing and health: More than bricks and mortar. In D. Raphael (Ed.), *Social determinants of health: Canadian perspectives* (2nd ed.) (pp. 235–249). Toronto: Canadian Scholars' Press.

The Caledon Institute. (2001). The Harris record. In R. Cohen (Ed.), *Alien invasion: Ontario politics and government 1995–2003.* Toronto: Insomniac Press.

Coleman, W.D., Skogstad, G.D., & Atkinson, M.M. (1997). Paradigm shifts and policy networks: Cumulative change in agriculture. *Journal of Public Policy, 16*(3), 273–301.

Dunleavy, M. (1981). *The politics of mass housing in Britain, 1945–75.* Oxford: Clarendon Press.

Fischer, F. (2003). *Reframing public policy: Discursive politics and deliberative practices.* New York: Oxford University Press.

Government of Ontario. (1997). *Tenant Protection Act (Bill 96).* Toronto: Queen's Printer.

Grabb, E. (2007). *Theories of social inequality* (5th ed.). Toronto: Harcourt Canada.

Habermas, J. (1968). *Knowledge and human interests* (J.J. Shapiro, Trans.). Boston: Beacon Press.

Hall, P.A. (1993). Policy paradigms, social learning, and the state: The case of economic policy making in Britain. *Comparative Politics, 25*(3), 275–296.

Hall, P.A. (2013). Brother, can you paradigm? *Governance, 26*(2), 189–192.

Ham, C., & Hill, M. (1984). *The policy process in the modern capitalist state*. Brighton: Wheatsheaf Books.

Hawkesworth, M.E. (1988). *Theoretical issues in policy analysis*. Albany: SUNY Press.

Hawkesworth, M.E. (1994). Policy studies within a feminist frame. *Policy Sciences, 27,* 97–118.

Heclo, H. (1974). *Social policy in Britain and Sweden*. New Haven, CT: Yale University Press.

Heclo, H. (1978). Issue networks and the executive establishment. In A. King (Ed.), *The new American political system* (pp. 270–303). Washington: American Enterprise Institute.

Kendrick, M., & Slade, K. (1993). *Spirit of life: The story of Women's College Hospital.* Toronto: Women's College Hospital.

Krieger, J. (1987). Social policy in the age of Reagan and Thatcher. *Socialist Register, 23,* 177–198.

Kuhn, T.S. (1970). *The structure of scientific revolutions*. Chicago: University of Chicago Press.

Lexchin, J. (2006). Pharmaceutical policy: The dance between industry, government, and the medical profession. In D. Raphael, T. Bryant, & M. Rioux (Eds.), *Staying alive: Critical perspectives on health, illness, and health care* (pp. 325–345). Toronto: Canadian Scholars' Press.

Lexchin, J. (2013). Health Canada and the pharmaceutical industry: A preliminary analysis of the historical relationship. *Healthcare, 9*(2), 22–29.

Lownsbrough, J. (1990). The insurrection: How the anti-merger troops seized control of Women's College Hospital. A blow-by-blow account. *Toronto Life, 24*(10), 43–93.

Milward, H.B., & Wamsley, G. (1984). Policy subsystems, networks, and the tools of public management. In R. Eyestone (Ed.), *Public policy formation and implementation* (pp. 105–130). New York: JAI Press.

Mintrom, M., & Vergari, S. (1996). Advocacy coalitions, policy entrepreneurs, and policy change. *Policy Studies Journal, 24*(3), 420–434.

National Advisory Committee on SARS and Public Health. (2003). *Learning from SARS: Renewal of public health in Canada; A report of the National Advisory Committee on SARS and Public Health*. Ottawa: Health Canada.

Park, P. (1993). What is participatory research? A theoretical and methodological perspective. In P. Park, M. Brydon-Miller, B. Hall, & T. Jackson (Eds.), *Voices of change: Participatory research in the United States and Canada* (pp. 1–19). Toronto: Ontario Institute for Studies in Education Press.

Progressive Conservative Party of Ontario. (1995). *The Common Sense Revolution*. Toronto: Progressive Conservative Party of Ontario.

Raphael, D. (2014). Beyond policy analysis: The raw politics behind opposition to healthy public policy. *Health Promotion International, 30*(2), 380–396.

Romanow, R.J. (2002). *Building on values: The future of health care in Canada*. Saskatoon: Commission on the Future of Health Care in Canada.

Sabatier, P.A. (1993). Policy change over a decade or more. In P.A. Sabatier & H.C. Jenkins-Smith (Eds.), *Policy change and learning: An advocacy coalition approach* (pp. 13–40). Boulder, CO: Westview Press.

Shapcott, M. (2004). Housing. In D. Raphael (Ed.), *Social determinants of health: Canadian perspectives* (pp. 201–215). Toronto: Canadian Scholars' Press.

Teeple, G. (2000). *Globalization and the decline of social reform: Into the twenty-first century.* Aurora, ON: Garamond Press.

Towers, B. (1989). Running the gauntlet: British trade unions under Thatcher, 1979–1988. *Industrial and Labour Relations Review, 42*(2), 163–188.

Tuohy, C.J. (1999). *Accidental logics: The dynamics of change in the health care arena in the United States, Britain, and Canada.* New York: Oxford University Press.

Weir, M., & Skocpol, T. (1985). State structures and the possibilities for Keynesian responses to the Great Depression in Sweden, Britain and the United States. In P. Evans, D. Rueschemeyer, & T. Skocpol (Eds.), *Bringing the state back in* (pp. 107–168). Cambridge: Cambridge University Press.

Chapter 5

INFLUENCES ON PUBLIC POLICY

INTRODUCTION

Numerous influences impinge upon the public policy change process. At a broad level, political, economic, and social forces related to the workings of the economic system, the state or government, and the attitudes and beliefs of the citizenry shape policy development. Closer to the ground, various groups and interests compete to influence the public policy change process. Advocacy organizations play an important role in the public policy change process by drawing attention to and informing the public about issues and offering policy solutions. These advocacy organizations differ widely in the resources they possess to further their aims. They also vary in their political influence and political clout to realize their health policy goals.

Specific groups' ability to influence policy development depends on the area in which they are engaged. There may be some policy areas in which the interests that support opposing policy options are more entrenched than in others. Ability to influence public policy will also be shaped by the extent to which specific policy areas—and the potential for policy change—are informed and consistent with the political ideology of the government of the day.

Political ideology is important because it provides a context for understanding state receptivity, as well as resistance, to some perspectives rather than others. Receptivity to policy options will clearly be less when policy advocates challenge components of the ruling governments' ideological commitments and beliefs. In short, most governments tend not to be receptive to criticism of their policies and programs. Any government of the day can privilege some interests over others, such that some groups can be deliberately shut out of the policy change process (Gamson & Wolfsfeld, 1993; Bryant, 2013). This chapter considers some of the dynamics and influences on health policy in Canada. These influences include the state itself and various groups that are part of civil society. The chapter also examines different frameworks by which these influences on public policy development can be classified. The assumption guiding this examination is that the public policy process in general and the health policy arena in particular are heavily influenced by politics (Rachlis, 2004; Raphael, 2014).

POLICY INFORMED BY POLITICS

Many theories of public policy present a rational process in which governments receive inputs—such as information on an issue from a variety of sources—calculate the benefits and liabilities of various policy options, and then make a carefully reasoned decision about public policy. The issue of the politics of policymaking challenges this view. Critical perspectives make explicit that public policy decisions are not based solely on what is usually termed evidence (Bryant, 2015; Raphael, 2014). In reality, policymaking is part of the political process and can be characterized as a highly conflictual process that different groups in civil society, such as the corporate, labour, and health and social service sectors, among others, vie to influence. The objective of these activities is to ensure policy change that protects and enhances their interests.

In the health policy field, these forces include the health professions (physicians, nurses, psychologists, and others), citizen activists organized into social movements such as the Canadian Health Coalition and Citizens for Medicare, professional policy analysts, and policy institutes such as the Caledon Institute on Social Policy, the Fraser and C.D. Howe institutes, and the Canadian Centre for Policy Alternatives, among others.

Corporate influences such as the nursing home and home care industry, the pharmaceutical industry, the medical testing business, and the insurance industry are well organized and well resourced to carry out advocacy activities. They lobby governments to develop policy approaches that support their interests and tend to have close relationships with government agencies.

These varied interests themselves are associated with or even embedded in ideologies that both shape and result from the political, economic, and social institutions, the economy, the state or government, and citizen beliefs and values that structure society. Together, these institutions and ideas shape the context and form of public policy discourse and debate. Understanding where these groups come from and their policy goals is critical for understanding the policy change process, as well as those instances when policy does not change.

What are the motivations for such advocacy actions? In many cases, advocacy groups work for policy goals that clearly benefit their economic interests. One example is that of a major pharmaceutical company lobbying governments to make available a vaccine, Gardisil, manufactured by Merck, against the human papillomavirus, which is said to cause cervical cancer. Clearly, economic interests in the form of substantial profits for pharmaceutical companies shape these activities. The federal government initiated a massive immunization campaign for Gardasil, in spite of evidence showing that incidence and mortality of cervical cancer has declined in Canada (Lippman, Melnychuk, Shimmin, & Boscoe, 2007). Indeed, although the incidence and mortality from cervical cancer among indigenous women is higher than for non-indigenous women, overall Canada experienced a dramatic reduction in mortality from cervical cancer prior to the development of any vaccine to prevent it.

In other cases, advocacy groups seek policy changes that are consistent with a set of values and beliefs. For example, advocacy groups may work to ensure that socially disadvantaged populations have greater access to health care services. Members of these advocacy groups may themselves not be socially disadvantaged, but they pursue these efforts in support of their values and beliefs about what the nature of society should be. Similarly, members of housing-related advocacy groups may work to end homelessness, but may not be at risk of becoming homeless themselves.

These groups present different types of evidence to convince governments of the need for policy changes that reflect their understanding of the issue and the means by which they could be addressed. While it would be hoped that these groups would advocate for policy change based on available evidence, frequently such information is not available. These groups must, however, carry on with their efforts even in the face of these limitations. Not surprisingly, some suggest that even governments frequently make policy decisions in the face of limited available evidence (Lindblom, 1959).

These are all critical factors that ensure that the public policymaking process is an explicitly political process. And this process also involves economic and social forces, such as values and beliefs that shape the state and public policy decision making (Walt, 1994). All these factors play a role in the policy development process, but vary in their influence on the health policy process.

KEY INFLUENCES ON THE PUBLIC POLICY PROCESS

As discussed in chapter 3, a range of macro-, meso-, and micro-level theories attempt to explain different inputs or factors that influence public policy outcomes. For example, the pluralist model offers a generally micro-level perspective of the political process that considers how rival interest groups vie to influence the public policy process. Pluralism focuses on how interest groups act as inputs into the policymaking system, with the assumption that no one group or set of groups will always dominate policy discussion and action.

New institutionalism is primarily a meso-level perspective concerned with the role that institutions such as governments, organizations, and agencies play in shaping policy discourse and debate. It emphasizes how institutions and their associated ideas influence public policy outcomes. Political economy is primarily a macro-level perspective concerned with how the organization, production, and distribution of economic and social resources, political ideology, and other forces influence public policy decisions related to the organization of the health care system. Public policy shapes citizens' living and working conditions.

A number of models have been developed to identify and explain the important influences on policy change. Some theories provide category systems or typologies to make sense of these various influences on public policy. For example, Leichter (1979) identified four groups of factors that influence the public policy change process:

1. Situational factors
2. Structural factors
3. Cultural factors
4. Environmental factors

Leichter's Framework and Its Implications

In Leichter's framework, situational factors can be sudden or violent events, such as the 9/11 attack on the US, Hurricane Katrina, the oil price crisis of the 1970s, or the onset of wars that are associated with policy development and change. These events can sometimes enable governments to introduce policy changes leading to innovations or other policy responses that might otherwise be unacceptable to the public or usually dominant groups (Walt, 1994). For example, during the Second World War, the UK government annexed private, voluntary hospitals to ensure a coordinated and national health service (Walt, 1994). This experience during the war showed that it was feasible to provide publicly organized health care that ensured all citizens had access to health care services on the basis of need. That this policy innovation was positively received helped to make this experience a template for the postwar creation of the National Health Service in Britain and public health care systems in other developed Western countries. Taking advantage of such governmental upheavals or shocks to introduce policies that may not normally be easily implemented has received increased attention recently (see Box 5.1). That these policy innovations may benefit some groups at the expense of others is also being examined.

Box 5.1: Shocks and Public Policymaking

Review of *The Shock Doctrine: The Rise of Disaster Capitalism*, by Naomi Klein
By Lenora Todaro
Village Voice

In *The Shock Doctrine*, journalist Klein trains her sharp investigator's eye upon the flaws of neoliberal economics. This meticulously researched alternative history, ranging from economist Milton Friedman's "University of Chicago Boys" to George W. Bush, brings Klein's argument into the present. Using stirring reportage, she shows the ways that disasters—unnatural ones like the war in Iraq, and natural ones like the Asian tsunami and Hurricane Katrina—allow governments and multinationals to take advantage of citizen shock and implement corporate-friendly policies: Where once was a Sri Lankan fishing village now stands a luxury resort. *The Shock Doctrine* aims its 10-foot-long middle finger at the Bush administration and the generations of neo-cons who've chosen profits over people in war and disaster; the effect is to provide intellectual armor for the now-mainstream anticorporatist crowd.

Source: Todaro, L. (2007, November 27). Review of *The shock doctrine*, by Naomi Klein. *Village Voice*. Retrieved from www.villagevoice.com.

Sometimes situational factors enable governments to introduce changes that are unpopular, such as cutbacks to the funding of social programs. The budget and debt crisis of the early 1990s in Canada was used to justify profound cuts in federal transfers to the provinces and territories in both health care and other health-related areas. Sometimes what seems like a progressive policy change can be used to justify not-so-progressive changes. The 2008 economic collapse necessitated stimulus funding, which many national governments implemented to support their economies.

For example, in 1974, Minister of Health and Welfare Marc Lalonde published *A New Perspective on the Health of Canadians: A Working Document* (Lalonde, 1974). This was the first federal report to discuss factors such as the environment and health-related behaviours as important influences on health. In practice, health professionals seized on lifestyle factors as the means to promote better health, to the exclusion of environmental factors (Legowski & McKay, 2000; Schrecker & Bambra, 2015). More importantly, another effect of the report was to justify changes brought about by the *Established Programs Financing Act of 1977*. The shift away from health care's role focusing solely on health allowed the federal government to consider withdrawing from some of its health care financing commitments (Rachlis, 2004). This act shifted the federal government's contribution to health care from 50:50 cost-sharing to a block-funding arrangement between the federal and the provincial and territorial governments.

This change represented a profound shift in health policy. The previous cost-sharing arrangement had helped the provincial and territorial governments accept medicare at its inception in 1961. This 1977 act effectively ended cost-sharing as the mode of financing health and social services and increased the provincial and territorial governments' financial burden for these services. Lalonde's report—usually seen as a progressive advance in health policy—may have inadvertently justified the federal government's decision to reduce its transfers to provincial and territorial health care insurance plans (Rachlis, 2004).

Structural factors can also lead to policy changes (Walt, 1994). A radical change in political leadership can trigger health policy change. Following his election in Venezuela in 1998, for example, socialist Hugo Chavez initiated health reforms to ensure the provision of health care to poor and marginalized citizens (Muntaner, Salazar, Benach, & Armada, 2006). The reforms signified a shift away from health care as a commodity to be bought in the marketplace to the provision of health care as a social right by means of a public health care system. This shift was especially important for the marginalized poor living on the periphery of large urban centres who previously did not have access to health care (see Box 5.2).

As another example of how structural factors can affect the organization of the health care system, consider the United States, which has a private health care system rooted in its free market economic system. Instead of having a public health care system primarily organized by the state, which is the case in every other developed nation, the US has numerous private insurance plans that provide differing levels of health coverage. President Barack Obama's *Patient Protection and Affordable Care Act* forces citizens to

Box 5.2: Structural Change and Health Policy in Venezuela

Upon election in 1998, Hugo Chavez embarked on health care reforms that would ensure the health care provision as a social right particularly to marginalized populations. Muntaner and colleagues (2006) argue that the reforms signified a movement away from health as a commodity to the provision of health care as a social right. This social right would be provided by means of a public health care system that provided care to all, including the marginalized poor who lived on the periphery of large urban centres in the country.

During the 1980s, most Latin American countries had significantly reduced health and social programs. These deep funding cuts, characteristic of structural adjustment policies during this period, gradually led to conditions that fostered neoliberal reforms, the destabilization of the welfare state, and the erosion of social services such as health care. In Venezuela, the erosion of welfare institutions throughout the 1990s fuelled calls for health care reform. During the election campaign, Chavez campaigned vigorously against further neoliberal reform. Once in office, Chavez called for a referendum on a new "Bolivarian" constitution, prepared by a special constituent assembly. Three articles in the new constitution contained important implications for health care reform. First, health was viewed as a fundamental human right that the state was obliged to ensure (Article 83); second, the state had the duty to create and manage a universal, integrated public health system providing services that were free at point of access and prioritized disease prevention and health promotion (Article 84); and third, this public health care system must be publicly financed through taxes, social security, and oil revenues, with the state regulating both the public and private elements of the system and developing a human resource policy to train professionals for the new system (Article 85).

join one of these plans. The act also outlaws the practice of underwriting, in which insurance companies screened applicants for previous health conditions (Hall & Lord, 2014).

Most Americans now have some form of insurance coverage, but many must pay additional health care costs that are not covered by their plans. The *Patient Protection and Affordable Care Act*—or Obamacare—aimed to insure all Americans in 2010 (Hall & Lord, 2014). The act does not change how private insurance remunerates physicians or hospitals. It expands Medicaid to insure those living near the poverty line, and subsidizes private insurance for people who are not poor but have no coverage through their employer. Under the act, private insurers cannot deny health coverage. But, the act does not create universal coverage or change the structure of the US health care system. It requires all Americans to purchase their health insurance from the private health insurance industry or face exorbitant fines.

The US continues to outspend all other countries in health care at 17.7 percent of its GDP, the equivalent of USD $8,508 per person per year (Organisation for Economic Co-operation and Development, 2013). This is approximately 50 percent to 100 percent more than other nations.

Demographic and social factors are also social and structural determinants that can affect public policy (Leichter, 1979). The extent to which a country is urbanized affects the structures that are developed to provide health and other services. The age structure of the population affects the type of health services that are provided (Walt, 1994). For example, depending on the perceived health of seniors, governments might move to ensure provision of long-term care and palliative services, such as expanding medicare to include a national pharmacare program, as many have urged the federal government to implement in Canada (Gagnon & Hebert, 2010; Morgan et al., 2015) (see Box 4.3). These kinds of issues inform current debates about wait times, especially as hip replacement appears to be an emerging issue. Such surgeries tend to be more prevalent among the elderly.

Culture affects policy. The political and cultural environment can influence levels of participation and trust in government and the possibility of political change (Leichter, 1979). In a situation where the populace does not trust government, their subsequent disengagement from the political system can further hinder policy change. Believing that they have no influence on the political process, more and more people decide not to vote at election time. Lack of interest and delays between elections may make it unlikely that a government will do anything to change public policies.

It has also been suggested that the dominant religions of a country can influence policy positions and policy change (Walt, 1994). For example, some analysts identified the tenor of the US presidential election in 2004 as being strongly influenced by conservative Christian issues and perspectives (Hillygus & Shields, 2005). There were several reasons for this development. Membership in these groups had grown, and the George W. Bush campaign seized on this demographic. By highlighting his Christian faith, he used this demographic to his political advantage. Indeed, exit polls from the election found that among voters who considered morals to be a pressing issue for the country (about 22 percent of the total number of voters), 80 percent indicated they had voted for Bush.

In addition, the same study notes that campaigns organized around defeating same-sex marriage proposals in 11 US states seemed to provide further evidence of the importance of conservative moral issues for many voters (Hillygus & Shields, 2005). Issues such as the war in Iraq and the economy were downplayed by a perception that voters were concerned with a need to reinforce and protect traditional nuclear family values. Few Canadian studies have examined religion as a factor in shaping Canadian politics.

Finally, environmental factors can affect policy (Leichter, 1979). Walt suggests that these factors may be better understood as external or international factors (Walt, 1994). Some of these factors are changes in the international political and economic arena that can affect the domestic policies of states. These forces sometimes result in radical changes to national policies.

For example, the economies of states are increasingly interdependent as a result of international trade treaties such as the General Agreement on Trades and Services (GATS) (Grieshaber-Otto & Sinclair, 2004). These agreements integrate participating countries' economies and enhance the mobility of international capital to move from location to location. The North American Free Trade Agreement (NAFTA) was signed by Canada, the US, and Mexico, and integrates the economies of these countries (Grieshaber-Otto & Sinclair, 2004; Walt, 1994). Canada recently signed a trade agreement with the European Union (the Comprehensive Economic and Trade Agreement [CETA]) (Walkom, 2014), and the Trans-Pacific Partnership (TPP). These agreements may further commodify different health goods and services by identifying them as sites for investment. Such trade agreements have implications for national policymaking, and this is especially the case for health care and health-related policy. These issues are taken up later in this book.

Some analysts suggest that increasing interdependence between nations may be jeopardizing democratic processes. This may be occurring because civil society actors are losing the ability to influence national policies, which are increasingly required to meet the requirements of international trade and capital mobility agreements (Teeple, 2000).

Leichter's framework therefore provides a useful conceptual tool for identifying and classifying various types of influences on the political system and its related public policymaking. It enables both the identification and the examination of broader factors that can influence the public policy process and public policy change outcomes.

Leichter does not explicitly consider the important role that civil society actors play in policy change or the impact of political ideology on public policy. Nor does he consider how structures and interests influence public policy outcomes. For example, the development of medicare in Canada was not solely about the forging of an agreement between the medical profession and the government, as Tuohy (1999) suggests. The establishment of medicare was also an achievement for the working class, which pressured for social change in the immediate postwar period (Teeple, 2000; Armstrong & Armstrong, 2003, 2010). Returning Second World War veterans wanted something in return for their sacrifices, and governments felt obliged to respond to these demands—and financial resources were available. In addition, Canadians who had suffered deprivations as a result of the Depression of the 1930s wanted increased security during periods of unemployment. These civil society actors advocated for social change that would improve their living conditions.

And while many changes in the international and national political arenas have impeded the capacity of civil society actors to influence policy, these individuals continue to try. This is particularly the case in the health policy field. As will be seen, the motivations and interests of civil society actors are increasingly in conflict with international market forces. The outcomes of these conflicts will shape national health policy as well as the health status of a population.

Easton's Framework and Its Implications

Easton (1965) presents an analytic framework that contains many institutions and processes concerned with what he terms the authoritative allocation of values for society (see Figure 3.1). *Values* refer to those objects that have meaning for people. These can be material consumer goods, such as home appliances or cellphones, or services, such as educational opportunities or health care. They can also be symbolic or spiritual entities, such as the right to free speech or a fair trial, or other rights citizens expect in a democratic society.

Inputs

Easton identifies inputs into the political system as values, demands, support, and resources. Governments select which of these inputs they will afford greater attention to and which they will ignore. These choices then shape their process of making or changing policies.

More explicitly, *demands* represent the expressed wishes of groups who desire particular policies that address their own objectives and interests. In the health care arena, for example, this could be a health coalition demanding that governments not allow public financing to private health care providers, or that governments ensure universal access to all health care services. It could also include efforts to have the government develop a policy to ensure universal access to prescription medications and dental care services.

Resources refer to the means available to governments to address the demands made by these interest groups. Does the government have the financial resources or policy levers to gain such resources in order to provide these services? *Support* refers to the public acceptance of these demands. Is there any reason that the government needs to respond to these demands?

The State

The middle box of Easton's model represents government institutions. Easton's initial insights concerning the various forms of the welfare state seem especially relevant here. Social democratic, conservative, and liberal welfare states are guided by fundamentally different sets of structures and interests that shape the development of institutions, values, and ideological principles in each regime. These factors come to influence state receptivity to various policy directions.

Briefly, Figure 5.1 lays out the fundamental forms that the welfare state takes in wealthy industrialized nations. Of particular interest are their guiding principles and dominant institutions. Canada is a liberal welfare state (Saint-Arnaud & Bernard, 2003). The dominant institution is the marketplace. Liberal welfare states generally provide the least support and security to their citizens.

Within liberal welfare states, the dominant ideological inspiration is liberty, which leads to minimal government intervention in the workings of the marketplace (Saint-Arnaud & Bernard, 2003). Within this framework, the increasing receptivity of Canadian governments to the marketplace as a source for health care policy ideas can be understood. In terms of meeting the needs of citizens, the greatest focus is on the most deprived. Canada, the US, the UK, and Ireland are the best exemplars of this form of the welfare state.

The opposite situation is seen among social democratic welfare states. The ideological inspiration for the central institution of these nations—the state—is the reduction of poverty, inequality, and unemployment. Rather than a concern with governments meeting the basic needs of the most deprived, the organizing principle here is universalism and providing for the social rights of

Figure 5.1: Ideological Variations in Forms of the Welfare State

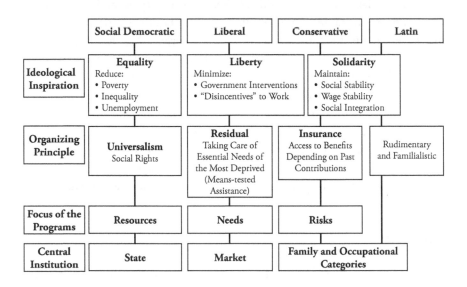

Source: Saint-Arnaud, S., & Bernard, P. (2003). Convergence or resilience? A hierarchical cluster analysis of the welfare regimes in advanced countries. *Current Sociology, 51*(5), 504.

all citizens. Denmark, Finland, Norway, and Sweden are the best exemplars of this form of the welfare state. In these nations, private involvement in health care delivery has been strongly resisted.

The conservative and Latin welfare states provide somewhat superior economic and social security to their citizens than do liberal welfare states, but rather less so than social democratic nations (Esping-Andersen, 1999). Maintaining social stability, wage stability, and social integration is accomplished by providing benefits based on insurance schemes geared to a variety of family and occupational categories (Saint-Arnaud & Bernard, 2003). These states have also tended to resist private involvement in health care delivery.

Within the welfare state typology, differences in state receptivity to differing policy approaches can be understood. Nations already focused on the market as the dominant institution in society will have greater difficulty resisting private involvement in health care delivery. The issue of welfare states and their influence on health-related public policy is considered in greater detail in a later section of this volume.

Outputs

The outputs in Easton's model are those goods and services that the government agrees to provide. These will involve all the issues related to how health care services are organized and delivered. These issues involve macro-, meso-, and micro-level decisions that concern all aspects of how health care is delivered within a nation. The details of the history and present configuration of the health care system in Canada are described in the next chapter.

Evaluation of the Leichter and Easton Models

Like Leichter, Easton provides useful tools for identifying and assessing inputs and policy outcomes. However, Easton's model focuses primarily on state institutions and too little on categories of actors and other influences on the political system. These models are primarily concerned with the political advocacy activities of experts, with a focus on state responses. There is little consideration of the structures and interests that influence policy outcomes. In addition, the models seldom consider the political activities of other civil society actors as contributing to and influencing the policy process. Civil society organizations, such as social movements, are either absent from these theories, or they are described in generally apolitical terms, strangely unattached to the political process. In short, these models may provide helpful tools for evaluating public policies, but they are static and fail to capture the conflict that is inherent in public policy discourse.

The health policy field comprises a wide range of government, corporate, health profession, and citizen activists and groups that bring their knowledge of issues and policy proposals for consideration and implementation. Citizen coalitions form to address pressing political issues and have been particularly influential in directing attention to issues of access to care and the sustainability of the public health care system. Such groups play an important role by informing and educating the public about key health issues, usually related to access, and advocating policy solutions to ensure universal access to health care services.

CIVIL SOCIETY AND HEALTH POLICY

Civil society refers to politically engaged citizens, professional policy analysts, and associational networks (such as unions and other social movements) that attempt to influence public policy decisions (Walzer, 1995). Social movements are organizations formed with the explicit purpose of carrying out collective action. They may come to exist for extended periods of time. The environmental, labour, and women's movements are good examples.

Civil society also includes associations and relational networks such as faith communities and educational institutions (Bryant, 2001). These institutions may form outside the state and act in partnership with larger social movements to promote health policy change. Informal organizations that advocate and champion policy change can also form within the state apparatus among senior civil servants. An especially relevant type of social movement is health coalitions that have come together in support of a public approach to health care organization and provision. Few theorists consider the important role played by these civil society organizations in the political process (see Box 5.3).

Box 5.3: Civil Society and Social Capital

Smith examines Putnam's (1995) controversial work on social capital and his arguments concerning the decline of social capital in the United States. He also analyzes Foley and Edwards's response to Putnam. Putnam's definition of social capital refers to social networks, connections between individuals, and norms of reciprocity and the sense of trust that develops between them (Putnam, 2000). He notes that some equate social capital with "civic virtue." Putnam argues that social capital highlights civic virtue and becomes "more powerful when it is embedded in a dense network of reciprocal social relations" (Putnam, 1993, pp. 173, 176). In contrast, a society with many virtuous but isolated individuals does not necessarily have abundant social capital. Putnam laments the decline of social capital in American society as fewer people join community organizations, as they once had in droves in previous generations.

In response to Putnam, Foley and Edwards identify two concepts of civil society (Foley & Edwards, 1996). Civil Society I is based on de Tocqueville's work on the contributions of American associational life to democratic governance. This approach argues that apolitical associations that intersect with major lines of conflict within a society help to cultivate the qualities needed to develop a sense of community that are essential for efficient democratic governance. Civil society, then, solely comprises organizations that mediate social and political divisions, and excludes organizations that foster social and political cleavages. Civil Society II is defined as consisting of politically mobilized social actors outside the usual political associations.

Foley and Edwards argue that "[de] Tocqueville ... identified specifically political associations" as essential features of the rich associational life that he observed in the United States in 1832 (Foley & Edwards, 1996, p. 42). Foley and Edwards argue that both versions of civil society fail to consider the political factors that influence and explain where or how civil society meets the political order. Both exclude "the nature and form of explicitly political institutions—including electoral systems and political parties—that structure relations between citizens and the State" (Smith, 1998, p. 93). Moreover, excluding political organizations from conceptualizations of civil society seriously downplays critical sources of civil engagement and social formation.

Smith suggests that this observation can also apply to studying transnational political associations that function in an increasingly global political arena (Smith, 1998). She argues that transnational social movement organizations similarly play an important role in fostering social capital, even in the event that they do not engender face-to-face contact among members.

The concept of social capital has been poorly defined in the literature. Much has been attributed to social capital, to the point that it has little meaning and is not a useful analytic tool. But, as Muntaner (2004) compellingly argues, the issue is not social capital, but class solidarity in identifying the public good and working together to advance public policies to achieve social and political change.

ADVOCACY GROUPS AND THE OPPORTUNITY STRUCTURE

A fundamental problem with much theory and research is their failure to consider the outcomes and consequences of social movements (Giugni, 1998). In other words, few studies consider the impact of social movements or politically engaged civil society organizations on public policy (Anyon, 2014). This is a peculiar gap in the literature, given that many social movements become politically engaged in their efforts to promote policy change.

A focus of early work on social movements and their impacts is the political opportunity structure (Burstein, Einwohner, & Hollander, 1995). The political opportunity structure refers to the larger context of social support and alliances that can form as a political resource to achieve political objectives, including policy change. Social movements devise many different strategies to increase their impact, and this theoretical perspective analyzes their capacity to broker activities with allies and opponents as means to achieve their objectives.

Other perspectives consider how social movements achieve their ends through comparisons of their efforts in different countries. How is it that health systems evolve differently in response to the same pressures? What role do social movement activities play in shaping public policy in differing jurisdictions? What lessons can we learn by studying these differing scenarios?

Giugni (1998) argues that this approach enables explicating how the political context mediates, and perhaps mutes, the impact of movements on policy outcomes. It is important to identify and understand the strategies social movements employ to achieve their impact.

Social movements may influence health policy discourses and shape what issues will even be addressed in the political system. For example, the emphasis on anti-smoking bans in Canada and other jurisdictions reflects the ability and success of the anti-smoking lobby in having the evidence of the negative impact of tobacco use on human health integrated into policy development. Twenty years ago, smoking was permitted in most public places, but current bans prevent smoking inside public buildings, in public vehicles, or on commercial flights.

Contrast this success with that of the anti-poverty community and related social movements' failure to have the health impacts of poverty integrated and applied in the service of policy development. A poverty and health discourse in Canada is very rare and reflects numerous difficulties in having a structural approach to health determinants integrated into health policy development and application (Raphael, 2007b).

MEDIA

The media are a critical influence on public policy activity within a society. The media play an important role in identifying—and may play a role in defining—what issues are health policy issues. The media usually claim to be impartial and would have us believe that they take seriously their responsibility to present a variety of perspectives. In reality, the media rarely present all views on an issue, especially when dealing with health policy issues. It has been argued that their selective coverage of health care issues has been instrumental in creating public perception of numerous health care crises, where in reality such crises do not exist. And, as with most institutions in modern society, media activities—like those of the state—are more likely to reflect the views of ruling elites than an objective presentation of the evidence available.

A set of articles on media coverage and understanding of health determinants demonstrates not only the persistent biases of the media, but also their ability to shape public perceptions (Hayes et al., 2007). Of 4,732 stories from 13 Canadian daily newspapers that considered the determinants of health and disease, 65 percent of these stories were on health care topics, such as disease treatments, service provision, and health care research. Only 13 percent of stories were concerned with physical environments and their effects on health, and only 6 percent considered the effects of socio-economic circumstances on health (Hayes et al., 2007).

Issues such as income, housing insecurity, and working conditions and their impacts upon health are unmentioned. Considering the explosion of research demonstrating that these issues are the primary determinants of health and disease, the results of the study are rather disturbing (Marmot & Wilkinson, 2006; Raphael, 2004, 2011). Health reporters' understanding of these issues was either lacking or undeveloped (Gasher et al., 2007).

The media's focus on health care contributes to public perceptions concerning the determinants of health. Canadians are strikingly unaware of the primary influences on their health (Canadian Population Health Initiative, 2004). It is not surprising, then, that the health policy discourse is strikingly devoid of any mention of socio-economic circumstances as being important determinants of health (Legowski & McKay, 2000). Considering this ignorance and the associated lack of public activity to raise these issues, it is not surprising that health policy in Canada is undeveloped compared to other developed nations in addressing them (Raphael, 2007a; Mackenbach & Bakker, 2002).

Another effect of the media preoccupation with health care has been increasing concern about the sustainability of the public health care system. In reality, health care spending in Canada is not out of control, and in some accounts, satisfaction levels with the system have been stable during the past decade (Organisation for Economic Co-operation and Development, 2005).

Yet, frequent front-page headlines that highlight wait times as a grave health care crisis have led to the preoccupation of Canadian politicians with reducing wait times as a health policy priority. Statistics Canada suggests that public perceptions regarding wait times for care may be influenced by the "intense focus and attention paid to this issue by both policymakers and the media" (Statistics Canada, 2006, p. 5). This perception may fuel support for the development of a parallel private system. The rationale for a parallel health care system is to relieve pressure on the public system. While there is evidence that indicates such a system will do the opposite—that is, it will increase wait times—such a perception serves the interests of those who wish to introduce private, for-profit health care.

POLITICAL IDEOLOGY

In addition to the activities of social movements and embedded interests, political ideology can play a role in shaping health policy. Existing at an abstract level, societal acceptance of one political ideology over another can serve as a potent stimulus to policy development. This may especially be the case in the health policy areas (see Box 5.4).

Box 5.4: The Patient Protection and Affordable Care Act, or Obamacare

As an example of how structural factors can affect the organization of the health care system, consider the United States, which has a private health care system rooted in its free-market economic system. Instead of having a public health care system primarily organized by the state, which is the case in every other developed nation, the US has numerous private insurance plans that provide differing levels of health coverage.

Prior to 2012, private health insurers in the US tended to be managed care (Hall & Lord, 2014). Managed care refers to a type of insurance that restricts which doctors or hospitals will be fully covered. This includes negotiating discounts with physicians and assessing medical necessity of treatments that are covered. Over half of Americans had private insurance. Private health insurers engaged in a practice known as medical underwriting, in which they screened potential applicants for health status. Upon the identification of a previous health condition, insurers declined coverage to people with costly medical conditions, charged them more, or denied them coverage for their existing health conditions. This left about 15 percent of Americans (approximately 50 million people) without any health coverage.

Most Americans had some form of insurance coverage, but many paid additional health care costs that were not covered by their plans. Only a small percentage (6 percent) of Americans had individual private insurance. The remainder had health insurance through their employers.

During the 2008 US election campaign, a key feature of Democratic candidate Barack Obama's campaign was health care reform (Young & Schwartz, 2014). Indeed, he vowed to bring universal health care to the US. Several polls showed that most Americans supported a single-payer universal health insurance program similar to Canadian medicare (Young & Schwartz, 2014). Most Americans considered it appropriate that government should ensure access to healthcare for all Americans. Indeed, a poll held just prior to the 2008 election showed that 77 percent of all people polled—including 57 percent of those who intended to support Republican candidate John McCain—agreed that the US government "should be responsible for ensuring" that all citizens' basic health care needs were met (Young & Schwartz, 2014). These polls demonstrated that Americans were often well ahead of politicians in their support of a universal health care system. It is unclear to what extent public opinion influenced the public policy agenda on this issue. Doubtless, it played a role in getting health care reform on the public policy agenda, but it was marginal to the process.

In the first year of his first term in office, Obama began consultations on health care reform. He appealed to the Republican Party for a bipartisan effort to provide health care to all Americans, and to the private health insurance industry to support the legislation. The private health insurance industry lobby called on Obama to require Americans to buy private health insurance from them (Kirk, 2010). The industry was opposed to the public option that had been proposed, and they wanted to ensure that Americans were forced to buy their insurance from them and no one else. In short, the industry secured its own interests while appearing to be supportive of Obama's plan.

Under the new *Patient Protection and Affordable Care Act*, all Americans must purchase their health insurance from the private health insurance industry. The primary achievement of the *Affordable Care Act* was to make all Americans insurable (Hall & Lord, 2014). In other words, private insurers can no longer deny coverage to Americans for pre-existing medical conditions.

Political ideology is a system of ideas and meanings that guides interpretation of events and political action (Hofrichter, 2003). Ideology becomes embedded in the social and political structures of a society, such as public policies and institutions. It plays a key role in legitimating and obscuring structures of political power that are related to class, race, and gender (Metzaros, 1989; Deetz, 1992). If policy-makers and the public come to believe that the market is the best source of the means to carry out health care organization and provision, policy development will increasingly move toward the creation of private systems of delivery. If policy-makers and the public believe that the primary determinants of health are biomedical indicators and healthy lifestyle choices, little policy development in support of improved living conditions will be seen.

Interestingly, few political theories consider the influence of political ideology and power on public perceptions of health issues and on public policy change, and on the influence of different civil society organizations on public policy. As noted in chapter 3, political economy emphasizes these dimensions of health policy as it considers how the organization, production, and distribution of social and economic resources influence the organization of the health care system and the living conditions to which the population is exposed. The political economy approach also places these issues within the context of dominant political ideologies and how they shape policy understandings and policymaking.

For example, political economists have identified the rise of neoliberalism as a significant force in bringing about economic globalization (Grieshaber-Otto & Sinclair, 2004; Coburn, 2000, 2006; Armstrong, Armstrong, & Coburn, 2001; Poland, Coburn, Robertson, & Eakin, 1998). These studies attribute increased attention to the private delivery of health care, as well as growing inequalities in health between rich and poor within advanced nations such as Canada, to neoliberal policies that emphasize a reduced state role in policymaking and social provision.

Box 5.5: Neoliberalism: A Political Ideology of the Market

As another example, neoliberalism is defined as a political ideology that advocates the market as the best vehicle for the production and distribution of resources in what is termed the post-industrial capitalist economy, which is economic globalization. Economic globalization requires the liberalization of trade and the mobility of capital across national borders, and increased interdependence between nations. Interdependence means that national economies are more open to foreign investment and trade. Neoliberal ideology provides the rationale for economic globalization (Coburn, 2000; Teeple, 2000; Schrecker & Bambra, 2015).

Increased economic interdependence among countries has raised concerns about the capacity of civil society actors to influence public policy outcomes. This issue is particularly salient in the social and health policy fields, which have experienced radical changes over the last 20 to 30 years (Laxer, 1997; McQuaig, 1993; Teeple, 2000). In response to changes in the global economy, Canadian governments at all levels have undertaken measures to balance budgets and reduce deficits, often at the expense of social programs. The Canada Health and Social Transfer has replaced such social programs as the Family Allowance

Program and the Canada Assistance Plan. The transfer provides block funding for health and social services. Some observers perceive such changes as enhancing international economic activity (Laxer, 1997; Teeple, 2000). Others perceive increased global interdependence as undermining the capacity of domestic governments to make domestic policy, thereby diminishing the influence of both state and civil society actors (Teeple, 2000). Both perspectives reflect different ideological commitments. Those who support the enhancement of international economic activity support neoliberalism. Opponents to neoliberalism reflect another political ideology, such as social democracy (which is pro-redistribution), and are committed to reducing inequalities between groups and maintaining a public voice in public policy decisions. The spectre of neoliberalism as an ideology has influenced the decline in social programs in Canada and elsewhere.

This perspective highlights the role that ideology can play in legitimating and reinforcing systems of inequality (Howe, 1994). Political ideology is conceived as tied to economic relations. Ideology can help to promote a sense of inevitability of existing economic relations. For example, the power of neoliberalism lies in its ability to promote economic globalization as somehow inevitable. A dominant political ideology can suppress other ideologies or explanations for social situations, particularly those that conflict with the ideas promoted by the dominant ideology. Harden's (1999) examination of health care restructuring in Ontario during the 1990s shows how the agenda of the Common Sense Revolution radically altered health care and politics in the province. The government appropriated the idea of common sense to market their policies and make them more palatable and acceptable to Ontario voters. It promoted what Howe (1994) terms an ideology of individualism that he describes as so influential "that it is commonsensically true" (p. 10; Hutson & Jenkins, 1989, p. 115). Equating a political ideology with common sense makes it especially powerful.

The broader political context takes into account what is presented as fact versus opinion. As demonstrated here, ideology can influence what is defined as fact. For example, while globalization and the perceived need for deficit reduction can be presented as inevitable, they may be seen as constructions of the social world asserted by certain groups in society. By examining specific cases of social policy change, the role of civil society in the policy change process can be identified and explained. Other structural factors, such as the economic base of a country, the way in which the labour force is organized, or the role of the state, can affect the types of policy changes that occur. For example, if a country's economy is mixed, as it is in countries with a social democratic welfare state, the role of the state is larger than in a country with a laissez-faire or market approach. With the advent of the welfare state in Western countries such as Canada, the UK, and western European countries following the Second World War, the state became involved in health, housing, social welfare, and other social policy areas that had been considered the responsibility of private charity or the market. Problems such as poverty or the inability to find appropriate, affordable housing shifted from private problems to public issues, and hence it became the responsibility of the state to respond.

As an example of a political economy analysis, the Canadian Centre for Policy Alternatives examined the potential implications of the General Agreement on Trades and Services and the North American Free Trade Agreement for medicare (Grieshaber-Otto & Sinclair, 2004). Coburn attributes the decline of the welfare state and changing class structures in advanced capitalist societies to neoliberalism (Coburn, 2000). Political economy presents issues concerning the system of production and distribution as social processes that reflect the dominant political ideology. We live in a capitalist society, and the dominant ideology reflects the interests of the capitalist class—that is, those who own the means of production and distribution and employ those who will produce goods and services to earn an income.

Although chapter 11 will pick up these issues related to the impact of globalization on health care and health policy in general, it is important here to note the importance for civil society groups to understand the influence of political ideology, particularly neoliberalism, and its implications for domestic health policy and their ability to influence national health policy.

THE INFLUENCE OF HEALTH COALITIONS AND HEALTH PROFESSIONS

The Canadian Health Coalition and related provincial health care coalitions have lobbied the government about the importance of maintaining a public rather than private approach to the provision of health care. They have prepared studies and reports to document their concerns about medicare and the problems that people face trying to access health care services.

They have been joined in their concern by numerous nurses' associations, such as the Canadian Nurses Association. Such support, however, has not been forthcoming from mainstream physicians' organizations, including the Canadian Medical Association, which have increasingly stressed private approaches to health care organization and delivery.

Medicare proponents now often compete with powerful lobbies such as the corporate sector and physicians' associations. The influence of these powerful groups on the public policy process cannot be underestimated. Although all health professions have associations that protect the interests of the professions they represent, the health professions are not equal in their ability to influence public policy.

The corporate sector and physicians' associations are powerful lobbies that have already significantly influenced the direction of health discourses. Both of these sectors possess substantial resources that enable them to mount effective lobbies to protect their interests.

Corporate and physician groups sometimes work in tandem to achieve a particular health policy outcome. For example, the new program to inoculate all 13-year-old girls in Canada against the human papillomavirus with Gardasil reflects the capacity of the corporate sector to lobby the political system and create new markets for its products. In spite of the lack of definitive evidence of the cost effectiveness of the vaccine as compared to other approaches to disease prevention, the federal government is financing provincial programs to vaccinate all adolescent girls against the virus believed to cause cervical cancer (see Box 5.6).

Box 5.6: How Politics Pushed the HPV Vaccine
By André Picard
The Globe and Mail

Not since the Salk vaccine was triumphantly unveiled in 1955 as the miracle drug that would end the scourge of polio has there been as much hoopla surrounding a vaccine as there is today about one that is being touted for having potential to eradicate cervical cancer.

Unlike polio, where children were dying and crippled in large numbers and immunization stopped an epidemic in its tracks, cervical cancer develops slowly, and the positive or negative effects of a vaccine for human papillo-virus (HPV), which can cause cancer of the cervix, will not be seen for decades.

There remain many unanswered questions about the vaccine: Will it actually prevent cervical cancer or just prevent infection with some strains of the virus? ... Conservative politicians have embraced the drug as a means of bolstering their street cred, and winning women's votes.... [O]n March 19, during his budget speech, Finance Minister Jim Flaherty short circuited the scientific and economic discussions by announcing $300-million to kick-start an HPV vaccination program.

Ottawa's move stunned public health officials, as well as the provinces.... "Aside from the polio vaccine in the fifties, it was the first time that the federal government made a direct medical decision," said Noni MacDonald, an infectious disease specialist and professor of pediatrics at Dalhousie University in Halifax. "Why are politicians making medical decisions? This is not how health-care delivery should be decided."

Anne Rochon Ford, coordinator of Women and Health Protection, agrees. The lack of transparency in a program that could have a dramatic impact on women's health is troubling, she said, and doubly so because governments seem to have succumbed to backroom lobbying from the massive marketing campaign of Gardasil's maker, Merck Frosst Canada Ltd., and its international parent.... Ms. Rochon Ford said the rhetoric about the vaccine with no long-term track record has been unbelievable, and the media has mindlessly and uncritically parroted outrageous claims, while ignoring the importance of proved measures of reducing cervical cancer like Pap testing.

The result of all the attention to Gardasil has been to drive public demand. A poll released earlier this week showed that 81% of parents want their daughters to get the vaccine and 77% favour a universal, school-based program.... "What has happened here is a milking of public sentiment around the fear of cancer and politicians, along with some other well-meaning people, have bought into it," Ms. Rochon Ford said.

Source: Picard, A. (2007, August 11). How politics pushed the HPV vaccine. *The Globe and Mail,* A1, A11.

Also, in recent years, both sectors have publicly expressed their acceptance of private sector involvement in the financing and delivery of care. At its annual meeting in 2007, the Canadian Medical Association (CMA) voted to support allowing physicians to practise in both the public and the private systems (Canadian Broadcasting Corporation, 2007; Priest, 2007). Although the motion violates the provisions of the Canada Health Act, this decision fuels governments' efforts to accelerate activities to increase private sector involvement in health care delivery.

The Registered Nurses of Ontario opposed the CMA's motion, noting the vast research on the high costs associated with private health care. Conflicts arise between health professions, and such developments provide additional support for the view that health policy development and implementation are highly contested areas. Such conflict between physicians and other groups is not new and represents only one example of a situation where physicians clearly have greater influence in policymaking than the allied health professions.

THE CORPORATE SECTOR

The corporate sector is well organized in Canada. Through a strong network of institutes, media outlets, and policy analysts, it advocates for greater private involvement in all aspects of public policy, especially with regard to health care organization and delivery. The idea of public-private partnerships (P3s) in health care provision is one such focus and is taken up in later sections of this book. Box 5.7 summarizes the corporate policy advocacy network in Canada (Langille, 2004).

Box 5.7: The Network of Corporate Advocacy Groups in Canada

Business Associations

Business Council of Canada: The voice of big business, representing the 150 CEOs of the major transnational corporations, formerly known as the Business Council on National Issues. John P. Manley is president and CEO.

Canadian Bankers Association: The leading lobby group for the chartered and foreign banks. Terry Campbell is president and CEO.

Canadian Manufacturers and Exporters: Canada's oldest business lobby group represents large manufacturers and exporters. Jayson Myers is president.

Canadian Chamber of Commerce: A coalition of local Chambers of Commerce representing the interests of many large and small businesses. Perrin Beatty is president and CEO.

Think Tanks

C.D. Howe Institute: The voice of the Bay Street business elite, led by president and CEO William B.P. Robson.

Fraser Institute: Founded in 1974 by Michael Walker to represent the "new right" devotion to free markets. Niels Veldhuis is president.

Institute for Research on Public Policy: A liberal response to the economic challenges of the 1970s, allowing more scope for government. Graham Fox is president.

Citizens' Front Groups

Canadian Taxpayers Federation: A watchdog for the well-to-do against the "special interests" responsible for "runaway spending." Aaron Wudrick is the federal director.

National Citizens Coalition: Funded by business leaders to defend individual freedom against government intervention. Peter Coleman is president and CEO.

Lobbyists

Lobbyists are "government relations consultants" hired to help firms increase their influence and gain favours from government; lobbying has become a growth industry in recent years as dozens of firms enter the market. Examples include Earnscliffe, GCI, Hill and Knowlton, and Strategy Corp.

Source: Adapted from Langille, D. (2008). Follow the money: How business and politics define our health. In D. Raphael (Ed.), *Social determinants of health: Canadian perspectives* (2nd ed.) (pp. 305–317). Toronto: Canadian Scholars' Press.

CONCLUSIONS

Numerous complex factors influence the public policy development process, particularly in the development of health policy. Important determinants of health policy are the structures of government itself; the extent of the organization and activities of civil society actors; dominant political ideologies and the understandings concerning health care and the determinants of health held by policy-makers and the public; media activities; and the influence of health professions. It is clear that health policy is a highly contentious policy area.

Of particular concern should be the impact of media coverage, neoliberal political ideology, the corporate sector, and the dominant health professions on health policy. Media coverage is a concern because of its narrow emphasis on health care and biomedical approaches to health, and its tendency to highlight health care crises. Neoliberal ideology is a concern as it clearly represents a policy approach known to threaten universal health care and overall population health.

The corporate sector is primarily concerned with generating profits, and such a concern may be a threat to the public health care system and public policies that support health. And, finally, physician receptiveness to private organization and delivery of health care is a cause for concern as physician influence upon public policymaking is clearly stronger than may be the case for the allied health professions, which tend to support public approaches to health care organization and delivery.

Few models of the public policy process capture all of the forces that shape health policy. Numerous forces play a role in shaping the health discourses and public perceptions about key health issues within which policymaking is made. These forces can prey on public fears about health care and health maintenance, and shape the responses of policy-makers to perceived health policy issues. As with other policy areas, health policy can be manipulated to serve particular interests in a society. The best means of avoiding this is to be aware of the wide range of forces that influence policy change and recognize that these forces will usually advocate an agenda that supports their interests. Whether these interests represent the views of a majority of Canadians requires careful analysis and reflection.

CRITICAL THINKING QUESTIONS

1. What is it about the current political system that makes citizens feel disengaged from the process and with little influence on the political process?
2. What are some ways that citizens can influence health policy? What resources do they need to make their voices heard?
3. What do you think are the dominant influences on the political process? How can citizens challenge these forces in the interests of saving the public health care system?
4. How can citizens contribute an alternative discourse on health policy and key health issues affecting citizens?
5. What kind of model would you devise to show how the health policy development process works?

FURTHER READINGS

Armstrong, P., & Armstrong, H. (2010). *Wasting away: The undermining of Canadian health care* (2nd ed.). Toronto: Oxford University Press.

Armstrong and Armstrong examine the rationalization of health care from the perspective of health care workers and family caregivers. The book is based on research they have carried out based on interviews with these two groups.

Gamson, W., & Wolfsfeld, F. (1993). Movements and media as interacting systems. *Annals of Political and Social Sciences, 528,* 114–125.

This article considers how the media influence social movements and their impact on the political process in the US. A key finding is that the message of a movement plays a significant role in determining its overall impact on the political process.

Hayes, M., Ross, I.E., Gasher, M., Gutstein, D., Dunn, J.R., & Hackett, R.A. (2007). Telling stories: News media, health literacy, and public policy in Canada. *Social Science & Medicine, 64,* 1842–1852.

This article examines the literacy of the media on social determinants of health.

Hofrichter, R. (2003). The politics of health inequities: Contested terrain. In R. Hofrichter (Ed.), *Health and social justice: Politics, ideology and inequity in the distribution of disease* (pp. 1–58). San Francisco: Jossey Bass.

Hofrichter writes cogently about the political economy of inequalities in health. The entire volume pulls together important essays on current political economy issues in health and the current influences on health policy and population health, such as economic globalization.

Rochon, T.R., & Mazmanian, D.A. (1993). Social movements and the policy process. *Annals of the American Academy of Political and Social Science, 528,* 75–87.

This article discusses the importance of social movements in the political process. The authors argue that participating in the public policy process is essential for social movements to influence public policy outcomes.

Staggenborg, S. (2012). *Social movements* (2nd ed.). Toronto: Oxford University Press.

This volume provides a comprehensive introduction to the major theories and historical background of social movements, focusing on how they originate, mobilize participants, and bring about social change.

RELEVANT WEBSITES

Canadian Centre for Policy Alternatives
www.policyalternatives.ca

The Canadian Centre for Policy Alternatives is an independent, non-partisan research institute concerned with issues of social and economic justice. Founded in 1980, the CCPA is one of Canada's leading progressive voices in public policy debates.

Canadian Council for Public-Private Partnerships
www.pppcouncil.ca

The newly established Crown corporation PPP Canada Inc. pledges to work with the public and the private sectors toward increasing the presence of P3s in Canada. The development of such an agency within the federal government reflects the growing interest of Canadian governments in increasing the presence of the private sector in health care.

Canadian Health Coalition
www.healthcoalition.ca

The Canadian Health Coalition is a not-for-profit, non-partisan organization dedicated to protecting and expanding Canada's public health system for the benefit of all Canadians. The CHC was founded in 1979 at the Canadian Labour Congress–sponsored S.O.S. Medicare conference, which was attended by Tommy Douglas, Justice Emmett Hall, and Monique Begin. The coalition includes organizations representing seniors, women, churches, nurses, health care workers, and anti-poverty activists from across Canada.

Douglas-Coldwell Foundation
www.dcf.ca

Founded in 1971, the Douglas-Coldwell Foundation was formed to support the movements on the political left in Canada and to stimulate discussion on key public issues such as health care. The foundation provides scholarships and publications on poverty, health, and other public policy issues.

Fraser Institute
www.fraserinstitute.org

The Fraser Institute examines the impact of competitive markets and government interventions on Canadians and Canada as a whole. Its peer-reviewed research on the impact of economic policy is internationally renowned.

REFERENCES

Anyon, J. (2014). *Radical possibilities: Public policy, urban education, and a new social movement* (2nd ed.). New York: Routledge.

Armstrong, H., & Armstrong, P. (2003). *Wasting away: The undermining of Canadian health care.* Toronto: Oxford University Press.

Armstrong, P., & Armstrong, H. (2010). *Wasting away: The undermining of Canadian health care* (2nd ed.). Toronto: Oxford University Press.

Armstrong, P., Armstrong, H., & Coburn, D. (Eds.). (2001). *Unhealthy times: The political economy of health and care in Canada.* Toronto: Oxford University Press.

Bryant, T. (2001). *The social welfare policy change process: Civil society actors and the role of knowledge* (Unpublished PhD thesis). University of Toronto.

Bryant, T. (2013). Policy change and the social determinants of health. In C. Clavier & E. de Leeuw (Eds.), *Health promotion and the policy process* (pp. 63–81). Oxford: Oxford University Press.

Bryant, T. (2015). Implications of public policy change models for addressing income-related health inequalities. Special Issue on public policy and health inequalities. *Canadian Public Policy, 39*(4), S1–S9.

Burstein, P., Einwohner, R.L., & Hollander, J.A. (1995). The success of political movements: A bargaining perspective. In J.C. Jenkins & B. Klandermans (Eds.), *The politics of social protest.* Minneapolis: University of Minneapolis Press.

Canadian Broadcasting Corporation. (2007, July 31). Ontario nurses condemn CMA's health-care plan. *CBC News.* Retrieved from www.cbc.ca.

Canadian Population Health Initiative. (2004). *Select highlights on public views of the determinants of health.* Ottawa: CPHI.

Coburn, D. (2000). Income inequality, social cohesion, and the health status of populations: The role of neo-liberalism. *Social Science & Medicine, 51*(1), 135–146.

Coburn, D. (2006). Health and health care: A political economy perspective. In D. Raphael, T. Bryant, & M. Rioux (Eds.), *Staying alive: Critical perspectives on health, illness, and health care* (pp. 59–84). Toronto: Canadian Scholars' Press.

Deetz, S.A. (1992). *Democracy in an age of corporate colonization: Developments in communication and the politics of everyday life.* Albany: State University of New York.

Easton, D. (1965). *A framework for political analysis.* Englewood Cliffs, NJ: Prentice-Hall.

Esping-Andersen, G. (1999). *Social foundations of post-industrial economies.* New York: Oxford University Press.

Foley, M., & Edwards, B. (1996). The paradox of civil society. *Journal of Democracy, 7*(3), 38–52.

Gagnon, M-A., & Hebert, G. (2010). *The economic case for universal Pharmacare: Costs and benefits of publicly funded drug coverage for all Canadians.* Ottawa: Canadian Centre for Policy Alternatives and Montreal: Institut de recherché et d'informations socioeconomiques.

Gamson, W., & Wolfsfeld, F. (1993). Movements and media as interacting systems. *Annals of Political and Social Sciences, 528*, 114–125.

Gasher, M., Hayes, M., Ross, I., Hackett, R., Gutstein, D., & Dunn, J. (2007). Spreading the news: Social determinants of health reportage in Canadian daily newspapers. *Canadian Journal of Communication, 32*(3), 557–574.

Giugni, M. (1998). Was it worth the effort? The outcomes and consequences of social movements. *Annual Review of Sociology, 24*(1), 371–393.

Grieshaber-Otto, J., & Sinclair, S. (2004). *Bad medicine: Trade treaties, privatization, and health care reform in Canada*. Ottawa: Canadian Centre for Policy Alternatives.

Hall, M.A., & Lord, R. (2014). Obamacare: What the *Affordable Care Act* means for patients and physicians. *British Medical Journal, 349*, g5376.

Harden, J.D. (1999). The rhetoric of community control in a neoliberal era. In D. Drache & T. Sullivan (Eds.), *Market limits in health reform: Public success, private failure* (pp. 204–221). London: Routledge.

Hayes, M., Ross, I.E., Gasher, M., Gutstein, D., Dunn, J.R., & Hackett, R.A. (2007). Telling stories: News media, health literacy, and public policy in Canada. *Social Science & Medicine, 64*, 1842–1852.

Hillygus, D.S., & Shields, T.G. (2005). Moral issues and voter decision making in the 2004 presidential election. *PS: Political Science and Politics, 38*(2), 201–209.

Hofrichter, R. (2003). The politics of health inequities: Contested terrain. In *Health and social justice: Politics, ideology and inequity in the distribution of disease* (pp. 1–56). San Francisco: Jossey Bass.

Howe, L. (1994). Ideology, domination and unemployment. *Sociological Review, 42*(2), 315–340.

Hutson, S., & Jenkins, R. (1989). *Taking the strain: Family unemployment and the transition to adulthood*. Milton Keynes: Open University Press.

Kirk, M. (2010). *Frontline: Obama's deal*. Boston: WGBH Educational Foundation.

Lalonde, M. (1974). *A new perspective on the health of Canadians: A working document*. Retrieved from www.hc-sc.gc.ca.

Langille, D. (2004). The political determinants of health. In D. Raphael (Ed.), *Social determinants of health: Canadian perspectives* (pp. 283–296). Toronto: Canadian Scholars' Press.

Laxer, J. (1997). *In search of a new left: Canadian politics after the neoconservative assault*. Toronto: Penguin.

Legowski, B., & McKay, L. (2000). Health beyond health care: Twenty-five years of federal health policy development. *CPRN Discussion Paper No. H04*. Ottawa: Canadian Policy Research Networks.

Leichter, H.M. (1979). *A comparative approach to policy analysis: Health care policy in four nations*. Cambridge: Cambridge University Press.

Lindblom, C.E. (1959). The science of "muddling through." *Public Administration Review, 19*(2), 79–88.

Lippman, A., Melnychuk, R., Shimmin, C., & Boscoe, M. (2007). Human papillomavirus, vaccines and women's health: Questions and cautions. *Canadian Medical Association Journal, 177*(5), 484–487.

Mackenbach, J., & Bakker, M. (Eds.). (2002). *Reducing inequalities in health: A European perspective*. London: Routledge.

Marmot, M., & Wilkinson, R. (2006). *Social determinants of health* (2nd ed.). Oxford: Oxford University Press.

McQuaig, L. (1993). *The wealthy banker's wife: The assault on equality in Canada*. Toronto: Penguin.

Metzaros, I. (1989). *The power of ideology*. New York: New York University Press.

Morgan, S.G., Martin, D., Gagnon, M-A., Mintzes, B., Daw, J.R., & Lexchin, J. (2015). *The future of drug coverage in Canada*. Vancouver: The Pharmaceutical Policy Research Collaboration, University of British Columbia.

Muntaner, C. (2004). Commentary: Social capital, social class, and the slow progress of psychosocial epidemiology. *International Journal of Epidemiology, 33*(4), 674–680.

Muntaner, C., Salazar, R.M.G., Benach, J., & Armada, F. (2006). Venezuela's barrio Adentro: An alternative to neoliberalism in health care. *International Journal of Health Services, 36*(4), 803–811.

Organisation for Economic Co-operation and Development. (2005). *Health at a glance: OECD indicators 2005.* Paris: Organisation for Economic Co-operation and Development.

Organisation for Economic Co-operation and Development. (2013). *Health at a glance 2013: OECD indicators.* Paris: Organisation for Economic Co-operation and Development.

Poland, B., Coburn, D., Robertson, A., & Eakin, J. (1998). Wealth, equity, and health care: A critique of a population health perspective on the determinants of health. *Social Science & Medicine, 46*(7), 785–798.

Priest, L. (2007, August 1). Debate among doctors builds over CMA health-care proposal. *The Globe and Mail.* Retrieved from http://www.theglobeandmail.com/news/national/debate-among-doctors-builds-over-cma-health-care-proposal/article18141459.

Putnam, R.D. (1993). *Making democracy work: Civic traditions in modern Italy.* Princeton: Princeton University Press.

Putnam, R.D. (1995). Bowling alone: America's declining social capital. *Journal of Democracy 6*(1), 65–78.

Putnam, R.D. (2000). *Bowling alone: The collapse and revival of American community.* New York: Simon and Schuster.

Rachlis, M. (2004). *Prescription for excellence: How innovation is saving Canada's health care system.* Toronto: HarperCollins.

Raphael, D. (Ed.). (2004). *Social determinants of health: Canadian perspectives.* Toronto: Canadian Scholars' Press.

Raphael, D. (2007a). Canadian public policy and poverty in international perspective. In D. Raphael (Ed.), *Poverty and policy in Canada: Implications for health and quality of life* (pp. 335–364). Toronto: Canadian Scholars' Press.

Raphael, D. (2007b). The politics of poverty. In D. Raphael (Ed.), *Poverty and policy in Canada: Implications for health and quality of life* (pp. 303–333). Toronto: Canadian Scholars' Press.

Raphael, D. (2011). Mainstream media and the social determinants of health in Canada: Is it time to call it a day? *Health Promotion International, 26*(2), 220–229.

Raphael, D. (2014). Beyond policy analysis: The raw politics behind opposition to healthy public policy. *Health Promotion International, 30*(2), 380–396.

Saint-Arnaud, S., & Bernard, P. (2003). Convergence or resilience? A hierarchical cluster analysis of the welfare regimes in advanced countries. *Current Sociology, 51*(5), 499–527.

Schrecker, T., & Bambra, C. (2015). *How politics makes us sick: Neoliberal epidemics.* Houndmills, UK: Palgrave Macmillan.

Statistics Canada. (2006). *Access to health services in Canada. January to June 2005.* Ottawa: Minister of Industry.

Smith, J. (1998). Global civil society? Transnational social movement organizations and social capital. *American Behavioral Scientist, 42*(1), 93–107.

Teeple, G. (2000). *Globalization and the decline of social reform: Into the twenty-first century.* Aurora, ON: Garamond Press.

Tuohy, C. (1999). *Accidental logics: The dynamics of change in the health care arena in the United States, Britain, and Canada.* New York: Oxford University Press.

Walkom, T. (2014, September 30). CETA a much-announced trade pact of dubious value. *Toronto Star*. Retrieved from www.thestar.com

Walt, G. (1994). *Health policy: An introduction to process and power*. London: Zed Books.

Walzer, M. (1995). The civil society argument. In R. Beiner (Ed.), *Theorizing citizenship* (pp. 153–174). New York: State University of New York.

Young, K., & Schwartz, M. (2014). Healthy, wealthy, and wise: How corporate power shaped the *Affordable Care Act*. *New Labor Forum*, *23*(2), 30–40.

Chapter 6

OVERVIEW OF THE CANADIAN HEALTH CARE SYSTEM

INTRODUCTION

Canadians are proud of medicare. For many, it symbolizes what it means to be Canadian. Medicare distinguishes Canada from the United States, where, in 2010, about 50 million Americans (approximately 16 percent of the US population) lacked any form of health care insurance coverage (Hall & Lord, 2014). As discussed in the previous chapter, the purpose of the *Patient Protection and Affordable Care Act* was to ensure that all Americans could obtain health insurance. It did not create a universal, single-payer system as exists in Canada. Under Canadian medicare, Canadians share the cost of risk, and it is a single-payer system in which provincial and territorial governments are the sole providers of health care services (Armstrong & Armstrong, 2003, 2010). Health care is provided on the basis of need, not income.

Health care is an important public policy area in the 21st century. A convergence of social, economic, and political factors brought about medicare in Canada. A particularly important determinant of medicare is Canadian federalism. From a new institutionalist perspective, medicare signifies the impact of institutions in shaping social policy. Health care is a politically contentious policy area involving intergovernmental co-operation, and has become a political football as the federal and provincial governments wrangle over the financing of provincial health care programs (McIntosh, 2004; Maioni, 2010). This is so not only because it is the most expensive social program, but also because it reflects ongoing conflict that is intrinsic to relations between the federal, provincial, and territorial governments, particularly in the health care policy arena in Canada.

From a critical social science perspective, the creation of medicare is considered a compromise between the state and the capitalist class (Teeple, 2000). Medicare is a welfare state program in the health field and represented a significant gain for the working classes. It is therefore seen as reflecting an implicit or explicit class struggle (Teeple, 2006, 2010).

This chapter examines the important role of federalism and other factors in the development of medicare, and the nature of the Canadian health care system. It also examines the key federal acts that have determined the financing and administration of public health care, and emerging issues in Canadian health care policy.

HISTORY OF PUBLIC HEALTH CARE IN CANADA

Political interest in a public health care system began as early as 1919, when then federal Liberal leader William Lyon Mackenzie King pledged to establish public health care in his party's election platform (Rachlis, 2004). In fact, the federal government did not act immediately to implement a national health care program. In 1947, Premier Tommy Douglas and his newly elected Co-operative Commonwealth Federation government in Saskatchewan established the first universal hospital health care plan in Canada, indeed in North America (Health Canada, 2005). The health program had the support of the province's doctors and hospitals because they received regular remuneration, in contrast to the past, when more than 10 percent of hospitals' and physicians' bills were unpaid (Rachlis, 2004).

During the 1950s, changes in the leadership at the federal level and in Ontario in the immediate postwar era contributed to more conciliatory relations between the federal and the provincial and territorial governments (Tuohy, 1999). Prior to this time, there were few policies and programs in which the two levels of government agreed to co-operate. The positive intergovernmental relations thus contributed to a political climate that was more favourable to developing innovative social programs such as medicare, which required co-operation between the two levels of government. Out of these negotiations, the single-payer system, which has become synonymous with Canadian health care, emerged.

In 1957, then federal Minister of Health and Welfare Paul Martin Sr. introduced a national hospital insurance program. The medical profession, insurance companies, and business opposed the program. In 1960, the Canadian Medical Association, a powerful lobby that represents all physicians in Canada, opposed all publicly funded health care. In 1962, the NDP government of Premier Tommy Douglas in Saskatchewan met opposition from doctors and citizens who associated public health insurance with socialism (Rachlis, 2004). More than 90 percent of the doctors in the province went on strike in opposition to the introduction of public medical insurance in the province (Tuohy, 1999). The dispute between the doctors and the Saskatchewan government went to arbitration.

In 1960, the settlement that emerged from the strike, known as the Saskatoon Agreement, permitted doctors to charge patients above fees negotiated with the provincial government. In other words, the agreement allowed doctors to extra-bill their patients for services they provided. Both parties agreed to private fee-for-service medical practice. This agreement became a template for the national program when it was established in 1966 with the federal government's passage of the *Medical Care Act* (Tuohy, 1999; Rachlis, 2004). Under the federal plan, the provincial and territorial governments became the single payers of a comprehensive range of physicians' and hospital services, with Ottawa cost-sharing 50 percent of provincial and territorial health care costs and the provinces and territories paying the other 50 percent.

In 1961, the Canadian Medical Association lobbied then Prime Minister John Diefenbaker to appoint a Royal Commission to study health care, hoping the commission would highlight the problems associated with a publicly financed health care system (Rachlis, 2004). In 1965, Justice Emmett Hall's commission not only supported a national medical insurance program, but it also recommended expanding the program to include home care, mental health, pharmaceuticals, and dental and optical programs for children. These programs are still not covered by medicare.

The provinces were required to comply with the five principles of medicare, which were the national standards for health care programs to ensure access and equity in health care services across the country (see Box 6.1).

Box 6.1: A Brief History of Canada's Health Care System

1947   The Saskatchewan Government, led by leader Tommy Douglas, introduces the first provincial hospital insurance program in Canada.

1957   Paul Martin Sr. introduces a national hospital insurance program. Doctors, insurance companies, and big business fight against it.

1960   The Canadian Medical Association opposes all publicly funded health care.

1962   Saskatchewan's NDP government introduces the first public health care program. Doctors walk out, but the strike collapses after 3 weeks.

1965   A Royal Commission headed by Emmett Hall calls for a universal and comprehensive national health insurance program.

1966   Parliament creates a national medicare program with Ottawa paying 50% of provincial health costs.

1977   Trudeau Liberals retreat from 50:50 cost-sharing and replace it with block funding.

1978   Doctors begin extra-billing to raise their incomes.

1979   Canadian Labour Congress convenes the S.O.S. medicare conference to fight extra-billing and joins with community groups to form the Canadian Health Coalition. The Clark Conservative government in Ottawa invites Justice Emmett Hall to chair an inquiry into federal financing of health care and how the provinces use these transfers.

1980   Justice Emmett Hall releases his second Commission Report recommending the abolition of extra-billing and user fees.

1984   Canada Health Act is passed unanimously by Parliament. Extra-billing is banned.

1993   Mulroney government grants 20-year patent protection to brand-name drugs.

1995   Paul Martin Jr. introduces Canada Health and Social Transfer (CHST), causing massive cuts in transfer payments to health and social programs.

1997   National Forum on Health calls for medicare to be expanded to include home care, pharmacare, and a phasing out of fee-for-service for doctors.

1998   Premiers demand say in interpreting the *Canada Health Act*. Chrétien caves in.

2000   Ralph Klein introduces legislation to allow private hospitals.

2000   Federal Budget offers 2 cents for health care for every dollar of tax cuts, ignoring pleas of Canadians to save medicare.

2002   The Romanow Royal Commission on the Future of Health Care in Canada conducted cross-country public hearings. Final report was tabled in Ottawa on November 28, 2002.

2003   First Ministers' meeting results in a new "Health Accord." Targeted funding in key areas (as prescribed by the Romanow report) shows promise. However, there are no accountability mechanisms and no restrictions on public funding being spent on for-profit health care.

2005   Jacque Chaoulli (backed by the Canadian Medical Association) wins Supreme Court of Canada case. Evidence from the lower courts was ignored. It resulted in increased calls for a two-tiered private insurance and for-profit health care delivery.

2006 CMA elects Dr. Brian Day as President and begins a highly public 4-year push to break Medicare and allow extra-billing and double-dipping doctors. The split within CMA leads to the formation of a new organization: Canadian Doctors for Medicare.

2009 Ontario doctors elect a pro-Medicare doctor, Jeffrey Turnball, as the candidate for CMA President in 2010. Outspoken advocate for private, for-profit health care, CMA past-President Dr. Brian Day faces serious charges in a BC court, including illegal billing practices.

Source: Canadian Health Coalition. (2009). *A brief history of Canada's health care system.* Retrieved from www.medicare.ca.

FEDERALISM: CATALYST FOR INNOVATION?

Federalism is a critical element in the development of health care in Canada (Hutchison, Abelson, & Lavis, 2001; McIntosh, 2004). The institution of federalism has tended to lead to a focus on particular issues while obscuring other key health care issues. Some policy analysts view Canadian federalism as having both constrained and facilitated innovation and opportunities for change (Tuohy, 1999; Hutchison et al., 2001).

Federalism divides political authority between federal and regional/sub-national governments (i.e., provinces and territories) and is considered to be the property of constitutions (Brooks, 1996). This means that it is based on state power. Federalism institutionalizes regions by relating them to different governments. The federal and regional governments have constitutional authority to enact laws and collect revenues. In other words, political authority is decentralized. The regionalism that results from the acceptance of a federal constitution is reinforced by the political administrative rivalries between national and regional governments that gave rise to it.[1] In Canada, much of this tension between the two levels of government stems from the Constitution, which sets out the powers and responsibilities of each level of government.

Sections 91 and 92 of the Constitution Act

The Canadian Constitution contributed to, and intensified, the rivalry between the federal and the provincial and territorial governments by investing responsibility for health care provision in the latter. Neither the federal nor the provincial and territorial governments have exclusive constitutional responsibility for health care (Commission on the Future of Health Care in Canada, 2002; Statistics Canada, 2001; Braen, 2004; Leeson, 2004). The terms set out in sections 91 and 92 of the Constitution Act, 1867, and the various constitutional interpretations of the meaning of these sections, provide the core for the federal and the provincial and territorial governments' claims for a continuing role in health care provision (McIntosh, 2004). While these sections appear to present the exclusive and shared responsibilities of each government, this is not the case. There is some ambiguity which has contributed to tensions between governments.

McIntosh (2004) notes that most of the health and social services that Canadians now consider valid areas of state involvement in actual delivery or regulation were considered to be the responsibility of charitable or religious organizations—that is, private matters—in the 19th century. In the 20th and 21st centuries, however, the state role evolved into these areas. The courts increasingly determine which level of government is responsible for specific policy initiatives.

In health care, the provinces and territories have primary responsibility for the organization, administration, and delivery of most health care services (Braen, 2004; Leeson, 2004). Section 92(7) of the Constitution Act, 1867, supports provincial responsibility over the administration and delivery of health care services, but many constitutional provisions authorize provincial responsibility in this area. The federal government has a role in criminal law, patents, and its often controversial spending power. The original act does not identify the territories, but territorial governments have the same powers as provincial governments.

The federal government can intervene in health care only through its spending power. It has used this power to set the terms and conditions of medicare. Although since the 1980s it has consistently reduced its transfer payments to the provinces and territories, the federal government retains considerable control over the terms of medicare and also over the provincial and territorial governments in the administration of their health insurance plans. Interestingly, it has rarely penalized a province or territory for violating the principles of medicare, although some provinces and territories have routinely allowed extra-billing and the imposition of user fees.

The Charter of Rights and Freedoms, as part of the Constitution Act, 1982, exerted a new thrust in public policy debates by enabling individuals and groups to use the courts in efforts to hold governments accountable for policy choices by asserting any of the rights listed in the Charter. The Charter has been used to challenge the state's role in a policy area. In 2005, the Charter provided the basis of a challenge to Quebec's ban on private insurance for medicare-covered services (Rachlis, 2005). For some, this challenge seemed the death knell for medicare.

Single-Payer System

Under medicare, the provincial governments are termed *single payers* for most medical and hospital services (Tuohy, 1999; Rachlis, 2004; Yalnizyan, 2006). Each province and territory has a single government insurance plan that provides a comprehensive range of medical and hospital services. From the outset as the system developed, there was no provision for private insurance alternatives for these services. Provincial and territorial governments were intended to be monopsonists—sole purchasers—of medical and hospital services. *Monopsony* is an economic term that refers to a state in which demand comes from one source (Tuohy, 1999). If there is only one customer or purchaser for a certain good, that customer has a monopsony in the market for that good or service, or one employer controls a sector by providing that good or service exclusively. It is similar to a monopoly, but on the demand side, not the supply side.

Since the inception of medicare, various cost-sharing schemes between the two levels of government were devised to ensure the sustainability of the health care system. The financing of provincial and territorial health care programs has also been the primary source of tension between the two levels of government as the federal government has reduced its contributions, but continues to dictate to the provinces and territories the terms on which services are to be delivered. It is considered that the federal spending power has helped to protect the principles of medicare as intended by its founder, Tommy Douglas (see Box 6.2).

Box 6.2: The Five Principles of Medicare

1. *Universality of coverage*: The provinces have to cover 100 percent of their residents for hospital and physicians' services.
2. *Portability of coverage*: The provinces have to cover their residents for care in other provinces at the rates that pertain in other provinces. They are supposed to cover their residents while out of the country, at least at the rates that would have applied in their home province.

3. *Reasonable accessibility to services*: The provinces are to ensure that services are "reasonably accessible" and that financial charges or other barriers do not impede access. This criterion also requires the provinces to pay reasonable compensation to their health professionals.

4. *Comprehensiveness of services*: The provinces are supposed to cover all "medically necessary" services provided by doctors or within hospitals. This criterion is actually a misnomer because community services (such as home care) are not covered and neither are the services of other providers (except dental services within hospitals—a rare event these days).

5. *Public administration*: The provinces have to administer their health insurance programs either themselves or through a body that is accountable to the provincial government. This criterion is also a bit of a misnomer because it expressly forbids neither for-profit insurers acting on contract with a province nor for-profit providers of services.

Source: Rachlis, M. (2004). *Prescription for excellence: How innovation is saving Canada's health care system* (p. 37). Toronto: HarperCollins.

Cost-Sharing Arrangements

Cost-sharing arrangements have evolved and changed radically since the inception of medicare in Canada. At the outset, the focus was on financing hospital and physician services. Services provided by allied health professionals were covered, provided patients had a physician's referral for such services. Over time, a broader range of institutional and community health settings, such as community health centres that combine health and social services, were recognized.

In 1957, the Hospital and Diagnostics Service Act provided federal-provincial cost-sharing of hospital and physician services (Rachlis, 2004; Tuohy, 1999). This act provided a template for future health care programs (Rachlis, 2004). The federal government contributed 50 percent of the costs of these services. The act required that provincial plans comply with the five principles of medicare: (1) universality, (2) portability, (3) comprehensiveness, (4) accessibility, and (5) public administration.

Medical Care Act

In 1966, the federal government implemented the Medical Care Act, which enshrined the principle of public payment for private medical practice only (Tuohy, 1999; Rachlis, 2004). The act entrenched private fee-for-service, which became the chief mode of practice for the organization of physician payment in Canada. The act was considered a compromise to appease both opponents and supporters of medicare. The federal government also promised to continue to pay 50 percent of the costs of provincial and territorial programs, provided the provinces and territories complied with the principles of medicare (Rachlis, 2004). Under the terms of the act, which are still in force, physicians send claims for payment to the provincial and territorial health insurance plans (Scott, 2001). They are reimbursed on the basis of the fee schedule negotiated by the government and medical association in each province or territory.

When the Medical Care Act came into force, only Ontario refused to comply. All of the other provinces and territories agreed within the first year (Rachlis, 2004). Ontario Premier John Robarts preferred a market system similar to that of the US, whereby the government would insure only those who could not afford private care. Prime Minister Pierre Trudeau threatened to withhold the transfer from Ontario, forcing Robarts to agree to the federal formula in 1971.

Some attribute the inclusion of private practice to good fiscal buoyancy/health, positive federal-subregional (i.e., provincial and territorial governments) relations at the time, broad political support for access to health care on the basis of need regardless of income, and physicians' willingness to accept limitations on their entrepreneurial discretion in exchange for professional independence in clinical decision making (Tuohy, 1999; Hutchison et al., 2001). A strong economy at the time enabled the government to draw physicians into the program on generous terms, including continued fee-for-service remuneration, clinical autonomy, and control over the location and organization of medical practice. This arrangement placed physicians at the centre of health care at all levels. In short, they became the gatekeepers of the health care system. It was this promise of power and control that ensured physician support for the system. The legislation did not change the existing structure of health care delivery (see Box 6.3).

Throughout the 1970s and 1980s, both federal and regional governments were concerned about controlling social spending. With growing inflation at the time, the federal government was uneasy about its spending commitments

Box 6.3: Canada's Health Care System

Canada's publicly funded health care system is best described as an interlocking set of 10 provincial and three territorial health insurance plans. Known to Canadians as medicare, the system provides access to universal, comprehensive coverage for medically necessary hospital and physician services. These services are administered and delivered by the provincial and territorial (i.e., state or regional) governments, and are provided free of charge. The provincial and territorial governments fund health care services with assistance from the federal (i.e., national) government.

What Happens First (Primary Health Care Services)

When Canadians need health care, they generally contact a primary health care professional, who could be a family doctor, nurse, nurse practitioner, physiotherapist, pharmacist, and so on, often working in a team of health care professionals. Services provided at the first point of contact with the health care system are known as primary health care services, and they form the foundation of the health care system.

In general, primary health care serves a dual function. First, it provides direct provision of first-contact health care services. Second, it coordinates patients' health care services to ensure continuity of care and ease of movement across the health care system when more specialized services are needed (e.g., from specialists or in hospitals).

Primary health care services often include the prevention and treatment of common diseases and injuries; basic emergency services; referrals to and coordination with other levels of care, such as hospital and specialist care; primary mental health care; palliative and end-of-life care; health promotion; healthy child development; primary maternity care; and rehabilitation services.

Fee-for-service scheduled negotiated between each provincial and territorial government and sub-national medical associations set the fees. Doctors in private practice are generally paid through fee-for-service schedules negotiated between each provincial or territorial government and the medical association in its respective jurisdiction. Those in other practice settings, such as clinics, community health centres, and group practices, are more likely to be paid through an alternative payment scheme, such as salaries or a blended payment (e.g., fee-for-services plus incentives). Nurses and other health professionals are generally paid salaries that are negotiated between their unions and their employers.

When necessary, patients are referred to specialist services (medical specialists, allied health services, hospital admissions, diagnostic tests, prescription drug therapy, etc.).

What Happens Next (Secondary Services)

A patient may be referred for specialized care at a hospital, at a long-term care facility, or in the community. The majority of Canadian hospitals are operated by community boards of trustees, voluntary organizations, or municipalities. Hospitals are paid through annual, global budgets negotiated with the provincial and territorial ministries of health, or with a regional health authority or board.

Alternatively, health care services may be provided in the home or community (generally short-term care) and in institutions (mostly long-term and chronic care). For the most part, these services are not covered by the Canada Health Act; however, all the provinces and territories provide and pay for certain home care services. Regulation of these programs varies, as does the range of services. Referrals can be made by doctors, hospitals, community agencies, families, and potential residents. Needs are assessed and services are coordinated to provide continuity of care and comprehensive care. Care is provided by a range of formal, informal (often family), and volunteer caregivers.

Short-term care, usually specialized nursing care, homemaker services, and adult day care, is provided to people who are partially or totally incapacitated. For the most part, health care services provided in long-term institutions are paid for by the provincial and territorial governments, while room and board are paid for by the individual; in some cases these payments are subsidized by the provincial and territorial governments. The federal department of Veterans Affairs Canada provides home care services to certain veterans when such services are not available through their province or territory. As well, the federal government provides home care services to First Nations people living on reserves and to Inuit in certain communities.

Palliative care is delivered in a variety of settings, such as hospitals or long-term care facilities and hospices, in the community, and at home. Palliative care for those nearing death includes medical and emotional support, pain and symptom management, help with community services and programs, and bereavement counselling.

Source: Health Canada. (2012). *Canada's health care system.* Retrieved from http://www.hc-sc.gc.ca/hcs-sss/pubs/system-regime/2011-hcs-sss/index-eng.php.

(Rachlis, 2004). The federal and the provincial and territorial governments wanted to adjust the funding rules. These concerns led to the passage of the *Established Programs Financing Act* in 1977.

Established Programs Financing Act: Shift to Block Funding

In 1977 the federal government passed the *Established Programs Financing Act* (EPF). The federal government threatened to act unilaterally unless the provinces and territories agreed to negotiate a block-grant arrangement (Tuohy, 1999). A block grant or fund is a sum of money given by one level of government to another for a specific purpose. Block grants signified a shift from the cost-sharing arrangements that characterized earlier funding arrangements in health care between the two levels of government. In other words, federal transfers for hospitals, medical care, and post-secondary education were placed in one funding envelope with a commitment to increase funding at the same rate as economic growth (i.e., the gross domestic product, or GDP) (Rachlis, 2004).

Under the EPF, federal transfers to health care—and post-secondary education—consisted of two equal allocations of a tax transfer and a cash transfer (Tuohy, 1999):

1. A cash transfer was conditional on provincial compliance with the five principles of medicare (i.e., universality, accessibility, comprehensiveness, portability, and public administration) and was determined on the basis of one-half of per capita transfer to a province or territory in 1975–1976. The amount would be determined partially by the rate of increase in GNP and growth in the population in a province or territory, but not at the rate of actual health care costs. In addition, an unconditional transfer was provided in the form of tax points. A tax point or tax room is fiscal compensation in the place of a cash transfer from the federal government to the provincial and territorial governments (Madore, 1997). Tax points lower the federal income tax rate and the provincial and territorial governments increase their tax rates by an equal amount. For example, when negotiating fiscal arrangements, the federal government would give the provinces and territories the option of opting out of a program and receiving an alternative for the federal contribution to a program, often in the form of tax transfers.

The new funding arrangement under the EPF gave the provincial and territorial governments greater discretion to allocate health care funding in accordance with their needs and priorities. The tax points were based on the revenues produced by a specific number of percentage points of the amount of income tax of the federal basic tax generated in a province or territory (Tuohy, 1999).

2. The impact of the shift to tax points made provinces and territories whose economies grew at less than the GNP financially less well off in the short term. The federal government provided transitional payments to prevent provinces and territories from being made worse off than if the provincial and territorial governments had received a cash transfer set at the rate of GNP and population growth. The federal government reduced its income tax rates by 16 percent, and the provinces and territories raised revenues to finance health care and institutions (Rachlis, 2004).

Overall, the shift to block grants heightened tensions between the two levels of government, particularly when the federal government initiated such actions without consulting the provincial and territorial governments. Ottawa's unilateral action would become the modus operandi when the provinces and territories refused to comply with federal plans. Other concerns in health care also emerged.

In Ontario and some of the other provinces and territories during the late 1970s, doctors grew concerned about the decline in their incomes (Begin, 2007). With the creation of medicare, they were paid for their work, whereas prior to the creation of medicare, about 10 percent of medical bills were not paid (Rachlis, 2004). Yet, by the 1970s, inflation had risen to over 10 percent, such that by 1975, physicians' incomes had begun to fall. To make up the shortfall, some physicians extra-billed patients above the fees set in the fee schedule in their region. The percentage of Ontario doctors who extra-billed their patients increased from less than 10 percent in 1978 to approximately 20 percent in 1979.

In 1979, the new federal Conservative Minister of Health David Crombie invited Emmett Hall once again to lead an inquiry on the health care system. In his second commission report, one of Hall's key recommendations was for the government to eliminate extra-billing and hospital user fees (Rachlis, 2004). Hall's main contention was that the two practices had led to a two-tiered health care system that jeopardized universal accessibility of health care services.

PROTECTING THE FIVE PRINCIPLES OF MEDICARE AND THE WAR ON EXTRA-BILLING

The *Canada Health Act* of 1984 enshrined the five principles of medicare: (1) universality, (2) accessibility, (3) portability, (4) comprehensiveness, and (5) public administration, and banned extra-billing (Rachlis, 2004; Tuohy, 1999). It included a provision that allowed Ottawa to reduce its financial contribution to provinces and territories that permitted physicians to extra-bill their patients as a measure to ensure provincial and territorial compliance (Tuohy, 1999). The federal government used this act to launch its attack on extra-billing, which triggered the 1985 doctors' strike in Ontario. The strike illustrates how Ontario served as a lightning rod for doctors' discontent during the war on extra-billing, as the act contributed to more conflict in Ontario than in any other province or territory (Tuohy, 1999; Rachlis, 2004). The relationship between the provincial government and the Ontario Medical Association (OMA) was already particularly confrontational. To add to existing tensions, the election of a Liberal government ended the 40-year Conservative rule in Ontario and also disturbed an accommodation reached by the OMA and the Conservative government.

The actions of the federal Liberal government of the early 1980s should not be construed as expressing an overwhelming commitment to medicare on its part (Tuohy, 1999). Rather, it acted out of concern for its declining popularity. As Tuohy (1999) argues, it "seized upon the issue of extra billing as a way of symbolizing its commitment to preserving the universality of the most popular social program" (p. 93). It threatened to reduce the federal transfer payment by the amount equal to the estimated amount of extra-billing occurring in an offending province or territory. Interestingly, the federal government hid behind the veil of this commitment while it whittled away at its financial contribution to provincial health care programs (Tuohy, 1999; Rachlis, 2004; Brooks, 1996).

CANADA HEALTH AND SOCIAL TRANSFER

The 1995 federal budget replaced the Canada Assistance Plan and the EPF funding for health and post-secondary education with the Canada Health and Social Transfer (CHST). The Canada Assistance Plan (CAP) provided funding for welfare and other provincial social services (Brooks, 1996). The CAP gave federal transfers to provincial and territorial welfare programs from 1965 to

1995 (Banting, 1997). Under the program, the provinces and territories were required to provide assistance to all residents in need.

The CHST is a single block transfer that empowers the federal government to freeze and cap the transfers to the provinces and territories that both federal Liberal and Conservative governments had done since the early 1980s (Brooks, 1996). This transfer effectively ended cost-shared programs between the federal and regional governments and signalled a retreat from Ottawa's commitment to national standards, which historically depended on the federal spending power.

Box 6.4: History of Health and Social Transfers

Health and social transfer payments have developed over the years from cost-sharing programs to block funding transfers. The illustration below shows the evolution of those transfers.

Figure 6.1: History of Post-Secondary Education, Social, and Health Funding in Canada

The following is a brief timeline of the evolution of health and social transfers within Canada:

1950s and 1960s: Health and social transfers were either provided as cash grants or were cost-shared to encourage the establishment of national social programs. In **1966**, the Canada Assistance Plan (CAP) was introduced, creating a cost-sharing arrangement for social assistance programs. Conditions were attached to federal funding, including the provision that provinces and territories not require a period of residency in the province or territory as a condition of eligibility for social assistance or for the receipt of social assistance.

1977: The *Established Programs Financing* (EPF) was introduced, replacing cost-sharing programs for health and post-secondary education. Federal funding provided through the EPF initially took the form of equal portions of a tax transfer and a cash transfer. Provinces received 13.5 percentage points of personal income tax (PIT) and 1 percentage point of corporate income tax (CIT), including some points carried over from the previous post-secondary education program. Provinces and territories received equal per capita total EPF support through a mix of cash and equalized tax points. The value of the tax points grew in line with the economy. The growth rate of the cash transfer was modified several times as the program underwent changes throughout the years.

1984: The *Canada Health Act* was enacted. EPF funding was made conditional on respect for the five criteria of the *Canada Health Act* (universality, accessibility, portability, comprehensiveness, and public administration) and provisions for withholding funding were introduced.

1995: The federal budget announced that the Canada Assistance Plan and *Established Program Financing* would be combined into one block fund—the Canada Health and Social Transfer, or CHST. The CHST provided funds to provincial and territorial governments in support of health care, post-secondary education, social assistance, and social services. Like the Established Program Financing transfer, the CHST was a combination of the 1977 tax transfer and a cash transfer, and the total was allocated on an equal per capita basis.

2000–2003: In 2000 and 2003, the Government of Canada and provincial and territorial governments entered into a series of agreements to strengthen and renew Canada's publicly funded health care system. These agreements also sought to improve accountability and reporting to Canadians.

As part of the First Ministers' Accord on Health Care Renewal in February 2003, First Ministers also agreed to restructure the CHST effective April 1, 2004, to create two new transfers—the Canada Health Transfer, or CHT, and the Canada Social Transfer, or CST—to improve the transparency and accountability of federal support to provinces and territories. Reflecting provincial spending patterns, 62 percent of the CHST was allocated toward health, and the remaining 38 percent was allocated toward post-secondary education, programs for children, and other social programs.

Budget 2003 allocated $16 billion over five years through a new Health Reform Transfer targeted to primary health care, home care, and catastrophic drug coverage.

2004: In September 2004, First Ministers signed the 10-Year Plan to Strengthen Health Care. In support of this 10-year plan, the Government of Canada committed additional funding to provinces and territories for health that included increases to the CHT through a base adjustment and an annual 6 percent escalator.

Under the 2004 10-Year Plan to Strengthen Health Care, the Health Reform Transfer was incorporated into the Canada Health Transfer effective April 1, 2005.

2007: Pursuant to the federal government's commitment to restore fiscal balance in Canada, Budget 2007 put all major transfers to provinces and territories on a legislated, long-term track out to 2013/14.

Budget 2007 restructured the CST to provide equal per capita cash support to provinces and territories. Additional investments were made to facilitate this transition and to enhance the stability and predictability of support to provinces and territories for post-secondary education, education programs for children, and other social programs. Total CST cash levels were also set in legislation to grow by 3 percent annually.

Respecting the 2004 10-Year Plan to Strengthen Health Care agreement, the CHT was legislated to move to equal per capita cash in 2014/15. For a smooth transition and to provide certainty in budget planning, Budget 2007 also ensured that no province or territory would receive lower cash transfers under the CST or CHT relative to what they would have received in 2007–2008, prior to the implementation of the new Equalization system and an equal per capita cash allocation for the CST.

2009: The Budget Implementation Act 2009 legislated a technical adjustment to ensure that Ontario, as an Equalization-receiving province, received the same per capita CHT cash as other Equalization-receiving provinces.

2011: The Government of Canada announced in December 2011 that the CHT will continue to grow at 6 percent annually until 2016/17. Starting in 2017/18, the CHT will grow in line with a three-year moving average of nominal gross domestic product (GDP) growth, with funding guaranteed to increase by at least 3 percent per year. In addition, the CST will continue to grow at its current rate of 3 percent annually in 2014/15 and beyond. The CHT and the CST will be reviewed in 2024.

Source: Department of Finance Canada. (December 15, 2014). *History of health and social transfers.* Ottawa: Minister of State (Finance). Retrieved from www.fin.gc.ca.

CURRENT ISSUES IN CANADIAN HEALTH CARE

Many issues in health care have arisen in recent years. Chief among them has been the decreasing federal contributions to provincial and territorial health care plans. Brooks and others have argued that the federal position has been to reduce its contribution toward provincial and territorial health services while continuing to set conditions on how those services will be delivered (Brooks, 1996; Armstrong & Armstrong, 2003, 2010). The reduced federal contribution has thus been the source of much tension between the federal and the provincial and territorial governments since the early 1980s. The provincial and territorial governments have had to shoulder a larger share of health care costs, which increase annually. Thus, declining federal transfers and growing health care costs have contributed to provincial and territorial governments opting for various privatization schemes to reduce their health care costs, such as public-private partnership arrangements (P3s) to build hospitals and other social services such as schools and highways. Provinces and territories have also delisted drugs covered by the provincial and territorial drug formularies and introduced user fees for a wide range of previously insured services.

Indeed, many are concerned that the 2004 Health Accord expired March 31, 2014. The Conservative federal government did not initiate discussions with the provincial and territorial governments to renew and renegotiate the agreement. In December 2011, then federal Minister of Finance Jim Flaherty announced that the 6 percent annual increase in the Canada Health Transfer and 3 percent annual increase in the Canada Social Transfer will continue until the 2016/17 fiscal year (Picard, 2011; Walkom, 2011). After 2017, until at least 2024, increases will be tied to economic growth, including inflation at about 4 percent, and will never fall below 3 percent.

A majority Liberal government led by Justin Trudeau was elected in the October 2015 general election. The Liberal campaign platform promised "collaborative federal leadership" (Liberal Party of Canada, 2015) and to negotiate a new health accord with the provincial and territorial governments. The accord will include a long-term funding agreement.

THE INFLUENCE OF NEOLIBERALISM

While reduced federal transfers have indeed undermined national standards in health care and other social policy fields, privatization is also driven by an ideological commitment characteristic of increasing neoliberalism in Canada. Neoliberalism is a market ideology in which the market is considered to be the most efficient allocator of economic and social resources in a society (Coburn, 2000). Many trace the rise of neoliberalism and globalization to the early 1970s oil crisis, which prompted many OPEC countries (i.e., participant countries in the Organization of Petroleum Exporting Countries) to ratchet back social programs (Teeple, 2000; Schrecker & Bambra, 2015).

Canadian governments raised alarm bells about the sustainability of medicare in its current form during the 1990s and into the 2000s. The issue of sustainability has fuelled interest in allowing private sector involvement in health care. A key issue is how to pay for the services and programs that promote health, and how to make it politically feasible and attractive (Yalnizyan, 2006). Affordability is expressed in terms of ability to pay. However, governments have not only the responsibility to pay, but also the capacity to control costs. Government decisions have implications for the public purse and household income, and influence total health care spending in the economy.

HEALTH CARE REFORM

Concern about the sustainability of medicare provides an opportunity to explore how it can be reformed to best serve the health care needs of Canadians. As noted elsewhere in this volume, Tommy Douglas and Emmett Hall recommended broadening the programs covered by medicare to include dental care, home care, and other services under medicare. Recent interest has focused on expanding medicare to include a national pharmacare program to provide coverage of the cost of prescription medications.

At the first SOS medicare conference in 1979, Tommy Douglas noted:

> Those of us who talked about the need for public health insurance back in the 1940s, '50s, and '60s kept reminding Canadians that there were two phases of Medicare. The first was to remove the financial barrier between those who provide health services and those who need them. We pointed out repeatedly that this first phase was the easiest of the problems we faced ... finding the revenue, ... setting up the organizational and administrative structure, ... exercising controls over costs ... Phase 2, however, would be a much more difficult one: altering our delivery system so as to reduce costs by putting emphasis on preventive medicine rather than on treatment and drugs. (Tommy Douglas, SOS Medicare, November 1979, in Douglas, 2007)

The current thrust of the system on diagnoses and curative treatments has increased the cost of health care provision. The system lacks a preventative component. In the view of some critics, prevention would involve addressing the social determinants of health, and in particular reducing the poverty rate among non-elderly families with children to improve their health. Research has established the relationship between income and health (Gordon, Shaw, Dorling, & Davey Smith, 1999; Brimblecombe, Dorling, & Shaw, 1999; Annals of the New York Academy of Sciences, 1999).

As noted elsewhere in this volume, Canada has significantly reduced health inequalities associated with medical conditions most conducive to medical treatment, but has done less well in reducing income-related inequalities in mortality from causes conducive to public health interventions, such as lung cancer and motor vehicle accidents (Bryant, Raphael, Schrecker, & Labonte, 2011). The next frontier is to address the social determinants of health and their unequal distribution across the Canadian population.

Medicare has many proponents and detractors. The latter seize upon any perceived failing of the system as evidence of the need to privatize health care. Both sides agree on the need to reform medicare, but there is no consensus on how to proceed. Public opinion polls show that Canadians value the health care system and support reforming it to improve delivery. Few Canadians support privatization as a solution. In addition, some health policy observers have warned that allowing private providers into the health care system would erode medicare in the long term and violate the principle of providing care on the basis of need. They advocate public solutions to addressing problems within the system (Rachlis, 2004; Yalnizyan, 2006; Canadian Doctors for Medicare, 2013).

WAIT TIMES

The federal, provincial, and territorial governments continue to wrangle over medicare. They focus their concern on reducing wait times for specialist care. Some provinces, such as Alberta, British Columbia, and Ontario, have privatized some health services, arguing that private sector involvement will relieve the backlog in the public system. Conservative think tanks such as the Fraser Institute and the C.D. Howe Institute have contributed to this view (see Barua & Clemens, 2015; Robson & Laurin, 2015).

A health care survey carried out jointly by Statistics Canada and the Centers for Disease Control and Prevention in the United States showed that 31 percent of low-income Americans reported poorer health, compared to 23 percent of low-income Canadians (Sanmartin & Ng, 2004). Interestingly, Americans were more likely to report being "very satisfied" with their health care services compared to Canadians, who were more likely to be "somewhat satisfied." How much of this concern is perceived rather than real is questionable. A more recent study shows that Canadians with low incomes continue to report poorer health outcomes overall compared to populations with higher incomes (Tjepkema, Wilkins, & Long, 2013). In addition, cause-specific mortality is highest for the lowest income groups in Canada. This illustrates the impact of income on health status and mortality (Tjepkema, Wilkins, & Long, 2013).

Studies on health spending in Canada and comparison nations with or without a public health system have shown that the public system is less costly. Table 6.1 shows the health spending for Canada, the United States, the United Kingdom, and Sweden. In all cases, public health care is less costly. Canada's public spending on health care is equated with the single-payer system, which has numerous advantages over a private system (Yalnizyan, 2006; Canadian Doctors for Medicare, 2011). For example, with one centre to receive bills and send out payments, the system reduces administrative duplication. Moreover, approximately 1.8 percent of Canada's provincial and territorial health care costs are directed to the structure responsible for paying physician and hospital claims.

In contrast, the US health expenditures were 17.7 percent of GDP in 2011, outspending all other countries (OECD, 2013). It spent $8,508 per person, which is 2.5 times the average of all developed countries. Health spending in the US rose by 1.5 percent in 2013, which is less than half the average annual growth rate before 2009.

Since 2010, Canada has experienced a sustained period of negative or low growth in its health expenditures (OECD, 2015). Between 2005 and 2009, its health spending grew 3.5 percent per year. Health spending fell from 2 percent per year in the 2009/10 fiscal year to 0.2 percent in the 2013/14 fiscal year. These data challenge claims that health spending will bankrupt the economy. Nonetheless, medicare has a number of issues that require redress. Chief among them is wait times for specialist and primary care.

The issue of wait times for care has led to discussion among provincial and territorial governments about considering an increased role for the private sector in health care, or allowing the development of a parallel private system to ease the pressure on the public system. Using public dollars to cover private health care services violates the principles of the Canada Health Act. As noted in the discussion on the terms of the Canada Health Act, provinces and territories that breach these provisions risk losing some federal health care dollars. The federal government has not acted on these violations. Such a state of affairs

Table 6.1: Demographic Aspects of Canada and Three Comparison Nations, 2010

	Canada	United States	United Kingdom	Sweden
GDP per capita, 2012	$44,319	$54,565	$39,561	$45,813
Annual GDP growth in %, 2010–2014	2.5	2.4	2.6	2.3
Income inequality 2010 (Gini coefficient)	.32	.38	.34	.27
% of population >65 years	14	13	16	18

Source: Organisation for Economic Co-operation and Development. (2014). *OECD annual national accounts database 2010*. Paris: OECD.

leaves the public wondering who will protect medicare and whether it will be there when they or a family member require emergency or long-term care.

Much has been written on how to reduce wait times. Some commentators attribute increased wait times to the lack of after-hours care available in communities (Canadian Doctors for Medicare, 2013). The Ontario auditor general notes that in 2010, about half of emergency room visits were non-urgent or for non-emergency problems (Office of the Auditor General of Ontario, 2010).

The most frequent recommendation among those who support medicare is *not putting more money into the system* (Priest, Rachlis, & Cohen, 2007; Canadian Health Coalition, 2009; Canadian Doctors for Medicare, 2013), but deploying existing resources more efficiently. This can include centralized intake of patients, using interdisciplinary teams, and doctors working in groups rather than on their own to address patient needs, among other suggestions. Another solution is to provide more after-hours primary care clinics to treat non-emergency patient needs. This would free up emergency departments to handle medical emergencies.

THE CANADIAN HEALTH SCENE IN INTERNATIONAL PERSPECTIVE

In this section, some indicators of Canadian health policy are placed within a comparative perspective. These measures include some demographic data, indicators of the health status of Canadians, and health care system functioning. Canada is often compared with the UK, the US, and Sweden. The US provides an exemplar of comparison with a market-driven approach to health policy, while the UK has a somewhat similar system to Canada, albeit with a separate, privately oriented system. Sweden represents a good example of a state-oriented social democratic approach to health policy governance, although the country has experienced some ratcheting back of its welfare system in recent years.

Demographics

The US is the wealthiest of these four nations on a per capita gross domestic product basis (Table 6.1). Per capita GDP for the US in 2014 was USD $46,405.26, which is rather more than for the other three comparison nations (Trading Economics, 2015). In terms of economic growth from the 1990 to 2005 and 2010 to 2014 periods, all nations showed rather similar rates of annual change in GDP. Striking differences are seen, however, in the degree of income inequality as measured by the Gini coefficient (OECD, 2014). The US shows the greatest income inequality, and Sweden the least.

Finally, in terms of the percentage of the population over the age of 65 years (a good indicator of the aging of the population), Sweden shows the highest proportion, and the US the lowest. Canada is currently near the low end on population aging at 14 percent. The OECD calculates aging support projections (OECD, 2014). The old-age support rate correlates with the number of those who can provide economic support to the number of older people who may be materially reliant on support from others. Its analysis suggests that the number of people who are non-elderly and who are able to support the elderly will decline over the next 40 years in most countries.

The Canadian Institute for Health Information (CIHI) reported that Canada's health spending would be $214.9 billion in 2014, or $6,045 per Canadian, up by $61 per person from 2013 (CIHI, 2014). The rate of growth in health spending is 2.1 percent less than inflation and population growth together. Overall, health spending in Canada fell by an average 0.4 percent per year between 2010 and 2014. Health spending represented approximately 11 percent of Canada's GDP in 2014. Most spending is on hospitals, drugs, and physicians.

Interestingly, the aging population is *not* a major driver of rising health care costs (CIHI, 2014). CIHI describes population aging as a "'modest cost driver,' estimated at 0.9 percent per year" (CIHI, 2014, p. 13). In fact, the proportion of public-sector health dollars spent on Canadian seniors has seen minimal change, from 44.6 percent in 2002 to 45.2 percent in 2012.

Among OECD countries, trends in the growth of total health expenditures have been identified since 1975 (OECD, 2014). The period between 1975 and 1991 was one of growth in health expenditures; between 1991 and 1996, governments cut health spending as they contended with fiscal deficits; and finally, 1996 to 2011 was a growth period of about 4 percent per year. During this last phase, health care became a priority for Canadians (OECD, 2014). This was the period during which the federal, provincial, and territorial governments signed the 2003 and 2004 health accords. As noted earlier in the chapter, these accords increased spending on human health resources, drugs, hospitals, and advanced diagnostics.

Health Status

Among the four countries compared, life expectancy is the greatest in Sweden and the lowest in the US (Table 6.2). Consistent with this pattern, the US shows the greatest number of premature years of life lost (prior to age 70) and Sweden the lowest. A similar pattern is seen for infant mortality and low birth weight rates. And, not surprisingly, this same pattern holds for obesity rates, where Sweden's rate of 11 percent is strikingly lower than the 36.5 percent rate seen in the US.

Table 6.2: Health Status in Canada and Three Comparison Nations, 2011

	Canada	United States	United Kingdom	Sweden
Life expectancy	81.0	78.7	81.1	81.9
Premature years of life lost/100,000 (2009)				
Males	4,168	6,133	3,988	1,916
Females	2,554	3,555	2,479	3,081
Infant mortality/1,000	4.9	6.1	4.3	2.1
Obesity %	25.4	36.5	24.8	11

Source: Organisation for Economic Co-operation and Development. (2013). *Health at a glance.* Paris: OECD.

Table 6.3: Usage of the Health Care System in Canada and Three Comparison Nations, 2017

	Canada	United States	United Kingdom	Sweden
Physicians/1,000	2.6	2.6	2.8	4.0
Nurses/1,000	9.5	11.1	8.2	11.2
Acute care hospital beds/1,000	1.73	2.48	2.3	2.0
Occupancy rate of acute care beds (%)	89	64.4	84.3	—
MRIs/1,000,000	8.5	35.5	5.9	—
Hospital discharges	83	125	129	163
Physician consultations per capita	7.7 (2010)	4.0 (2009)	5.0 (2009)	2.9

Source: Organisation for Economic Co-operation and Development. (2017). *Health at a glance: OECD indicators.* Paris: OECD.

Usage of the Health Care System

Table 6.3 provides data about the health care systems in the four countries. Sweden has the highest number of physicians available to the population, while Canada has the lowest (2.6). Th e US has the highest number of acute care beds in hospitals (2.48). Of interest is the high number of MRI machines available for use in the US (35.5 per million people). In 2013, Canada's high occupancy rate for acute care beds is mirrored in its having the highest number of physician consultations. Canada, however, has the lowest rate of hospital discharges among the nations compared.

Health Expenditures

Total expenditures on health on a per capita basis in equivalent US dollars is presented in Table 6.4. Th e US spends, on average, $8,508, up from $6,401 in 2005. Canada and the US spend more than the UK and Sweden on an absolute

Box 6.5: Health Council's Demise "Just Made Sense," Spokesman Says

As the 2004 federal-provincial health accord expires, so will the independent body monitoring it
CBC News

Health Canada is winding down the funding for the Health Council of Canada, the independent body responsible for monitoring the results of the federal-provincial health accord struck in 2004. But with the $41 billion deal set to expire in 2014, a spokesman for Health Minister Leona Aglukkaq says wrapping up the council's work "just made sense."

Steve Outhouse says the Health Council measured results in the health care system across Canada, work already being done by the Canadian Institute for Health Information (CIHI).

He says Aglukkaq has already announced it will be renewing and expanding funding for CIHI.

The minister's spokesman said it is possible for the provinces to take over the council and "keep it going." But although the offer has been made, so far there has been no interest from them, and no complaints, says Outhouse.

The council's chief executive, John Abbott, said Health Canada told him last week that its $6.5 million funding would continue through this fiscal year, but come to an end after that, with $4 million to close up shop in 2014–15. The council relies entirely on federal money to fund its operations. Abbott said the "federal fiscal environment" was cited in the explanation offered to him for the decision. "This did come right out of the blue," Abbott told The Canadian Press on Tuesday.

Federal spending to focus on 'front-line' services

Outhouse said the federal government is instead focusing its health spending "on patient-oriented research, things that are connected to front-line health-care service to Canadians, including transfers that go to provinces and territories."

"It seemed like a natural time to make that transition," he explained.

When the current accord expires next year, the federal government will continue to increase its health transfers to the provinces for 2014 to 2024, but at a lower rate of increase, and with no strings attached. Finance Minister Jim

Flaherty abruptly unveiled a take-it-or-leave-it plan at a meeting of provincial and territorial finance ministers in Dec. 2011. He committed to a six per cent annual increase in funding for each of the first three years. After that, annual increases will be a minimum of three per cent—or more, if the economy is strong.

In a letter sent earlier this month to provincial health ministers, who also act as corporate members of the council, Aglukkaq said it is up to the provinces and territories to decide whether to keep funding the organization. "I should emphasize that this is a decision about federal funding for the council, and that formal decisions about its future as an entity will need to be made collectively by us, the council's corporate members," Aglukkaq wrote.

The council was formed to follow on from the work of the Romanow Commission and focus on both performance monitoring and accountability in the health care system. Some credit its work for helping to lower wait times and encouraging innovation in the public health care system to ensure access is maintained across regions and age groups.

Abbott said he sees a role for the council after the current accord expires. For instance, he noted, there will still be a need to hold governments accountable for health-care delivery and spending. "Most of our reports were written so that the Canadian public could certainly have a better understanding of the issues at play and that they can use those reports to help hold governments accountable at the provincial and national level."

National standards at risk?

Dr. Anna Reid, the president of the Canadian Medical Association, said in a news release Tuesday that "Canada's health care system needs all the information it can get, but instead we are about to lose one of the few bodies responsible for monitoring and measuring progress toward ensuring the health care system is able to meet the needs of Canadians."

The Canadian Health Coalition urged the provinces to pick up where the federal government is leaving off so the work continues.

"National surveys consistently show that Canadians and the provincial and territorial governments want federal leadership," said Michael McBane, the coalition's national coordinator in another release. "Instead Harper is choosing to cut and run—cut the funding and then put distance between his government and universal health care."

"Universal health care in Canada is about to fragment into 14 separate systems operating independently from each other. The federal government is running away from its essential role as guardian of national standards and universal access to care for all Canadians regardless of where they live," said McBane.

The left-leaning Council of Canadians called the funding decision "scandalous."

"The Council of Canadians views this as an intentional and very serious attack on the public health-care system in Canada and a clear indication that the federal government is not interested in the health of Canadians," Adrienne Silnicki, the group's health-care spokeswoman, said in a statement.

Canadian Doctors for Medicare also criticized the move. "The federal government is no longer walking away from health care, it's sprinting at full speed," Dr. Ryan Meili, the group's vice-chairman, said in a statement. "Cutting funding to the Health Council means cutting information on sustainability, quality and efficiency of our health care system—information that Canadians should be able to expect from their government."

NDP health critic Libby Davies said there remains a role for the council, so cutting its funding is a mistake. "It's a lack of planning and a lack of foresight at minimum, and at worst, it's another indication that the federal government is abandoning its role in health care," she said.

"So I think either way you look at it, it's bad news."

Source: Health Council's demise "just made sense," spokesman says. (2013, April 17). *CBC News.* With files from Amanda Pfeffer, The Canadian Press. Retrieved from www.cbc.ca.

dollar basis. US expenditures represent almost 20 percent of its GDP. However, Canada ranks sixth highest among the 30 OECD nations for whom data is available. Of note is that of Canada's $4,522 per capita expenditures, about 70 percent—or $3,183—is publicly financed. Annual growth in spending from 2000 to 2011 was only 3.25 percent in Canada.

Per capita spending on pharmaceuticals is highest in the US ($985). Canada's spending on pharmaceuticals is USD $701, compared to USD $443 in Sweden. In terms of average growth in health expenditures from 2000 to 2009, the UK had the highest growth rate compared to the other three nations.

Table 6.4: Health Expenditures in Canada and Three Comparison Nations

	Canada	United States	United Kingdom	Sweden
Total per capita expenditures (USD)	$4,522	$8,508	$3,405	$3,925
Public per capita expenditures (USD)	$3,183	$4,066	$2,821	$3,204
Total expenditures as % of GDP	11.2	17.7	9.4	9.5
Percentage of expenditures that are public	68.5	47.8	82.8	81.6
Average annual growth in health expenditures 2009–2011 (%)	0.8	1.3	-1.8	1.8
Per capita pharmaceutical expenditures (USD)	$701	$985	--	$443
Average annual growth in pharmaceutical expenditures 2000–2011 (%)	-0.3	-0.5	--	-0.9
Physician consultations per capita	7.4	4.1	5.0	3.0

Source: Organisation for Economic Co-operation and Development. (2013). *Health at a glance 2013: OECD health indicators.* Paris: OECD.

Public Share of Health Spending

Not surprisingly, only 47.8 percent of health care spending in the US is public. Canada's rate of 70 percent is stable from previous years, and while noticeably higher than is the case in the US, it is lower than the UK (82.8%) or Sweden (81.6%). Indeed, Canada's public coverage is among the lowest of OECD nations.

SUMMARY

While wealthier than Sweden, Canada shows greater income inequality. Canada provides a health status profile that, while superior to that seen in the US, falls well behind what is seen in Sweden. This is the case for life expectancy, infant mortality, premature years of life lost, low birth weight rate, and obesity rate.

Canada's health care system spends more than Sweden's on an absolute basis and also as a percentage of GDP. Also, in Canada, much less of that spending is publicly provided than in Sweden. The growth in health costs in Canada, however, is less than that seen in the other comparison nations. Canada provides fewer acute care hospital beds, and these show very high occupancy. Finally, Canada has significantly fewer physicians available than the other countries, and these physicians appear to be very busy, as indicated by the average number of consultations. The shortage of general practitioners is a problem in rural and remote communities, and also in large urban centres such as Toronto.

These findings suggest that Canada's health care system is operating at a higher capacity than is the case in other nations. Despite spending more than Sweden on health care in absolute dollars and percentage of GDP, health status indicators fall behind those seen in that nation. The sources of these health differences and the means by which the health care system can respond to these challenges are taken up in later chapters.

CONCLUSIONS

This chapter has described the organization and delivery of health care services in Canada. It has also chronicled the history of public health care and the role of Canadian federalism in shaping it. Medicare is Canada's most valued social program. A comparison of health spending in Canada and comparison nations shows that public systems are more cost-efficient than private systems and better serve the health needs of citizens.

Canadian federalism and ongoing federal-provincial conflict have shaped health care in Canada. Federalism, among other dynamics, led to the single-payer system that characterizes Canadian health care. The ongoing intergovernmental conflict has contributed to discussions about how to sustain the system into the future, not always with a view to strengthening the system to ensure its sustainability.

Comparatively, Canada provides a health profile that, while superior to the US, falls well behind Sweden. Canada's health care system spends more than Sweden with rather less to show for it. The system appears to be operating at very high capacity and with fewer physicians, and has more average consultations than three other comparison nations. The sources of these indicators are examined in later chapters.

APPENDIX 6.1: A DETAILED HISTORY OF CANADA'S HEALTH CARE SYSTEM

1867	British North American Act passed: federal government responsible for marine hospitals and quarantine; provincial/ territorial governments responsible for hospitals, asylums, charities, and charitable institutions.
1897–1919	Federal Department of Agriculture handles federal health responsibilities until Sept. 1, 1919, when first federal Department of Health created.
1920s	Municipal hospital plans established in Manitoba, Saskatchewan, and Alberta.
1921	Royal Commission on Health Insurance, British Columbia.
1936	British Columbia and Alberta pass health insurance legislation, but without an operating program.
1940	Federal Dominion Council of Health created.
1942	Federal Interdepartmental Advisory Committee on Health Insurance created.
1947	Saskatchewan initiates provincial universal public hospital insurance plan, January 1.
1948	National Health Grants Program, federal; provides grants to provinces and territories to support health-related initiatives, including hospital construction, public health, professional training, provincial surveys, and public health research.
1949	British Columbia creates limited provincial hospital insurance plan. Newfoundland joins Canada; has a cottage hospital insurance plan.
1950	Alberta creates limited provincial hospital insurance plan, July 1.
1957	Hospital Insurance and Diagnostic Services Act, federal, proclaimed (Royal Assent) May 1; provides 50/50 cost sharing for provincial and territorial hospital insurance plans, in force July 1, 1958.

1958	Manitoba, Newfoundland, Alberta, and British Columbia create hospital insurance plans with federal cost sharing, July 1. Saskatchewan hospital insurance plan brought in under federal cost sharing, July 1.
1959	Ontario, New Brunswick, and Nova Scotia create hospital insurance plans with federal cost sharing, January 1. Prince Edward Island creates hospital insurance plan with federal cost sharing, October 1.
1960	Northwest Territories creates hospital insurance plan with federal cost sharing, April 1. Yukon creates hospital insurance plan with federal cost sharing, July 1.
1961	Quebec creates hospital insurance plan with federal cost sharing, January 1. Federal government creates Royal Commission on Health Services to study need for health insurance and health services; appoints Emmett M. Hall as Chair.
1962	Saskatchewan creates medical insurance plan for physicians' services, July 1; doctors in province strike for 23 days.
1964	Royal Commission on Health Services, federal, reports; recommends national health care program.
1965	British Columbia creates provincial medical plan.
1966	Canada Assistance Plan (CAP), federal, introduced; provides cost sharing for social services, including health care not covered under hospital plans, for those in need, Royal Assent July, effective April 1. Medical Care Act, federal, proclaimed (Royal Assent), December 19; provides 50/50 cost sharing for provincial/territorial medical insurance plans, in force July 1, 1968.
1968	Saskatchewan and British Columbia create medical insurance plans with federal cost sharing, July 1.
1969	Newfoundland, Nova Scotia, and Manitoba create medical insurance plans with federal cost sharing, April 1. Alberta creates medical insurance plan with federal cost sharing, July 1. Ontario creates medical insurance plan with federal cost sharing, October 1.
1970	Quebec creates medical insurance plan with federal cost sharing, November 1. Prince Edward Island creates medical insurance plan with federal cost sharing, December 1.

1971   New Brunswick creates medical insurance plan with federal cost sharing, January 1. Northwest Territories creates medical insurance plan with federal cost sharing, April 1.

1972   Yukon creates medical insurance plan with federal cost sharing, April 1.

1977   Federal-Provincial Fiscal Arrangements and Established Programs Financing Act (EPF) federal cost-sharing shifts to block funding.

1979   Federal government creates Health Services Review; Emmett M. Hall appointed Special Commissioner to re-evaluate publicly funded health care system.

1980   Health Services Review report released August 29; recommends ending user fees, extra billing, setting national standards.

1981   Provincial/territorial reciprocal billing agreement for in-patient hospital services provided out-of-province/territory.

1982   Federal EPF amended; revenue guarantee removed, funding formula amended.

1983   Royal Commission on Hospital and Nursing Home Costs, Newfoundland, begins April, reports February 1984. Comite d'étude sur la promotion de la santé, Quebec, begins, ends 1984. La Commission d'énquête sur les services de santé et les services sociaux, Quebec, begins January, reports December 1987. Federal Task Force on the Allocation of Health Care Resources begins June, reports 1984.

1984   The Canada Health Act, federal, passes (Royal Assent April 17), combines hospital and medical acts; sets conditions and criteria on portability, accessibility, universality, comprehensiveness, public administration; bans user fees and extra billing.
                Provincial/territorial reciprocal billing agreement for out-patient hospital services provided out-of-province/territory.

1985   Health Services Review Committee, Manitoba, begins, reports November.

1986   Federal transfer payments rate of growth reduced.
                Health Review Panel, Ontario, begins November, reports June 1987.

1987   Premier's Council on Health Strategy, Ontario, begins, ends in 1991.

	Royal Commission on Health Care, Nova Scotia, begins August 25, reports December 1989. Advisory Committee on the Utilization of Medical Services, Alberta, begins September, reports September 1989. All provinces and territories in compliance with the Canada Health Act by April 1.
1988	Provincial/territorial governments (except Quebec) sign reciprocal billing agreement for physicians' services provided out-of-province/territory. Commission on Directions in Health Care, Saskatchewan, begins July 1, reports March 1990. Premier's Commission on Future Health Care for Albertans, Alberta, begins December, reports December 1989. Commission on Selected Health Care Programs, New Brunswick, begins November, reports June 1989.
1989–1994	Further reductions in federal transfer payments.
1990	Royal Commission on Health Care and Costs, British Columbia, begins, reports 1991.
1991	National Task Force on Health Information, federal, reports; leads to creation of Canadian Institute of Health Information. Task Force on Health, Prince Edward Island, begins June, reports March 1992.
1994	National Forum on Health, federal, created to discuss health care with Canadians and recommend reforms, begins October, reports 1997.
1995	Federal EPF and CAP merged into block funding under the Canada Health and Social Transfer (CHST), to support health care, post-secondary education, and social services.
1996	Federal CHST transfers begin April 1.
1998	Health Services Review, New Brunswick, begins, reports February 1999.
1999	Social Union Framework Agreement (SUFA) in force; federal, provincial, and territorial governments (except Quebec) agree to collective approach to social policy and program development, including health. Minister's Forum on Health and Social Services, Northwest Territories, begins July, reports January 2000.
2000	First ministers' Communiqué on Health, announced September 11. Commission of Study on Health and Social Services (Clair Commission), Quebec, created June

	15, reports December 18. Saskatchewan Commission on Medicare (Fyke Commission), Saskatchewan, begins June 14, reports April 11, 2001. Premier's Advisory Council on Health for Alberta (Mazankowski Council), Alberta, established January 31, reports January 8, 2002. Premier's Health Quality Council, New Brunswick, begins January, reports January 22, 2002.
2001	Standing Senate Committee on Social Affairs, Science, and Technology review (Kirby Committee), federal, begins March 1, publishes recommendations October 2002. Commission on the Future of Health Care in Canada (Romanow Commission), federal, begins April 4, reports November 2002. British Columbia Select Standing Committee on Health (Roddick Committee), begins August, reports December 10. Northwest Territories Action Plan, begins November, reports January 2002. [Health] Consultation Process, Ontario, begins July, results released January 21, 2002. Health Choices—A Public Discussion on the Future of Manitoba's Public Health Care Services, Manitoba, begins January, reports December.
2003	First ministers' Accord on Health Care Renewal, announced February 5. Health Council of Canada established to monitor and report on progress of Accord reforms, December 9.
2004	Federal CHST split into two transfers: the Canada Health Transfer (CHT) and the Canada Social Transfer (CST), April 1. First ministers' A 10-Year Plan to Strengthen Health Care, September 16.

Source: http://www.hc-sc.gc.ca/hcs-sss/pubs/system-regime/2011-hcs-sss/index-eng.php#a13.

NOTE

1. See Stephen Brooks's *Canadian democracy: An introduction* (1996) for a full treatment of Canadian federalism and its implications for intergovernmental relations and public policy at the federal and provincial levels.

CRITICAL THINKING QUESTIONS

1. How can Canadian federalism contribute constructively to the preservation of medicare in Canada?
2. Why might the medical profession support the preservation of medicare?
3. Why might the medical profession support increased private involvement in the health care system?
4. What possible programs could you envisage as becoming part of the publicly organized health care system?
5. How can the allied health professions (e.g., nursing, physiotherapy, occupational therapy) become engaged in helping to maintain a public health care system?

FURTHER READINGS

Armstrong, H., & Armstrong, P. (2010). *Wasting away: The undermining of Canadian health care*. Toronto: Oxford University Press.

Canada's health care system is often referred to as Canada's best-loved social program. It has been one of the most accessible health care systems in the world and has played a significant role in prolonging the lives of many Canadians. This book examines how it has come under attack from a variety of sources and the effects these attacks have had on the system.

Carroll, A.E. (2012, April 16). 5 myths about Canada's health care system: The truth may surprise you about international health care. *AARP Real Possibilities*. Available online at www.pnhp.org.

This article discusses the difference between the Canadian and American health care systems. Among issues examined are wait times in Canada and the proportion of Canadians who travel to the US for medical care.

Rachlis, M. (2004). *Prescription for excellence: How innovation is saving Canada's health care system*. Toronto: HarperCollins. Available online at www.michaelrachlis.com.

In his latest book, Michael Rachlis argues that the cure for Canada's health delivery system is not more money and not privatization; he says the answer can be found in the system itself. He describes various innovations and best practices across the system that have improved health delivery and enhanced quality for the patients and health professionals.

Bryant, T., Raphael, D., & Rioux, M. (Eds.). (2010). *Staying alive: Critical perspectives on health, illness, and health care* (2nd ed.). Toronto: Canadian Scholars' Press.

Staying Alive provides a fresh perspective on the issues surrounding health, health care, and illness. In addition to the traditional approaches of health sciences and the sociology of health, this book shows the impact that human rights issues and political economy have on health. This provocative volume takes up these issues as they occur in Canada and the United States within a wider international context.

RELEVANT WEBSITES

Canada's Health Care System
www.hc-sc.gc.ca/hcs-sss/index_e.html
This government website provides background material and access to a range of sources about Canada's health care system.

Canadian Institute for Health Information
www.cihi.ca
The Canadian Institute for Health Information provides timely, accurate, and comparable information. Their data and reports inform health policies, support the effective delivery of health services, and raise awareness among Canadians of the factors that contribute to good health.

Canadian Doctors for Medicare
www.canadiandoctorsformedicare.ca
Canadian Doctors for Medicare formed in May 2006, when a group of physicians and friends became concerned about increased privatization in Canadian health care. They were also concerned about the development of a two-tier health care system that would allow the wealthy to buy private insurance for private care at the expense of the vast majority of Canadians. They advocate that health care reform must occur within the public system to benefit all Canadians.

Canadian Association of Community Health Centres
www.cachc.ca
The Canadian Association of Community Health Centres is the federal voice for community health centres and community-oriented, people-centred

primary health care across Canada. The association was established in 2012 to replace the previous Canadian Alliance of Community Health Centre Associations, which was first established in 1995.

Canadian Health Coalition
healthcoalition.ca
Formed at the 1979 SOS medicare conference, the Canadian Health Coalition is a public advocacy organization dedicated to the preservation and improvement of medicare.

REFERENCES

Annals of the New York Academy of Sciences. (1999). *Socioeconomic status and health in industrial nations: Social, psychological, and biological pathways* (vol. 896). Bethesda: Annals of the New York Academy of Sciences.

Armstrong, H., & Armstrong, P. (2003). *Wasting away: The undermining of Canadian health care*. Toronto: Oxford University Press.

Armstrong, P., & Armstrong, H. (2010). *Wasting away: The undermining of Canadian health care* (2nd ed.). Toronto: Oxford University Press.

Banting, K. (1997). The social policy divide: The welfare state in Canada and the United States. In K. Banting, G. Hoberg, & R. Simeon (Eds.), *Degrees of freedom: Canada and the United States in a changing world* (pp. 267–309). Montreal & Kingston: McGill-Queen's University Press.

Barua, B., & Clemens, J. (2015). Sorry Mr. Trump, Canadian health care is not working. *National News Watch*. Vancouver: Fraser Institute.

Begin, M. (2007). The Canada Health Act: Lessons for today and tomorrow. In B. Campbell & G.P. Marchildon (Eds.), *Medicare: Facts, myths, problems & promise* (pp. 46–49). Toronto: James Lorimer & Company.

Braen, A. (2004). Health and the distribution of powers in Canada. In T. McIntosh, P.-G. Forest, & G.P. Marchildon (Eds.), *The governance of health care in Canada* (pp. 197–232). Toronto: University of Toronto Press.

Brimblecombe, N., Dorling, D., & Shaw, M. (1999). Where the poor die in a rich city: The case of Oxford. *Health & Place, 5*(4), 287–300.

Brooks, S. (1996). *Canadian democracy: An introduction*. Toronto: Oxford University Press.

Bryant, T., Raphael, D., Schrecker, T., & Labonte, R. (2011). Canada: A land of missed opportunity for addressing the social determinants of health. *Health Policy, 101*, 44–58.

Canadian Doctors for Medicare. (2011, February). *Neat, plausible, and wrong: The myth of health care unsustainability*. Toronto: Canadian Doctors for Medicare.

Canadian Doctors for Medicare. (2013, July 21). *Strategies to reduce wait times*. Retrieved from www.canadiandoctorsformedicare.ca.

Canadian Health Coalition. (2009). *Medicare privatization: Privatized, for-profit health care; Pay more and get less*. Ottawa: Canadian Health Coalition. Retrieved from http://medicare.ca.

Canadian Institute for Health Information. (2014, October). *National health expenditure trends, 1975 to 2014*. Ottawa: Canadian Institute for Health Information.

Coburn, D. (2000). Income inequality, social cohesion, and the health status of populations: The role of neo-liberalism. *Social Science & Medicine, 51*(1), 135–146.

Commission on the Future of Health Care in Canada. (2002). *Building on values: The future of health care in Canada—Final report*. Saskatoon: Commission on the Future of Health Care in Canada.

Douglas, S. (2007). SOS medicare: A (cautionary) tale of two conferences. In B. Campbell & G. Marchildon (Eds.), *Medicare: Facts, myths, problems, and promise* (pp. 19–24). Toronto: James Lorimer & Co.

Gordon, D., Shaw, M., Dorling, D., & Davey Smith, G. (1999). *Inequalities in health: The evidence presented to the independent inquiry into inequalities in health*. Bristol: The Policy Press.

Hall, M.A., & Lord, R. (2014). Obamacare: What the Affordable Care Act means for patients and physicians. *British Medical Journal, 349*, g5376.

Health Canada. (2005). *Canada's health care system*. Ottawa: Minister of Health.

Hutchison, B., Abelson, J., & Lavis, J. (2001). Primary care in Canada: So much innovation, so little change. *Health Affairs, 20*(3), 116–131.

Leeson, H. (2004). Constitutional jurisdiction over health and health care services in Canada. In T. McIntosh, P.-G. Forest, & G.P. Marchildon (Eds.), *The governance of health care in Canada* (pp. 169–198). Toronto: University of Toronto Press.

Liberal Party of Canada. (2015). *A new health accord*. Retrieved from http://www.liberal.ca/realchange.

Madore, O. (1997). *The transfer of tax points to provinces under the Canada Health and Social Transfer*. Ottawa: Government of Canada.

Maioni, A. (2010, May 1). Health care funding: Needs and reality. *Policy Options, 31*(5), 69–72.

McIntosh, T. (2004). Introduction: Restoring trust, rebuilding confidence—The governance of health care and the Romanow Report. In T. McIntosh, P.G. Forest, & G.P. Marchildon (Eds.), *The governance of health care in Canada* (pp. 3–22). Toronto: University of Toronto Press.

Office of the Auditor General of Ontario. (2010). *Report of the Auditor General of Ontario to the Legislative Assembly*. Retrieved from www.auditor.on.ca/en/content/annualreports/arreports/en10/2010ar_en.pdf.

Organisation for Economic Co-operation and Development. (2013). *Health at a glance 2013: OECD indicators*. Paris: OECD.

Organisation for Economic Co-operation and Development. (2014). *Society at a glance 2014: OECD indicators: The crisis and its aftermath*. Paris: OECD.

Organisation for Economic Co-operation and Development. (2015). *Health at a glance 2015: OECD indicators*. Paris: OECD.

Picard, A. (2011, August 23). When even Dr. Optimism is losing faith in medicare, it's time to fix it. *The Globe and Mail*. Retrieved from http://www.theglobeandmail.com/life/health-and-fitness/when-even-dr-optimism-is-losing-faith-in-medicare-its-time-to-fix-it/article626869.

Priest, A., Rachlis, M., & Cohen, M. (2007). *Why wait? Public solutions to cure surgical waitlists*. Vancouver: BC Health Coalition and Canadian Centre for Policy Alternatives BC Office.

Rachlis, M. (2004). *Prescription for excellence: How innovation is saving Canada's health care system*. Toronto: HarperCollins.

Rachlis, M. (2005). *Public solutions to health care wait lists*. Ottawa: Canadian Centre for Policy Alternatives.

Robson, W.B.P., & Laurin, A. (2015). *Adaptability, accountability and sustainability: Intergovernmental fiscal arrangements in Canada. Commentary No. 431*. Toronto: C.D. Howe Institute.

Sanmartin, C., & Ng, E. (2004). *Joint Canada/United States survey of health, 2002–03*. Ottawa: Statistics Canada.

Schrecker, T., & Bambra, C. (2015). *How politics makes us sick: Neoliberal epidemics*. Houndmills, UK: Palgrave Macmillan.

Scott, C. (2001). *Public and private roles in health care systems*. Buckingham: Open University Press.

Statistics Canada. (2001). *The assets and debts of Canadians: An overview of the results of the Survey of Financial Security*. Retrieved from www.statcan.ca.

Teeple, G. (2000). *Globalization and the decline of social reform: Into the twenty-first century*. Aurora, ON: Garamond Press.

Teeple, G. (2006). Foreword. In D. Raphael, T. Bryant, and M. Rioux (Eds.), *Staying alive: Critical perspectives on health, illness, and health care* (pp. 1–4). Toronto: Canadian Scholars' Press.

Teeple, G. (2010). Foreword. In T. Bryant, D. Raphael, and M. Rioux (Eds.), *Staying alive: Critical perspectives on health, illness, and health care* (2nd ed.) (pp. 1–4). Toronto: Canadian Scholars' Press.

Tjepkema, M., Wilkins, R., & Long, A. (2013). Cause-specific mortality by income adequacy in Canada: A 16-year follow-up study. *Health Reports, 24*(7), 14–22.

Trading Economics. (2015). *GDP per capita*. Retrieved from www.tradingeconomics.com.

Tuohy, C. (1999). *Accidental logics: The dynamics of change in the health care arena in the United States, Britain, and Canada*. New York: Oxford University Press.

Walkom, T. (2011, April 20). Harper and the subtle erosion of medicare. *Toronto Star*. Retrieved from https://www.thestar.com/news/canada/2011/04/20/walkom_harper_and_the_subtle_erosion_of_medicare.html.

Yalnizyan, A. (2006). Controlling costs: Canada's single-payer system is costly—but least expensive. In *Mending medicare: Analysis and commentary on Canada's health care crisis* (pp. 11, 14–15). Ottawa: Canadian Centre for Policy Alternatives and the Canadian Health Coalition. Retrieved from https://www.policyalternatives.ca/sites/default/files/uploads/publications/National_Office_Pubs/2006/Mending_Mediare.pdf.

Chapter 7

HEALTH CARE REFORM IN CANADA

INTRODUCTION

From the 1980s to the mid-2000s, Canadian governments were preoccupied with issues related to the health care system and how to reform it. The penchant for reform has been driven by concerns that medicare is inefficient and overly costly as it is currently organized. This has fuelled support for allowing a parallel private system to develop to ease pressure on the public system. For example, perceptions of long wait times for specialist care and the non-responsiveness of the health care system to emerging issues have been used to build support for radically overhauling the system. Some critics have proposed privatizing some health care services and allowing private for-profit health care organizations to provide care.

Between 2000 and 2004, several major reports on health care reform were issued. These included the Mazankowski Report, prepared for the Government of Alberta; the Romanow Royal Commission on Health Care; the Kirby Report from the Canadian Senate; the Fyke Commission on Medicare in Saskatchewan; and the Clair Commission on the Study of Health and Social Services in Quebec (Clair Commission d'etude sur les services de santé et les services sociaux, 2001; Commission on Medicare, 2001; Kirby, 2002; Mazankowski, 2001; Romanow, 2002). Each report proposes a course of action for reforming medicare. The Mazankowski, Kirby, and Romanow reports proved to be the most influential. Their key recommendations and other reforms are the focus of this chapter. Health issues and other reforms that have emerged since the early 2000s are also examined.

All the authors of the major reports express their commitment to the sustainability of medicare, but differ sharply in their perspectives on medicare and how it can be repaired. Stone's distinction between the polis and the market can help to elucidate the varying concepts of society that inform the orientation of these reports and their recommendations (Stone, 1988). Is the efficient operation of the health care system best accomplished by understanding it to be a communal effort undertaken by society to benefit the community as a whole? Or is it best to allow the health care system's operation to be governed by principles of the marketplace driven by individual interest?

A FRAMEWORK FOR REFORM (THE MAZANKOWSKI REPORT)

This report was named after Don Mazankowski, who chaired the Premier's Advisory Council on Reform in Alberta. Mazankowski is best known for being Minister of Finance in Brian Mulroney's Conservative government in Ottawa during the 1980s. His 2001 report calls for fundamental changes in how health care services are financed and delivered to ensure their long-term sustainability (Mazankowski, 2001). Despite an extensive section on the broader determinants of health, most of which the Alberta government subsequently ignored (Raphael, 2003), the sections on the health care system have garnered virtually all health policy attention. Mazankowski's primary goal is to "ensure sustainability of the health system for years to come" (Mazankowski, 2001, p. 5).

First, Mazankowski contends that medicare was never intended to provide the full range of health services, treatments, drugs, and technology. Criticizing the current system as an "unregulated monopoly" (2001, p. 4), Mazankowski advocates a larger role for the private sector in health care and greater choice for consumers. He argues that the primary purpose of the report's recommendations is to stimulate innovation. Specific mechanisms include more direct payments from citizens for health care services, such as user fees, premiums, deductibles, and taxes for use of the system. One of his key recommendations was the creation of medical savings accounts (MSAs).

Medical Savings Accounts

MSAs are health accounts formed in conjunction with high-deductible health insurance—that is, the policy pays a significant portion of initial costs—that can be set up by individuals, employers, or governments (Ramsay, 1998). As an illustration, employers would set up MSAs for their employees. A portion of these funds would be used to purchase health care for those employees. When these funds were used up, employees would assume full responsibility for paying for their medical care up to a designated cap, at which catastrophic insurance would be provided.

Mazankowski argues that MSAs would be more cost-efficient than traditional insurance policies. It is claimed that MSAs foster "more prudent" spending of health care dollars without harming the health of individuals (Ramsay, 1998, p. 3). Rules governing MSA plans could vary with respect to how surplus funds in personal accounts can be used once coverage periods end. In theory, MSAs would reduce demand for services by making individuals financially responsible for their consumption of health services (Shortt, 2002).

Mazankowski argues that MSAs and other co-payment strategies would discourage inappropriate use of health care services, and also "give people more control over their health care spending" (Mazankowski, 2001, p. 17). He sees these reforms as increasing personal choices in health care services, thereby enabling more competition and increased accountability for health care services organization and delivery. He recommends delisting—or removing from public health care system coverage—some services that would now be paid for privately, arguing that "private innovators could do wonders for our health care system" (Mazankowski, 2001, p. 27).

Further, Mazankowski recommends that private, for-profit health care facilities receive public financing. He also calls for increased development of public-private partnerships (P3s) to build hospitals and provide health care services. A P3 is an arrangement in which a government contracts with the private sector to finance, develop, construct, own, and operate infrastructure and public service (Savas, 2005). The key aspect of P3 arrangements such as those already initiated by Canadian provincial governments is that, following the construction of a facility such as a new hospital or other public building, the private corporation that built it would own it and make it available to health care authorities on a lease-back or rental basis.

Regional Health Authorities

Another important aspect of Mazankowski's recommendations is a larger role for regional health authorities (RHAs) in health care. RHAs would work with other regions to provide health services and also develop service agreements with a range of private or not-for-profit health providers or facilities. These agreements would consider identifying specific areas of specialization.

These collaborations would provide "joint administration," direct contracts with hospitals, and "alternative ownership arrangements and payment mechanisms" (Mazankowski, 2001, p. 50). Authorities would be authorized to raise revenues by charging fees for a range of services that would include instituting co-payments for long-term care and home care, restaurant inspections, environmental assessments, and public health education programs. Acknowledging that RHAs have faced numerous challenges since their inception in Alberta in 1995, Mazankowski believes that his recommendations will address many of these problems (Mazankowski, 2001).

Health Care Guarantee

Mazankowski recommends health care guarantees to reduce wait times for specialists and other specialized health care services (Mazankowski, 2001). Health care guarantees are predetermined wait-time deadlines for various medical procedures. The purpose of these would be to ensure timely access to care. Specifically, if Albertans could not be assured access to needed health services within 90 days, the RHA where the individual resides would be required to arrange for those services to be provided by either a public or private sector provider. The travel costs for the patient and the costs of the service provision would be charged to the region in which the patient resides. The concept of provincial health care guarantees has been endorsed by the federal government as a means of reducing wait times for various medical procedures and treatments (see Box 7.1).

Box 7.1: Why Ontario Keeps Sending Patients South
By Lisa Priest
The Globe and Mail

More than 400 Canadians in the full throes of a heart attack or other cardiac emergency have been sent to the United States because no hospital can provide the lifesaving care they require here.

Most of the heart patients who have been sent south since 2003 typically show up in Ontario hospitals, where they are given clot-busting drugs. If those drugs fail to open their clogged arteries, the scramble to locate angioplasty in the United States begins.

"They rushed me over to Detroit, did the whole closing of the tunnel," said Eric Bialkowski, 47, of the heart attack he had on March 14, 2007, in Windsor, Ont. "It was like Disneyworld customer service."

While other provinces have sent patients out of country—British Columbia has sent 75 pregnant women or their babies to Washington State since February, 2007—nowhere is the problem as acute as in Ontario.

At least 188 neurosurgery patients and 421 emergency cardiac patients have been sent to the United States from Ontario since the 2003–2004 fiscal year to Feb. 21 this year. Add to that 25 women with high-risk pregnancies sent south of the border in 2007.

Although Queen's Park says it is ensuring patients receive emergency care when they need it, Progressive Conservative health critic Elizabeth Witmer says it reflects poor planning.

That is particularly the case with neurosurgery, she said, noting that four reports since 2003 have predicted a looming shortage.

"This province and the number of people going outside for care—it's increasing in every area," Ms. Witmer said.

"I definitely believe that it is very bad planning.... We're simply unable to meet the demand, but we don't even know what the demand is."

Tom Closson, the Ontario Hospital Association's president and chief executive officer, said 30 per cent of Ontario's hospital medical beds are currently occupied by patients awaiting more appropriate placements, such as assisted living centres, a nursing home, a rehabilitation facility or even their own homes with proper home-care supports.

That squeezes the system at both ends: Patients in intensive care units whose condition improves cannot get into step-down units, and some emergency patients can't get a bed at all, he said, adding that "everything is jam-packed at the moment."

A method for determining the right mix of beds and health services required in Ontario needs to be developed, he said, noting that that task has not been undertaken on a provincial basis for a decade.

Laurel Ostfield, press secretary to provincial Health Minister George Smitherman, said that in emergencies, where the patient goes becomes a clinical decision.

It is preferable for someone with a heart attack in Windsor to be sent to Detroit, a few kilometres away, rather than on a long ride to London, Ont.

When demand has peaked, government has responded, she said. It struck a neurosurgery expert panel to study the problem and $4.1-million has been provided to stem the tide of US neurosurgery patients.

As well, stand-alone angioplasty services were created in Windsor in May.

Canadian Medical Association president Brian Day said he couldn't speak about the Ontario problem, but noted this country is the last in the Organisation for Economic Co-operation and Development to finance hospitals with global budgets.

Under that model, patients—and often doctors—are sometimes viewed as a financial drain.

"We keep coming back to the same root cause," Dr. Day said in a telephone interview from Ottawa. "The health system is not consumer-focused."

Patients first learn of the problem when they are critically ill.

Jennifer Walmsley went to Headwaters Health Care Centre in Orangeville in October and was diagnosed with a cerebral hemorrhage due to a ruptured aneurysm. That acute-care hospital does not have neurosurgery and no Ontario hospital that does could take her. She was then rushed to a Buffalo hospital.

Headwater's chief of staff, Jeff McKinnon, said three neurosurgery patients have been sent to Buffalo in the past year. Others have gone to Toronto, Mississauga, Hamilton and London.

Radiologist Louise Keevil said Headwaters has an arrangement with neurosurgeons at other Ontario hospitals to send electronic images for their assessment, but "the limiting factor is availability of beds in their hospital."

"The physicians are very accommodating but their hands are tied by availability of service."

Kaukab Usman had a heart attack after a gym workout in Windsor on Dec. 9. She was rushed to hospital and given clot-bursting drugs.

When they failed, she was sent to Henry Ford Hospital in Detroit, where she had angioplasty on one clogged artery and two stents inserted.

"It was a miracle for me to be alive," Ms. Usman said in a telephone interview from Somerset, New Jersey, where she is recuperating.

Aaron Kugelmass, director of the cardiac catheterization laboratory at Henry Ford Hospital, said a system is in place to get these patients the care they need expeditiously.

"We try to make their length of stay in the US as short as possible," said Dr. Kugelmass, associate division chief of cardiology. "If they are stable for discharge, we discharge them to home in Windsor, with clear follow-up plans."

Cross-border emergency health care should become less frequent when Amr Morsi, an interventional cardiologist currently in Orlando, Florida, comes to work at Hôtel-Dieu Grace Hospital in Windsor in April; a second interventional cardiologist is to come on board there by end of year.

When the program is fully functional, Dr. Morsi expects Hôtel-Dieu Grace to be able to do 500 angioplasties a year.

"The idea of starting the program in Windsor is that we will be able to do more of the angioplasty procedures in Windsor without having to send them to Detroit or London," said the Toronto native who did his cardiology training at the University of Toronto.

"It will take some time to decrease the numbers entirely, but that certainly is the long-term plan."

Mr. Bialkowski of Lakeshore, a town east of Windsor, had angioplasty and received four stents. The stents, typically made of self-expanding, stainless steel mesh, were placed at the site of the fully blocked artery to keep it open.

The price to treat him, including a two-day hospital stay in March, 2007, was $40,826.21 (US). With a 35 per cent discount from Henry Ford Hospital, the bill to the Ontario Health Insurance Plan tallied $26,537.03 (US), according to a health ministry document, a copy of which was sent to Mr. Bialkowski.

The father of six, a human resources manager for a manufacturing company based in Windsor, is back at the gym and feels great. It didn't matter where he received the lifesaving care, he said, just so long as he obtained it.

"I guess the Canadian government took care of me," he said.

Source: Priest, L. (2008, March 1). Why Ontario keeps sending patients south. *The Globe and Mail*, A1.

In summary, the key message of the report is that the health care system should be financed less by general taxation and more by direct payments from citizens (Mazankowski, 2001). To further this objective, Mazankowski asserts that such a shift would encourage people to stay healthy, such that they would make less use of the health care system. Mazankowski emphasizes that consumers need to be more aware of the cost of providing health care by paying out of pocket for health care services that they receive. In essence, Mazankowski argues that commercialization schemes through user fees and private sector involvement will foster better-quality and more timely care.

THE HEALTH OF CANADIANS: THE FEDERAL ROLE (THE KIRBY REPORT)

Senator Kirby initiated a Senate study of the Canadian health care system at the same time as Romanow began his Royal Commission on behalf of the federal Liberal government of Prime Minister Jean Chrétien. Kirby wrote a number of reports in which he identifies the different roles of the federal government in health and health care, the principles of medicare, and health care financing. The focus here is the sixth report, which presents the final recommendations to reform and renew medicare.

Independent Health Commission

Kirby recommends the creation of an evaluation body or council that would function independently of government to monitor the operation of the health care system. Its primary responsibilities would be to prepare an annual report on the state of the health care system and the health of the Canadian population. Such reporting would provide an important impetus to improve health care delivery and health outcomes (Kirby, 2002). This body would consist of one provincial/territorial representative from each of the five major regions in Canada and five representatives from the federal government. The federal government would provide $10 million annually for council operations. As discussed in chapter 6, the Health Council was abolished in 2012.

Public versus Private Administration and Delivery of Health Care Services

Kirby argues that it is not important who funds or owns health care services, as he believes that the quality would be the same: "The patient and the funder/insurer will be served equally well no matter what the corporate ownership of a health care institution might be" (2002, p. 38). He asserts that the principle of public administration articulated in the Canada Health Act and other health care legislation refers only to the funding of hospital and physician services, but "*not to the delivery* of those services" (2002, p. 7; italics in source). He asserts there has been widespread misunderstanding about the meaning of publicly funded and administered health insurance, and the delivery of health care services. He stresses that under the Canada Health Act, health care services "do not have to be delivered by public agencies" (2002, p. 8).

Cost Efficiency and Medical Savings Accounts

Similar to Mazankowski, Kirby is convinced of the need to make the health care system more effective and efficient (Kirby, 2002). Further, he sees the system as not sustainable, given existing funding levels. He argues for an infusion of $5 billion annually from the federal government, which he believes is required to reform and renew the health care system. Thus, unlike Mazankowski, Kirby calls for a strong federal role in health care as key to ensuring its long-term sustainability, and also to maintaining national standards for medicare.

Like Mazankowski, Kirby also recommends medical savings accounts as a mechanism to prevent inappropriate use or overuse of the system (Kirby, 2002). Kirby, too, believes that MSAs will help limit (if not eliminate) unnecessary use of health services, thereby reducing financial pressures on public health care funding. Such accounts will also promote greater efficiency in health care operations (Kirby, 2002).

Health Care Guarantee

Although Kirby acknowledges the lack of reliable data on wait times for particular procedures, Kirby cites "strong" public perception of a waiting list problem as evidence of the need for action (2002, p. 110). Like Mazankowski, Kirby recommends establishing a national health care guarantee to reduce wait times for health services (Kirby, 2002). He argues that "such a guarantee would serve as a spur to the creation of the necessary standards, criteria and information systems" (p. 113) and that it will ensure governments provide patients with reasonable access to needed health services in their own or another Canadian province or territory. The guarantee is considered essential to (1) reform the system; (2) restore public confidence in the system; and (3) provide evidence of the capacity of government to spend tax dollars responsibly. Further, Kirby argues that not implementing a guarantee will increase the likelihood that the Supreme Court will approve the right of individuals to purchase private-issued insurance to pay for privately delivered health care outside of the public medicare system.

Primary Health Care Reform

Kirby reiterates the need for continuing primary health care reform, with emphasis on creating multidisciplinary primary health care teams (Kirby, 2002). He calls for alternatives to fee-for-service arrangements, such as capitation (health care providers being paid a set rate for serving a designated population) or some kind of blended approach. He also favours incorporating health promotion and illness prevention strategies into primary care. Kirby recommends that the federal government provide $50 million annually to help the provinces establish these primary-care groups. All of these arrangements are seen as serving to reduce health care expenditures.

Devolution to Regional Health Authorities

Kirby also favours expanding the role of regional health authorities (Kirby, 2002). Consistent with his interest in introducing mechanisms into the public health care system, Kirby argues for devolving responsibility from senior governments to RHAs to purchase a comprehensive range of health services (Kirby, 2002). RHAs would control finances and select providers on the basis of quality and cost.

Kirby considers that devolution to these authorities would encourage more effective management of health care services. Further, he argues that regionalization will ensure the timely provision of health care services (Kirby, 2002), because regional authorities would be responsible for finding timely care for an individual. If that was not possible, the authority would either have to go to a private health care provider in the local jurisdiction or to a public or private provider in another jurisdiction to provide needed care.

RHAs are also the mechanism by which internal markets would be created. Kirby defines internal markets as "the introduction of market-like mechanisms" into the health care system (Kirby, 2002, p. 70). He cites internal market reforms that involve devolving responsibilities to regional health authorities as having been implemented successfully in Sweden and the United Kingdom (Kirby, 2002).

Service-Based Funding

The current funding model for hospitals in Canada is global funding. In this model, health care service providers apply their funding to provide a range of services. Kirby recommends a shift to service-based funding, in which specific areas of activity, such as cardiac care or hip replacements, are provided with set funding envelopes. Service-based funding would replace all of the current hospital funding methods and include what are called line-by-line budgeting and population-based funding. This means that hospitals would receive funding based on the type and volume of services that they provide (MacDonald, 2002–2003). To this end, Kirby recommends that hospitals develop specializations, such as cardiology care (Kirby, 2002). He argues that service-based funding would reduce costs and make hospitals less dependent on government for financing.

Kirby's report reiterates many of the recommendations in Mazankowski's health reform report. The key message of both reports is to reduce the perceived dependency of the health care sector upon government financing of health care. Kirby recommends expanding the role of the private sector in health care and introducing a range of market mechanisms to finance the system. However, he also recognizes the need for stable federal financing of provincial and territorial health care programs.

BUILDING ON VALUES: THE FUTURE OF HEALTH CARE IN CANADA (THE ROMANOW REPORT)

Prime Minister Jean Chrétien appointed Roy Romanow, former premier of Saskatchewan, to lead a Royal Commission on health care reform (Romanow, 2002). Romanow was to initiate what was called a dialogue with Canadians about the future of the public health care system. Of specific concern was the long-term sustainability of the universally accessible, publicly funded medicare system.

Describing his report as "a roadmap for a collective journey by Canadians to reform and renew their health care system" (Romanow, 2002, p. xxiii), Romanow presents a vision that the health care system is sustainable (Romanow, 2002). His key recommendations focus on retaining a public over a private, for-profit service delivery and adding accountability as a principle of medicare in the Canada Health Act. In contrast to the Mazankowski and Kirby reports, he is committed to strengthening the existing public system. In terms of the sustainability of the public health care system, Romanow considers the focus on financing and money to be "narrow" and "inadequate." He argues that sustainability "means ensuring that sufficient resources are available over the long term to provide timely access to quality services" (Romanow, 2002, p. 1).

Public versus Private Care

Romanow notes that a key element of his commission's mandate was to make recommendations "to ensure the long-term sustainability of a universally accessible, publicly funded health care system" (Romanow, 2002, p. 1). He considers the role that MSAs, various user fees, public-private partnerships, and other market-related mechanisms could play in a reformed health care system. On the basis of the available evidence, including a very large number of commissioned reports, Romanow concludes that all of these have shortcomings, with serious implications for the accessibility and quality of health care services.

Not surprisingly, considering the title of his report—*Building on Values*—he calls for a recommitment to the principles of need over income as a guiding principle of medicare. Romanow provides evidence that health care systems are more effective when publicly financed and managed. Health and health care should not be seen as commodities, he argues, but rather as essential goods to which all citizens are entitled.

With regard to financial sustainability, Romanow notes that Canada's spending on health care compares favourably with that of other developed countries in the OECD with public health care systems (Romanow, 2002). He recognizes the funding imbalance that has appeared between the federal and the provincial and territorial governments as a result of steady declines in federal contributions since the 1980s. As a result, the provinces have been required to dedicate increasing proportions of their budgets to health care. He argues that the health care system is under-resourced and requires more federal dollars to maintain sustainability. He recommends "stable and predictable federal funding" in the form of a "cash-only" Canada Health Transfer (Romanow, 2002).

Health Care Guarantee

Romanow considers the matter of wait times for care and recommends caution in approaching care guarantees (Romanow, 2002). He acknowledges that care guarantees can reassure patients, and require health authorities, providers, and hospitals to initiate steps to ensure that the health care system can meet time limits established in a guarantee. Yet, he adds that guarantees must be based on an objective assessment of the capacity of the system to provide the required service or treatment within a specific period of time and on the urgency of the condition requiring treatment.

Overall, Romanow is concerned that provincial and territorial health care systems be provided with the flexibility to manage emergency and elective surgical procedures (Romanow, 2002). Care guarantees might introduce rigidity and could direct resources away from life-saving surgery or treatment to meet care guarantees for other health care services.

Direct and Ancillary Health Services

Romanow differentiates between direct and ancillary health services (Romanow, 2002). Ancillary health services are cleaning and food services within hospitals. He recommends public funding of diagnostic and treatment services, but supports contracting out ancillary services to reduce costs and make more resources available for medically necessary services.

Romanow advocates this distinction on the basis that most Canadians seem to accept the provision of ancillary services by for-profit agencies (Romanow, 2002). He adds that many non-profit hospitals currently contract out these services to for-profit corporations. He argues that, based on the available evidence, direct health care services should be provided in public and not-for-profit health care facilities, since the consequences of private delivery can be life-threatening.

Box 7.2: What Is Missing in the Royal Commission's Final Report?

The Report quite clearly fails to provide a gendered analysis of health care. Plans that fail to take women into account [are] not only inadequate but also inequitable.

The Report fails to recommend the prohibition of for-profit delivery, even though it presents evidence demonstrating the problems with such delivery.

The Report fails entirely to consider long-term care, chronic care or care for people with disabilities.

The Report fails to discuss reproductive issues and access to these services.

The Report does not apply the lessons on international agreements set out in the final chapter to the other recommendations in the Report, even though they could have a profound impact on them.

What Does the Report Mean for Women?

We applaud the Romanow Commission for demonstrating the sustaining of medicare. A publicly funded system delivered through non-profit services is crucial for all women in Canada. But like other reports on health care reform in the last decade, this Report fails to recognize the significant ways in which health care is an issue for women. Women are 80% of paid health care providers, a similar proportion of those providing unpaid personal care and a majority of those receiving care, especially among the elderly. The sustainability of the system is not just about finances, it is about women's work and women's care. Just as Canada should be a leader in seeing health as a human right, it should also be a leader in promoting gender equality in Canada and globally.

Investing in health care means investing in women. Unless this is understood, planning for care is bound to fail in its objectives.

Source: Adapted from The National Coordinating Group on Health Care Reform and Women. (2003). *Reading Romanow: The implications of the final report of the Commission on the Future of Health Care in Canada for women* (p. 53). Winnipeg: Centres of Excellence for Women's Health.

Expand Medicare

Romanow recommends expanding the scope of medicare to include home care and palliative home care services to support people in the final six months of their lives (Romanow, 2002). Romanow also recommends developing a program to provide ongoing support to informal caregivers by making them eligible for special benefits under Canada's Employment Insurance program.

Romanow recommends developing a national formulary of prescription medications to ensure consistent medication coverage in all provinces and territories. The National Drug Agency would work with the provinces and territories to ensure consistent coverage, objective assessments, and cost effectiveness.

Relationship to National Forum on Health Findings

Of all the health reform reports, Romanow's report is most consistent with recommendations made by the National Forum on Health. The National Forum was launched by then Prime Minister Jean Chrétien in 1994 to engage Canadians in a discussion about health care and to recommend innovative ways that the federal government could improve the health care system and the health of the population (National Forum on Health, 1998). The National Forum was set up as an advisory body to the prime minister and the federal minister of health. This body saw its role as considering the long-term and systemic issues associated with health and health care. The National Forum commissioned several papers on systemic issues and produced five volumes on key health issues. It provided several recommendations on how to improve the health care system and the health of the population.

Box 7.3: Recommendations of the National Forum on Health

Among the recommendations of the National Forum were:

- system is already sustainable
- public is preferred over private
- add accountability to the Canada Health Act principles of public administration, universality, accessibility, portability, and comprehensiveness
- include home care services
- improve timely access to services
- approach health care guarantee with caution, based on principles of fairness, appropriateness, certainty
- investigate pros and cons of private diagnostic services
- workers' compensation

ANALYSIS OF THE HEALTH REFORM REPORTS

The Mazanowski, Kirby, and Romanow reports reflect diverse perspectives—and a lack of consensus—on how to reform medicare. The system has become too large to leave responsibility to the health care professions to manage it. Increasing amounts of money are being made available to reform the system, but with little commitment on the part of politicians and government to strengthen the public health care insurance system. They seem unwilling to significantly reform the manner in which services are provided, health care providers are paid, and health care activities are monitored (Rachlis, 2004, 2005; Walkom, 2011).

Box 7.4: Preliminary Analysis of the Romanow Report from the Canadian Health Coalition and the Canadian Labour Congress

Overview and Broad Principles

The Romanow Report on the Future of Health Care concluded that there is a consensus among Canadians that medicare is a moral enterprise, not a commercial venture. Canadians believe that equal and timely access to medically necessary health services on the basis of need alone is a right of citizenship. The core values that underpin medicare remain the same: equity, fairness, and solidarity. As a result, Canadians reject diluting the principles of medicare, scrapping national standards, paying privately to get faster care, and treating health care as a business.

In his message to Canadians, Commissioner Romanow said, "I believe it is a far greater perversion of Canadian values to accept a system where money, rather than need, determines who gets access to care." The Report clearly states that Romanow challenged those advocating user fees, medical savings accounts, de-listing public services, greater privatization, and a parallel private system to provide him with evidence that these choices would improve or strengthen the health care system. He clearly said that "The evidence has not been forthcoming." There is no evidence that these solutions will deliver cheaper care or improve access to care. Further, the principles underlying these solutions are directly contradictory to the values of Canadians and the values of medicare.

For those reasons, the Romanow Report rejects a parallel tier of private, for-profit care for the delivery of what he calls direct health care services such as medical, diagnostic, and surgical care. This conclusion is to be applauded. It is based on evidence that for-profit care will harm, not improve, Medicare.

However, the Report mistakenly says that a line can be drawn between health services and ancillary services such as laundry, food preparation, cleaning, and maintenance services. These services are said to be appropriate for delivery in the private sector. The labour movement disagrees with this approach. These services are health services and those who provide them are health care workers, and see themselves as health care workers. These services are pertinent to the health of patients. Good nutrition is critical to people who are sick, and the cleanliness of hospitals is essential to patients, staff, and the public. While the Report has rejected a parallel tier of for-profit care, there does not appear to be a mechanism for ensuring that this does not happen. It does recommend that the Canada Health Act must be clarified to include these services under the act. The Report needs to be looked at more closely.

Overall, the Romanow Report offers some important steps forward to preserving and expanding medicare for today and for future generations, but it is just a starting point. It has established some fundamental principles that need to be built and expanded upon.

Public-Private Partnerships

The Report rejects the argument that [for] Public-Private Partnerships to design, build and operate health facilities, such as hospitals, will save the public money. Romanow notes that these agreements have been shown to cost more over the longer term, and can have the effect of hospital bed closures and a reduction in nurses and other health staff. Romanow stops short of recommending no Public-Private Partnerships.

Medical Savings Accounts, User Fees and Co-payments, Tax Credits, and Deductibles

Romanow rejects these alternative measures to raise more funding for medicare. In the end, all of these measures violate the core principle of equity and equal access to care based on need for care. These measures promote access based on ability to pay.

MRIs and CT Scans

The Report calls all diagnostic services required to assess a patient's need for health services to come under the conditions of the Canada Health Act, including the prohibitions of user fees, facility fees, and extra-billing. The CHA should be amended to clarify this.

CHST

The Report calls for federal health funding to be taken out of the CHST and put into a new transfer—The Canada Health Transfer. This transfer would be a cash-only transfer and have an escalator clause so that federal funding would keep pace with economic growth and our ability to pay. The CLC has called for this since the CHST was put in place in 1995.

Expansion of the Public System

The Report recommends that the Canada Health Act should be revised to include home care services in priority areas. This would include post-acute home care, including drugs and rehab services, as well as coverage of palliative care in the home during the last six months of life. Also, it would include a program of support for informal caregivers. Home mental health services should immediately come under the CHA. It calls for a Catastrophic Drug Transfer to help provinces with their drug plans. Eventually, the CHA would cover the cost of prescription drugs. It calls for a creation of a National Drug Agency to control costs and insure the safety of drugs and it also calls for the establishment of a National Drug Formulary to help control costs. Finally, it calls for a review of aspects of the Patent Act. There must be an effective dispute mechanism maintained in the CHA. The dedicated Health Transfer would be directly connected to the principle and conditions in the Act. The Report calls for the development of a Rural and Remote Access Fund to attract and retain health care providers, including opportunities for health professionals in training to gain experience for doctors, nurses and other health providers. The Report states that the current status of injured workers getting preferred access to care violates the principle of equal access to care for all Canadians. The Canada Health Act allows this to take place. This exception needs to be reconsidered.

Accountability

The Report calls for the establishment of a new Canadian Health Covenant which would state Canadian values and would be a guiding force for Medicare. A Health Council of Canada would be established to analyze and assess the national health system as a whole. Membership in the Council would include the public, providers, and governments. The Canada Health Act should be revised to include a Sixth Principle of Accountability.

Trade and Health Care

In recognition of the threat to health care from globalization, Romanow sends a clear message to the federal government that current protections for health care in trade agreements must not be weakened. Future expansions and actions must be protected in all future agreements. The right to regulate health care policy should not be subject to claims from foreign companies.

Primary Care Reform

The Primary Care Transfer should drive changes to the primary care system. We need a common national platform for health care reform. Prevention and promotion initiatives would be a part of this. Primary care needs to be delivered in multi-disciplinary teams in a community-based setting. All funding sources for Aboriginal health care should be pooled into a new Aboriginal Health Partnerships Fund. The goal is to improve access to care and provide adequate, stable funding. The system needs to reflect cultural diversity and language barriers to accessing care.

Funding: Making Medicare Sustainable

Civil Society organizations have called for the federal government to increase its share of health funding to 25% of publicly insured health services. The Romanow Report recommends that the federal government move to this standard by 2005–06 with increased funding in each of the next three years. The Report calls for new federal funds to bring the federal share up to 25% of insured health spending provided under current provincial plans. This will require additional investments to be added to the current level of funding. This would mean a new investment of $3.5 billion next year, 2003–04, followed by an additional $5 billion the next year, 2004–05, and a $6.5 billion increase in 2005–06. By 2005–06, these increases will bring the federal cash transfer to $15.3 billion per year. Romanow assumes that this will equal 25% of the public health services insured under provincial health plans. An escalator clause will increase this cash floor according to economic growth. These funding arrangements need to be stable and predictable. These funds would be targeted to specific spending areas over the next two years.

Table 7.1

	2003/04 ($ billion)	2004/05 ($ billion)
Diagnostic services fund	.75	.75
Rural and remote access	.75	.75
Primary health care	1.0	1.5
Home care	1.0	1.0
Drugs	—	1.0
TOTAL	3.5	5.0

In 2005–06, the federal transfer for that year would rise from $5 billion to $6.5 billion, bringing the total federal cash transfer to $15.3 billion that year.

Source: Canadian Health Coalition and Canadian Labour Council. (2002). *Preliminary analysis of the Romanow Report from the Canadian Health Coalition and the Canadian Labour Council.* Ottawa: Canadian Health Coalition and Canadian Labour Council.

As a result, the federal and provincial and territorial governments tinker at the edges of the system by delisting services and privatizing increasing elements of the system. All of this further reduces the role of government in providing publicly organized and managed health care. Already, the Canadian health care system provides significantly less public coverage of health services than do most developed nations (OECD, 2015). Thus, central to health care reform is the debate between public versus private financing and delivery of health care services.

Values, Principles, and World Views

Mazankowski's and Kirby's visions of health care are consistent with the market approach defined by Stone (1988, 2012). Stone explains how the market treats individuals as consumers and how public goods such as health care become commodities. The market is characterized by competition, as each individual works to acquire goods and services at the lowest possible cost. Competition, however, does not ensure quality of the goods and services traded and sold in a market when applied to health care.

Market approaches create inequities in access for vulnerable populations who lack the income to move up in line to receive the health care services that they require. If faced with paying health care costs such as user fees, people with low income will simply do without.

Of these reports, only Romanow recognizes these issues and expresses confidence in the overall purpose, function, and form of the public health care system, yet he also identifies areas for improvement. Romanow couches his report in the notion of values and reinforces the notion that medicare expresses a value of equality that Canadians continue to support.

Romanow confirms public confidence in public health care and recommends major new federal investments in the system to ensure its sustainability (Maioni, 2003). Observers wonder, however, if the required co-operation between the two levels of government is feasible, given their tendency toward reducing resources to the system and opting for privatization schemes that result in reducing the role of government in health care.

Box 7.5: New Institutionalism Concepts and the Prospects for Health Care Reform

From a new institutionalist perspective, institutions structure political debate and the solutions that will be considered to address public problems (Hall, 1993; Hall & Taylor, 1996). In health care, federal and provincial institutions tend to impede meaningful reforms of the health care system, particularly in relation to the provision of sufficient funding to ensure its sustainability. The ongoing wrangling between the federal and the provincial and territorial governments over the financing of health care has led to little productive debate on how to change the system with the goal of improving it. The two levels of government can be seen as structuring the health care debate, often by limiting the range of solutions that can be considered to reform the system and improve service delivery and health outcomes. There is also institutional resistance to expanding the system not only to provide sufficient resources to core functions of medicare, but also to expand the scope of the system to include dental care, home care, and pharmacare, as recommended as early as 1964 by Emmett Hall's report to the federal government.

In contrast to Romanow, Mazankowski and Kirby recommend introducing some privatization measures, such as user fees for services, in order to sustain the system. Opting for private measures or an expanded role for the private sector is an ideological position (Coburn, 2000, 2001; Langille, 2004, 2009; Savas, 2005). It prescribes roles and relationships for private institutions and government within a society. The private institutions identified to improve health care represent the market and market-oriented strategies such as user fees, medical savings accounts, and public-private partnerships (Stone, 1988, 2012). What happens in these arrangements is that the service or good charged to the private entity in the end belongs to that entity. Critics argue that once these arrangements are in place, it is difficult to bring these goods or services back into the public sector.

All three reports are concerned about the sustainability of medicare, but present very different solutions to ensure it. Mazankowski recommends user fees and medical savings accounts (MSAs) to reduce inappropriate use. Kirby recommends public over private funding, but also recommends MSAs for reasons similar to Mazankowski. Romanow unequivocally states that public funding makes the most sense and notes the lack of evidence that privatization will improve the quality of care. These and other aspects of the reports reflect different conceptions of society and how to deliver health care.

Drawing on Stone's distinction between the polis and the market (Stone, 1988; Romanow, 2002), it is clear that the market underlies Mazankowski's approach to health care reform. He implies that making the health care system run more like a private business will ensure its sustainability. He also recommends market or private solutions, such as MSAs, to ensure the sustainability of the health services system. His aim is to make consumers more aware of the cost of health care and to discourage inappropriate use or overuse of health care services.

In contrast, Romanow and Kirby reflect the polis in their emphasis on a strong federal role in health care. Neither considers health care a commodity to be bought and sold in the market, but rather a public good. Romanow cites evidence that shows that public health facilities provide better-quality care than private health facilities. He also cites the evidence showing that private health care systems are more costly than public health care systems. Romanow's findings and perspective are consistent with the views of the Canadian public.

Box 7.6: Walkom: Why the Harper Funding Diktat Endangers Medicare

Ottawa's plan to cut back health funding threatens to make medicare rules unenforceable. And this is only stage one.
By Thomas Walkom, National Affairs
Toronto Star

For medicare, the federal government's new health financing ultimatum is a clear and deliberate step backward. By scaling back cash contributions to provincial medicare plans, it will gradually and inevitably destroy Ottawa's ability to enforce the Canada Health Act. By tying these contributions to the vagaries of the overall economy, it will make it harder for provinces to forge long-term health-care strategies. And by cutting back health spending during slump periods, it will remove money and jobs from health care precisely at those times when they are needed most.

Most provincial governments were furious when federal Finance Minister Jim Flaherty formally unveiled his non-negotiable scheme Monday. Justly so. The new plan from Prime Minister Stephen Harper's Conservatives threatens to undo key medicare gains that Canada has made in the past eight years.

To understand those gains, we have to understand what medicare is. It is a national public health insurance scheme administered and partly funded by the provinces. The only incentive for individual provinces to adhere to national standards set out in the Canada Health Act is that doing so allows them to get cash from Ottawa. But since its inauguration by the Liberals in 1968, medicare has been under attack from those who think the federal government has no business in health care.

Indeed, it was a Liberal government that, in 1977, first devised a way to gradually extricate Ottawa from what had been a 50-50 cost sharing arrangement with the provinces. The Liberals did so by first tying annual federal health transfers to the ups and downs of the economy. Like Flaherty, they explained this as a cost-saving measure. More important, they began to count any tax room ceded to the provinces as part of their health contribution. The use of these so-called tax points allowed successive Liberal and Conservative governments to gradually reduce the actual cash they transferred to provinces.

By 2002, Ottawa was contributing only 18 per cent of the public cash going to medicare. An increasingly unenforceable Canada Health Act was on its way to becoming a dead letter. This is why Roy Romanow's 2002 Royal Commission into health care recommended a boost in federal cash contributions.

And it is why the federal-provincial health accord two years later was so important. That accord eliminated any linkage between federal health transfers and economic growth. More important, it committed Ottawa to put more real cash into medicare. Thanks to that accord, the federal government's cash share of health-care funding has gone back up to about 25 per cent.

Flaherty's new plan very carefully doesn't mention the accounting fiction known as tax points. But even so, the Conservative arrangement would eventually return the country to where it was in 2002—with Ottawa putting little into medicare and the federal government losing all ability to enforce national standards that Canadians accept as given. Think of this as stage one.

Stage two has not yet been announced. But it is intriguing to see that Ottawa still wants to continue talking to the provinces about health, even as it insists that the main topic of contention—money—is non-negotiable.

What will they talk about? My guess is "flexibility." Having warned the provinces that he plans to eventually starve them of cash, Prime Minister Stephen Harper can now tell the premiers that he'll turn a blind eye if they try to make up this shortfall through creative solutions—even if such solutions (delisting of all but core services? user fees?) run directly counter to the letter and spirit of medicare.

Source: Walkom, T. (2011, December 20). Why the Harper funding diktat endangers medicare. *Toronto Star.* Retrieved from www.thestar.com.

In short, the reports reflect two competing world views (Maynard, 2007). These are the collectivist and the libertarian ideologies. The collectivist approach promotes equality as the goal of the behaviour of social institutions. Romanow's and Kirby's reports represent the collectivist orientation. Kirby, however, favours user fees and other privatization mechanisms, while also supporting a strong federal role. In contrast, Mazankowski reflects a libertarian world view with his emphasis on incurring more out-of-pocket payments and a smaller state role.

Of particular interest is Kirby's recommendation to shift to service-based funding for hospitals and an expanded role for regional health authorities. It seems to contradict his overall support for a national health care system fortified by federal funding. It also highlights his desire to reduce the role of the state in health care.

Grieshaber-Otto and Sinclair (2004) argue that service-based funding represents a fundamental shift in hospital funding. Moreover, they add that Kirby's analysis fails to recognize that hospitals and local health authorities may become less accountable to the public as these institutions become more independent of democratically elected governments. They suggest that Senator Kirby and his Senate colleagues believe that these developments would improve the functioning of the system, thereby validating the policy changes that Kirby and his committee think are necessary (Grieshaber-Otto & Sinclair, 2004).

Kirby's recommendation that governments pay for people to receive treatment in other jurisdictions may not address the fundamental problem of the federal government's underfunding (Grieshaber-Otto & Sinclair, 2004). In essence, the proposed remedy could exacerbate the situation by authorizing additional spending outside the local setting at private market rates. Thus, Grieshaber-Otto and Sinclair and other policy analysts argue that such measures may result in increasing reliance on private, for-profit health entities to provide health care services (Grieshaber-Otto & Sinclair, 2004).

Box 7.7: Provincial Innovation or Federal Leadership?

Much ink has been spilled in describing and explaining the development of healthcare policy across Canada (see, inter alia, Taylor, 1987; Shortt, 1981; Maioni, 1998; Tuohy, 1999; Boychuck, 2009). These studies have pointed to a number of factors that account for the distinctively Canadian experience: some scholars point to the innovation edge of a social-democratic government in Saskatchewan and the demonstration effect of provincial experiments; some indicate the federal-provincial dynamic that allowed for the creation of a "collaborative" fiscal federalism framework; and some look to the elusive notion of "nation-building" that is sometimes attached to the historical experience.

Two enduring legacies stand out, however, in the historical narratives. The first is that institutions matter; the second is that politics paved the way for policy. The *absence of federal policy leadership,* combined with an *interventionist social-democratic government,* led to provincial innovation (the Saskatchewan experience). The stability, diffusion, and expansion of this experiment in Saskatchewan and across the other provinces, however, depended on the fiscal involvement of the federal government, which attempted to use *fiscal levers* in the absence of policy-making capacity.

But the history of these fiscal levers has shown that, while effective in deterrence and compliance, they are less useful in trying to deploy or encourage policy reform or system change. Instead, they have become part of the ebb and flow of fiscal federalism in Canada—an instrument of federal budgetary exigencies, rather than a specific instrument for health policy-making. The "pendulum" effect applies to a range of policy areas (see Simeon & Robinson, 1990), but the case of healthcare illustrates it best. In the earliest years of cost-sharing programs, through the Hospital Insurance and Diagnostic Services Act of 1957 and the Medical Care Act of 1966, there was a hefty financial commitment—an investment, in many ways—on the part of the federal government to pay specific amounts engendered by provincial spending. But between 1977 and 2003, block transfers became the financial instrument of choice, severing federal financing from provincial healthcare policy. Even with the introduction of the Canada Health Transfer and the Ten-Year Plan, as of 2004, federal fiscal involvement has amounted to the equivalent of a series of blank cheques rather than a commitment to policy leadership.

Source: Excerpt from Maioni, A. (2015). Politics and the healthcare policy arena in Canada: Diagnosing the situation, evaluating solutions. In A. S. Carson, J. Dixon, and K. R. Nossal (Eds.), *Toward a Healthcare Strategy for Canadians,* (p. 226). Kingston: Queen's School of Policy Studies.

Deregulation and Accountability

Kirby and Mazankowski believe greater competition will lead to more innovation and better quality of care, but cite little evidence to support these claims. They seem unconcerned about the lack of accountability that may result from an expanded private sector role and further deregulation of health care. Mazankowski criticizes medicare as an unregulated monopoly, yet favours further deregulation. It is unclear how further deregulation will improve the quality of services, or how it can maintain public accountability.

Moreover, experiences with deregulation in other jurisdictions suggest the need for caution (Grieshaber-Otto & Sinclair, 2004). Deregulation jeopardizes accountability and obscures lines of authority. For example, the House of Commons Transport Committee in the United Kingdom identified serious flaws in the organization of the privatized railway: "The constant theme throughout our work was the complaint that the current structure of the industry is too fragmented to provide clear lines of responsibility and leadership and a satisfactory basis for improved rail performance" (UK House of Commons Transport Committee, 2004, pp. 5–6). Such fragmentation and blurring of lines of accountability may affect the Canadian health care system, should Canadian governments allow further commercialization in health care.

There is need for more consideration of public solutions to remedy the problems of the health care system. Foremost is a need to renew the state's role in health care and recognize the benefits of the single-payer system.

Medical Savings Accounts: Path to Prudent Consumer Use of Health Care Services?

The Fraser Institute, a public policy think tank based in Vancouver, BC, favours an expanded role for the private sector, and the introduction of user fees and MSAs (Ramsay, 1998). Their premise is that MSAs and other user fees will reduce the cost of care, and, in particular, reduce taxes. They argue that American evidence shows that "MSAs are conducive to more prudent health spending without compromising individuals' health.... They have resulted in lower employer and employee costs" (Ramsay, 1998). Further, the Fraser Institute suggests that MSAs could lower health expenditures by up to 20 percent (Ramsay, 1998). The rationale for such measures is to make consumers more aware of the cost of health care to reduce their use of health care services.

Research literature on experiences in the public systems of Singapore and China, where such plans have been implemented, suggests that the approach does not control costs (Shortt, 2002). In fact, MSAs may increase costs. Moreover, MSAs may exacerbate inequalities in publicly funded systems. Low-income individuals are disadvantaged because they will choose to do without health care services if they use up the funds in their MSAs. Such actions may result in fatal consequences for some. They may not have the financial resources to purchase private health care services.

Mazankowski's and Kirby's emphasis on an expanded private sector role in health care raises concerns about meeting the five principles of medicare articulated in the Canada Health Act. As Romanow argues in his report, Canadians remain committed to a publicly funded and administered health care system (Romanow, 2002).

Regionalization of Health

Another important trend in health care reform has been the growing interest in the regionalization of health—that is, the devolution of decision making in health care to local authorities. Regionalization means that responsibility for the delivery of health services is referred to municipal or regional governments. The rationale for regionalization is that local or municipal governments are perceived as best positioned to identify, and are most responsive to, local needs. It is seen as compatible with their mandated responsibility for public health, such as sanitation, support for new mothers and families, and maintaining and improving the health of the population. Several provincial governments have opted for regionalization based not only on this rationale of local responsiveness, but also to reduce provincial health expenditures.

By the late 1990s, nine of 10 Canadian provinces had devolved health care decision making to local authorities (Lomas, Woods, & Veenstra, 1997). Regionalization meant the vertical integration of health care services. The vertical integration of health care refers to the entire range of health care services, from out-patient to hospital and long-term care services. By the late 1990s, Ontario had not regionalized its health care system, but health care and public health services were organized locally. In 2004, Ontario announced that it would regionalize health services by creating Local Health Integration Networks (LHINs). The Ontario government created LHINs in 2006 through the Local Health System Integration Act, 2006. The legislation invested significant decision-making power at the community level.

Problems with regionalization related to its design and implementation have been identified. The population health discourse has not translated into mandated programming. Population health and healthy community programs had long been key features of some local public health programs, such as those in the City of Toronto, Peterborough, and other cities across Canada. Concern centred on the potential effect of vertical integration on the public health identity and funding, and the idea that regionalization of public health could result in units that are too small to support local expertise and could impede the development and enforcement of province-wide programs. There was also concern that citizen involvement in health care decision making was merely political rhetoric. In addition, critics expressed concern that regionalization would increase rather than reduce costs (Sutcliffe, Deber, & Pasut, 1997). Regionalization in the 1990s was clearly different from previous plans to regionalize health care, since there was no consensus on whether devolution was good for Canadian health care.

Much of the interest in regionalization stemmed from the federal and the provincial and territorial governments' concern with reducing health spending, improving the efficiency of service delivery, improving equity in service provision, and ensuring more citizen participation and more accountability of decision makers (Church & Barker, 1998). In some provinces, regionalization had translated into reducing the scope of public health when it should have been amenable to expansion (Sutcliffe et al., 1997).

Public-Private Partnerships

Another reform adopted by provincial and territorial governments is public-private partnerships (P3s). The adoption of P3s is attributable to changes in health care financing, particularly by the federal government. Provincial and territorial governments increasingly consider expanding private sector involvement in health care delivery to reduce their health budgets. Health care costs increase annually. In addition, reduced federal transfers for health care result in provincial and territorial governments paying more for health care.

A P3 is an arrangement in which a government and a private entity—be it a private corporation, individual, or agency—jointly provide a public service or good (Savas, 2005). It refers to a relationship between one government unit and a consortium of private firms to build, for example, a highway such as the 407 in Ontario, a hospital, or a school. In other words, a government may contract with a private entity to enable that entity to finance, design, build, own, and operate infrastructure and services that were previously in the public domain. To many health coalitions, P3s signify "privatization by stealth" (National Union of Public and General Employees, 2006, p. 1). The National Union of Public and General Employees argues that P3s are privatization in secret. There is little opportunity for the public to challenge these arrangements as the best way to provide what are public services.

Savas (2005) argues that to consider privatization as merely a call to reduce government spending is a "serious misunderstanding of the concept" (p. 2). In contrast to the authors of *Bad Medicine*, Langille, and others, he argues that "privatization can be at least as compassionate as the welfare state; properly implemented, it offers even more for the less fortunate among us" (Savas, 2005, p. 2).

Savas considers three methods of privatization:

1. *Delegation:* The government maintains overall responsibility, but uses the private sector for service delivery, such as contracting for services, or outsourcing. Savas says that this can be understood as "partial privatization" because it still requires an active state role while the production or service activity is carried out by the private sector.

2. *Divestment:* The government withdraws its responsibility and presumably transfers it to the private sector. This is "competitive sourcing." Savas notes that this is the dominant form of privatization in the US and is used by federal, state, and local governments. He describes it as "the most direct form of delegation."

3. *Displacement:* The private sector expands and "displaces" (usurps) a government activity. Savas considers this development to be a "powerful incentive for public agencies" (2005, p. 5).

In contrast to critics of P3s and privatization of health and social services, Savas suggests that P3s are innocuous. Savas fails to demonstrate, however, how low-income and other vulnerable populations would benefit from such arrangements.

The Council of Canadians, the Canadian Centre for Policy Alternatives, and others argue that Canada must approach public-private partnerships and increased commercialization warily and with tremendous caution (Barlow, 2007; Grieshaber-Otto & Sinclair, 2004). Turning over any public good or service to the private sector to deliver for a profit violates the principles of medicare as outlined in the *Canada Health Act.* A preferable form of private involvement in a public health care system is one in which the private provider is non-profit and regulated by government statute. This relationship helps to ensure public accountability. For example, hospitals are private but not-for-profit. They are governed by their own board of directors, but are accountable to government for how they spend public dollars to deliver public health care services.

Interestingly, Savas cites Starr's (1989) opposition to privatization as an example of ideological and political opposition to P3s: "Privatization undermines the foundation of claims for public purpose and public service.... It shifts power to those who can more readily exercise power in the market. It may also shift income and wealth, depending on the specific form of that policy" (Savas, 2005, p. 14). Starr clearly identifies the movement toward the privatization of welfare state programs as a function of structures and interests.

An alternative definition of P3s is provided by Janusz Lewandowski, post-Communist Poland's first minister of privatization, otherwise known as "the Minister of Ownership Transformation." He defined it thus: "the sale of enterprises that no one owns, and whose value no one knows, to people who have money" (Savas, 2005, p. 2). He might have added, "And who will make more as a result of the transaction."

CURRENT HEALTH CARE ISSUES

Since these reports were released, little has changed. Many of the issues they identified remain issues today. Wait times for specialists and emergency care seem to have increased. This issue has intensified in part as a result of the increase in private health clinics that meet the needs of those with higher incomes.

CONCLUSIONS

Health care reform in Canada has focused on the financial sustainability of the public health care system. Much of the debate has centred on whether to allow private involvement to ease some of the pressure on the public system. Primary care is seen as the logical area to reform to address a number of other health care issues (Dixon, 2013).

Health care reform represents a locus site for governments to reduce public health care spending. The health reform reports of Mazankowski and Kirby welcome increased private sector involvement as a vehicle for innovation in health care. Kirby, however, supports the principle of public financing, but considers that there is little difference in whether non-profit or for-profit entities provide health care services. Both Mazankowski and Kirby support medical savings accounts as means to make Canadians aware of the cost of health care, and ostensibly to reduce utilization of health care services.

In contrast, echoing the sentiments of the National Forum on Health, Romanow urges renewing government commitment to medicare around the principles of universality and non-profit delivery of health care services. While he is open to private delivery of what he terms "ancillary services," such as food services, cleaning, and other non-medical care, Romanow acknowledges that he has found no evidence to support a larger private sector role in health care delivery. His main point is the need for stable and secure federal funding to the provinces and territories in order to provide universal and comprehensive health care programs (Maioni, 2003).

The three main reform reports vary in their commitment to allowing private care, reflecting in part the conflict between the polis versus the market concepts of society as devised by Stone (1988, 2012). The polis signifies a focus on the public interest and the collective in identifying and realizing goals. In contrast, the market society consists of individuals who, by competing with each other to promote self-interest, benefit the whole. In health care, as in many other areas, emphasis on the market may distort the operation of public policy and lead to ineffective and inequitable outcomes.

This examination of recent reform proposals in Canada demonstrates this tension between the polis and the market. In health care, the polis reflects the collective desire to provide access to health care to all members of society on the basis of need, and the market represents increasing privatization of health care and the commodification of care. Evidence suggests that such commodification is associated with growing inequities in access to health care and health care outcomes.

CRITICAL THINKING QUESTIONS

1. What do you think are the main drivers of the call for health care reform in Canada? How should medicare be reformed?
2. How can various sectors in Canadian society have their voices heard in health care reform?
3. To what extent do you think Canadians are aware of the various forces driving the health care reform debate?
4. What are your personal views concerning the future of the Canadian health care system?

5. To what extent do you think Canadians are engaged with these issues? Why might this be the case?

FURTHER READINGS

Grieshaber-Otto, J., & Sinclair, S. (2004). *Bad medicine: Trade treaties, privatization, and health care reform in Canada.* Ottawa: Canadian Centre for Policy Alternatives.

This report provides a critical analysis of the three major reports presented above.

Kirby, M.J. (2002). *The health of Canadians: The federal role.* Ottawa: Standing Senate Committee on Social Affairs, Science, and Technology.

This is another influential report that has fuelled the call for increasing private sector involvement in the health care system. It is available online at www.parl.gc.ca/37/2/parlbus/commbus/senate/Com-e/soci-e/rep-e/repoct02 vol6-e.htm.

Mazankowski, D. (2001). *A framework for reform: Report of the Premier's Advisory Council on Health.* Edmonton: Government of Alberta.

This report argues for a range of market-oriented innovations to medicare. It is available online at dsp-psd.pwgsc.gc.ca/Collection-R/LoPBdP/BP/prb0133-e.htm.

Romanow, R.J. (2002). *Building on values: The future of health care in Canada.* Saskatoon: Commission on the Future of Health Care in Canada.

Roy Romanow, head of the Commission on the Future of Health Care in Canada, recommended sweeping changes to ensure the long-term sustainability of Canada's health care system. This report is available online at publications.gc.ca.

RELEVANT WEBSITES

Canadian Centre for Policy Alternatives
www.policyalternatives.ca

The CCPA is an independent, non-profit research organization. It was created to promote research on economic and social policy issues from a progressive perspective.

Canadian Doctors for Medicare

www.canadiandoctorsformedicare.ca

The purpose of Canadian Doctors for Medicare is to provide a voice for Canadian doctors who want to strengthen and improve Canada's universal, publicly funded health care system. They advocate for innovations in treatment and prevention services that are evidence-based and improve access, quality, equity, and sustainability.

Canadian Health Coalition

www.healthcoalition.ca

The Canadian Health Coalition is a not-for-profit, non-partisan organization dedicated to protecting and expanding Canada's public health care system for the benefit of all Canadians. The coalition includes organizations representing seniors, women, churches, nurses, health care workers, and anti-poverty activists from across Canada.

Ontario Health Coalition

www.ontariohealthcoalition.ca

The primary goal of the Ontario Health Coalition is to protect and improve the public health care system in Ontario. The coalition works to honour and strengthen the principles of the Canada Health Act. Their work is guided by a commitment to core values of equality, democracy, social inclusion, and social justice, and by the five principles of the act: universality, comprehensiveness, portability, accessibility, and public administration. The OHC is a non-profit, non-partisan public interest activist coalition and network.

REFERENCES

Barlow, M. (2007). *Profit is not the cure*. Ottawa: Council of Canadians.

Boychuk, G. (2009). *National health insurance in the United States and Canada: Race, territory, and the roots of difference*. Washington: Georgetown University Press.

Church, J., & Barker, P. (1998). Regionalization of health services in Canada: A critical perspective. *International Journal of Health Services, 28*(3), 467–486.

Clair Commission d'étude sur les services de santé et les services sociaux. (2001). *Emerging solutions*. Quebec: Government of Quebec.

Coburn, D. (2000). Income inequality, social cohesion, and the health status of populations: The role of neo-liberalism. *Social Science & Medicine, 51*(1), 135–146.

Coburn, D. (2001). Health, health care, and neo-liberalism. In P. Armstrong, H. Armstrong, & D. Coburn (Eds.), *Unhealthy terms: The political economy of health and care in Canada* (pp. 45–65). Toronto: Oxford University Press.

Commission on Medicare. (2001). *Caring for medicare: Sustaining a quality system.* Regina: Government of Saskatchewan.

Dixon, J.A. (2013). *Backgrounder—Healthcare reform in Canada: Toward a Canadian healthcare strategy.* Kingston: Queen's School of Business and The Monieson Centre.

Grieshaber-Otto, J., & Sinclair, S. (2004). *Bad medicine: Trade treaties, privatization, and health care reform in Canada.* Ottawa: Canadian Centre for Policy Alternatives.

Hall, P.A. (1993). Policy paradigms, social learning, and the state: The case of economic policymaking in Britain. *Comparative Politics, 25*(3), 275–296.

Hall, P.A., & Taylor, R.C.R. (1996). Political science and the three institutionalisms. *Political Studies, XLIV,* 936–957.

Kirby, M.J. (2002). *The health of Canadians: The federal role.* Ottawa: Standing Senate Committee on Social Affairs, Science and Technology.

Langille, D. (2004). The political determinants of health. In D. Raphael (Ed.), *Social determinants of health: Canadian perspectives* (pp. 283–296). Toronto: Canadian Scholars' Press.

Langille, D. (2009). Follow the money: How business and politics define our health. In D. Raphael (Ed.), *Social determinants of health: Canadian perspectives* (pp. 305–317). Toronto: Canadian Scholars' Press.

Lomas, J., Woods, J., & Veenstra, G. (1997). Devolving authority for health care in Canada's provinces: 1. An introduction to the issues. *Canadian Medical Association Journal, 156*(3), 371–377.

MacDonald, L.I. (December 2002–January 2003). Health care: From reinvesting to reinventing: Interview with Michael Kirby. *Policy Options, 24*(1), 5–9.

Maioni, A. (1998). *Parting at the crossroads: The emergence of health insurance in the United States and Canada.* Princeton: Princeton University Press.

Maioni, A. (2003). Romanow—A defence of public health care, but is there a map for the road ahead? *Policy Options, 24*(2), 50–53.

Maynard, A. (2007). *How to protect a public health care system.* In B. Campbell & G.P. Marchildon (Eds.), *Medicare: Facts, myths, problems, and promise.* Toronto: James Lorimer.

Mazankowski, D. (2001). *A framework for reform: Report of the Premier's Advisory Council on Health.* Edmonton: Government of Alberta.

National Forum on Health. (1998). *Building on the legacy. Volume 5: Evidence and information.* Ottawa: National Forum on Health.

National Union of Public and General Employees. (2006). *Public-private partnerships: What they are, why they're a bad idea.* Retrieved from www.nupge.ca.

Organisation for Economic Co-operation and Development. (2015). *Health at a glance 2015: OECD indicators.* Paris: Organisation for Economic Co-operation and Development.

Rachlis, M. (2004). *Prescription for excellence: How innovation is saving Canada's health care system.* Toronto: HarperCollins.

Rachlis, M. (2005). *Public solutions to health care wait lists.* Ottawa: Canadian Centre for Policy Alternatives.

Ramsay, C. (1998). *Medical savings accounts: Universal, accessible, portable, and comprehensive health care for Canadians.* Vancouver: The Fraser Institute.

Raphael, D. (2003). Barriers to addressing the determinants of health: Public health units and poverty in Ontario, Canada. *Health Promotion International, 18,* 397–405.

Romanow, R.J. (2002). *Building on values: The future of health care in Canada*. Saskatoon: Commission on the Future of Health Care in Canada.

Savas, E.S. (2005). Privatization and public-private partnerships. Adapted from E.S. Savas, *Privatization in the City: Successes, failures, lessons*. Washington: CQ Press. Retrieved from www.cesmadrid.es/documentos/sem200601_MD02_in.pdf.

Shortt, S.E.D. (1981). *Medicine in Canadian society: Historical perspectives*. Montreal: McGill-Queen's University Press.

Shortt, S.E.D. (2002). Medical savings accounts in publicly funded health care systems: Enthusiasm versus evidence. *Canadian Medical Association Journal, 167*(2), 159–162.

Simeon, R., & Robinson, I. (1990). *State, society, and the development of Canadian federalism* (Vol. 71). Toronto: University of Toronto Press.

Starr, P. (1989). The meaning of privatization. In S.B. Kamerman & A.J. Kahn (Eds.), *Privatization and the welfare state* (pp. 15–48). Princeton, NJ: Princeton University Press.

Stone, D. (1988). *Policy paradox and political reason*. Glenview, IL: Scott Foresman.

Stone, D. (2012). *Policy paradox: The art of political decision making* (3rd ed.). New York: W.W. Norton & Company.

Sutcliffe, P., Deber, R., & Pasut, G. (1997). Public health in Canada: A comparative study of six provinces. *Canadian Journal of Public Health, 88*(4), 246–249.

Taylor, M.G. (1987). *Health insurance and Canadian public policy: The seven decisions that created the health insurance system and their outcomes* (2nd ed.). Kingston & Montreal: McGill-Queen's University Press.

Tuohy, C.H. (1999). *Accidental logics: The dynamics of change in the health care arena in the United States, Britain and Canada*. New York: Oxford University Press.

UK House of Commons Transport Committee. (2004). *The future of the railway*. London: Government of the United Kingdom.

Walkom, T. (2011, April 20). Harper and the subtle erosion of medicare: Stephen Harper isn't preparing a direct assault on medicare. But he's willing to stand by as others do the dirty work. *Toronto Star*. Retrieved from https://www.thestar.com/news/canada/2011/04/20/walkom_harper_and_the_subtle_erosion_of_medicare.html.

Chapter 8

MARKETS AND HEALTH POLICY

INTRODUCTION

Since the 1970s, social and economic changes have dramatically restructured the global economy, specifically the processes of production and investment (Schrecker & Bambra, 2015; Teeple, 2000; Grieshaber-Otto & Sinclair, 2004). In addition, concerns about rising deficits that began in the early 1980s drove both federal and provincial and territorial governments to reduce social and health spending (Scarth, 2004). Developed economies such as Canada, the United Kingdom, and the US responded to these changes by adapting their economies and deregulating business activities in a number of public policy areas.

One aspect of this increasing emphasis on economic functioning has been nations with public health care systems such as Canada and the United Kingdom increasingly looking to the private sector and market mechanisms to deliver health and social services. National governments justify these changes as essential to enhance their competitiveness in the new global economy (Banting, Hoberg, & Simeon, 1997; Bakker, 1996). From the perspective of the private sector, health care in particular represents an attractive investment opportunity (Grieshaber-Otto & Sinclair, 2004).

This chapter considers these increasingly important health care markets in Canada. It also analyzes the situation in the United Kingdom, where market approaches to health care delivery have become increasingly common. As discussed in chapter 7, a central and recurring theme in the debate over health care reform in Canada and in the United Kingdom is a call to expand the role of the private sector—or the market—in health care provision. This chapter considers the implications of an increasing emphasis on health care markets for both the health care system and population health.

WHAT IS A MARKET?

A market is a complex set of social institutions that enables the exchange of a commodity such as a good (housing) or service (health care) between a seller and buyer (Leys, 2001; Teeple, 2000). The market is thus a mode of exchange that meets the needs of society through the processes of buying and selling goods and services as private property or commodities. These goods and services can be health care services, but also include what are usually termed basic needs, such as housing, food, income, education, and recreation, among others.

In the market, the process of distribution is based on competitive supply and demand in the exchange process. The market also comes to represent a means by which labour power and capital, income, and wealth are distributed through processes of production and consumption. Inequalities in such distributions may also give way to differences in political power and influence.

Although often presented as a source of innovation, the effects of the market on societal processes may not always be beneficial or even benign. The market may come to represent significant and powerful economic forces that influence health policy and other public policy arenas. This is especially important since interwoven with markets are politics, ideology, and power (Leys, 2001). Markets have considerable capacity to carry influence beyond their purely economic realm into the broader society and the public policy arena.

Markets are "highly political" (Leys, 2001, p. 81) because politics shape market activities as much as do the processes of cost, revenue, and profit margins (Leys, 2001). Understanding the politics of markets and their power to influence many aspects of societal functioning, including health policy development, is integral to understanding their impacts on a society. Market-driven policies emerge when global economic forces influence and impede domestic policymaking. These issues are especially important in the financing and management of health care services (Leys, 2001; Whiteside, 2009).

CHARACTERISTICS OF MARKETS

Leys (2001) identifies the characteristics of markets that help explain how they function and influence health care policy. This is particularly helpful for understanding the current orientation of governments and others toward market mechanisms to control health care costs.

First, markets are systems consisting of rules and regulations set and enforced by both state and non-state agencies, including market actors through trade associations, informal agreements, and market power, such as price maintenance (Leys, 2001). Regulations govern what can be traded, as well as when and where trading can occur. Regulations also influence costs, profit margins, and other aspects of the trading process. Leys suggests that it is at this juncture of shaping regulations that market politics come into play. Despite the assumption that states or governments create regulations, increasing attention is being paid to how companies and corporations can adjust the rules to their own advantage. These companies and corporations possess considerable resources to accomplish this.

Second, markets are complex. This is the case since any one market actually consists of a complex of markets that involve transportation, raw and manufactured materials required for product development, insurance, and advertising, among others (Leys, 2001). That is, any one market is embedded directly or indirectly in a broad series of other social relations.

Those who work in markets also participate in other social relations, and are shaped by them. *Social relations* refers to the pattern of relationships between people in the group or organization in which they function (Hale, 1990). Markets shape social relations such that they come to accentuate other political issues. Leys suggests that the more important these social relations are, the more changes in a market tend to lead to and accentuate other larger political issues.

For example, changes in the rules and regulations by which health care services are organized and delivered may influence the ability of certain groups to access and influence health care services. If there is increased emphasis on delivering health care services, and these services are turned over to the market, then physicians and other allied health care professionals, such as nurses, may have less ability to influence the course of health policy. And if these newly empowered, privately organized service providers are less concerned with providing access to marginalized groups, then health consequences for these marginalized groups may emerge.

Increasing market mechanisms for health care delivery may also affect the distribution of income and other economic resources. To make the introduction of market approaches more attractive to citizens, governments may offer tax cuts that benefit primarily well-off, higher-income individuals and households. Since public health care systems tend to have distributional effects—the well-off pay more for health services in taxes, but tend to use them less—the creation of health service markets will lead to a transfer of income from lower-income groups to higher-income groups. The health care system then comes to be financed less out of general revenues and more by private sources, such as user fees. As discussed elsewhere in this volume, those least able to pay—who are also the most likely to require health services—are especially affected by policy shifts to market approaches.

Third, markets are inherently unstable (Leys, 2001). Their instability reflects the nature of competition. Instability is a function of industry and other market sectors always trying to increase their market share, which is the proportion of industry sales of a good or service that is controlled by an individual company or firm. These processes may be seen as beneficial to market competition, but it may be problematic when they include the provision of basic needs, such as health care services.

In addition, Leys (2001) argues that market success endows greater power in the market itself, possibly at the expense of society as a whole. As an example, Leys suggests that global firms can come to take over and control a national market, potentially curtailing or discarding certain services. Leys cites the example of Rupert Murdoch's News Corporation dominating the national newspaper market in the United Kingdom, but one can imagine health services coming to be dominated by exceptionally powerful private sector health corporations. Competition and its resultant side effects are central to how markets work.

THE RATIONALE FOR MARKET COMPETITION

The belief in the competitive market (or health care markets) is based on economic theory, which claims the superiority of markets over government control and regulation of health care (Rice, 1997; Leys, 2001). Some policy analysts and national and provincial/territorial policy-makers have come to believe that such markets are key to reducing health care costs and improving the quality of care.

The assumptions from economic theory include the following: (1) markets are the source of innovation; (2) deregulating and privatizing health and social services will facilitate such innovation; (3) these activities will allow a reduced state role in these policy areas; and (4) efficiencies in cost and operation will result (Coburn, 2001; Teeple, 2000; Leys, 2001; Schrecker & Bambra, 2015). And it is clear that such beliefs are increasingly being put forth in the health policy debate in Canada (see Box 8.1).

The emphasis on the market is supported by political ideologies that are consistent with the central tenets of neoliberalism and traditional economic theory. These ideologies provide the rationale for emphasizing market processes

Box 8.1: Privatizing Health Care is Risky for All of Us
By Danielle Martin and Irfan Dhalla
The Globe and Mail

In poll after poll, Canadians reaffirm their commitment to a health-care system in which access is based on need rather than wealth. So it stands to reason that opening up medicare to a private second tier would be bad for people who have no choice but to rely on the public system. With a relatively fixed number of health-care providers, wait times in the public system would increase as staff were recruited to the private sector. From Australia to Zimbabwe, this scenario has unfolded repeatedly around the world.

But, deep down, some of us wonder: If I had the money to buy my way to the front of the line, wouldn't I be better off in a two-tier system?

The answer, perhaps surprisingly, is probably not. Private health care would be almost as bad for the wealthy as for the poor, as long as the public system provides high-quality care (and most Canadians who use the system rate it highly).

The reason is, there's such a thing as too much health care—too many tests, too many interventions and too many pills. The emergence of for-profit health care in Canada would produce just this situation—not enough health care for some, and too much health care for others.

This is exactly what happens in the United States, where people with private health insurance find themselves subjected to the risks of unwarranted procedures. The U.S., for example, has the highest rate of invasive cardiac procedures in the world—45 per cent more than the next highest country. Yet, all these additional procedures have not bought Americans better heart health. Worse still, each invasive cardiac procedure carries a small but real risk of a serious complication—stroke, a torn coronary artery or even death.

Similarly, in a two-tier system, the wealthy would be bombarded with advice to get "checked out," and many would end up receiving unwarranted screening tests such as CT scans, which produce enough radiation to increase the risk of cancer.

Even if there were a well-developed private health-care system in Canada, the wealthy would still need to use the public system for many forms of health care—trauma care, for example—because the private system would focus on elective and outpatient care. The erosion of political support for medicare probably would result in worse public care for everyone.

A two-tier system also would be bad for business. In a world where wealth buys faster access to more health care, corporations would be expected to pay for their employees to jump to the front of the line. Some Canadian businesses do this already, purchasing too much health care—executive physicals, for example—for their most-favoured employees. The cost of providing too much health care for a large proportion of the work force would be enormous.

Bank CEOs understand this already. Charles Baillie, the former CEO of TD Bank, said a few years ago: "I choose to talk about health care as a banker—as a corporate leader—because I believe it's high time that we in the private sector went on record to make the case that Canada's health-care system is an economic asset, not a burden, one that today, more than ever, our country dare not lose."

Source: Martin, D., & Dhalla, I. (2010, November 11). Privatizing health care is risky for all of us. *The Globe and Mail.* Retrieved from www.theglobeandmail.com.

in several public policy areas, but their effects are especially important when considering health care policy.

One of the central tenets of neoliberalism is that a market economy best allocates resources, including income and wealth, in a society (Coburn, 2001; Schrecker & Bambra, 2015). Government policy-makers and elected representatives concerned with health care are especially susceptible to neoliberal arguments for several reasons. Health care services provided by the state do not generate revenues and consume among the most resources of all public policy areas.

Box 8.2: The Cost of Medicare

In a recent report on medicare, the Fraser Institute argues that Canada spends more on health care than other industrialized countries in the Organisation for Economic Co-operation and Development, and provides "inferior" health care compared to those countries without a public health care system (Esmail & Walker, 2005). Further, the institute argues that all of the countries that have fewer years of life lost to disease and lower mortality have private health care systems and user fees at point of access to health care services.

Neoliberal arguments become attractive because policy-makers can view health services as a potential site for private investment, which will absolve governments of funding and other responsibilities. By turning to domestic and international private health care agencies to finance and provide health care services, costs and responsibilities can be reduced, yet turning to the private sector leads to the creation of health care markets. Health care then becomes a commodity and not a public service. People become reliant on their incomes to obtain health care services. In addition, privatization increases the responsibility for health care on individual households and primary family caregivers, most of whom are women (Armstrong & Armstrong, 2010). Front-line health care workers, especially nurses, are also adversely affected by reduced government transfers and increasing privatization. Armstrong and Armstrong (2010) document the fragmentation of nursing work, which is reflected in the growing number of categories of workers providing care—registered nurses, nurses-in-training, nursing assistants, nursing aides and orderlies, and therapists, among others. The increasing division of nursing work has implications for the quality of patient care. Armstrong and Armstrong (2010) attribute the fragmentation not only to medical developments, but also to pressures "from governments and hospital administrators concerned about finances" (p. 102; see Armstrong & Armstrong, 2010, for a full discussion). We are back to the reason health care was made into a public affair: to have health services provided on the basis of need, not income! When the state provides health care, health care is decommodified; in other words, it is not a market commodity for which people must pay out-of-pocket for the care they receive.

HEALTH CARE MARKETS

Private financing comes in different forms, but what they all share in common is the creation of health care markets. In addition to medical savings accounts, user fees, and contracting out services, among others identified in chapter 7, a government can transfer the financing and delivery of a health care service to the private sector as represented by public-private partnerships (P3s).

As discussed in chapter 7, a P3 is an arrangement between the public and private sectors to provide a project or service that the public sector has usually delivered (Grieshaber-Otto & Sinclair, 2004; Savas, 2005). There is a continuum of P3 models, with considerable variation in the degree to which the private sector is involved. At one end, public assets might be privatized or transferred to the private sector to operate and manage. Other P3 arrangements may involve contracting out services normally provided by public servants to private for-profit firms (Grieshaber-Otto & Sinclair, 2004). Still other arrangements may have the private sector operating and managing publicly or privately owned facilities. All of these arrangements may be done under short-term, long-term, or indefinite periods. P3 arrangements may also vary in their degree of accountability, government control, and private risk involved.

Box 8.3: Policies for the Market

Tim Rice (1997), a professor in the School of Public Health at the University of California at Los Angeles, identifies the different types of policies espoused by advocates of market mechanisms in health care:

- providing low-income people with subsidies to allow them to purchase health insurance, rather than paying directly for the services they use
- having people pay more money out-of-pocket in order to receive health care services, especially for services whose demand is most responsive to price
- requiring people to pay more in premiums to obtain more extensive health insurance coverage
- allowing the market to determine the number and distribution of hospitals and what services they provide, and the total number of physicians and their distribution among specialties
- deregulating the development and diffusion of medical technologies
- eschewing government involvement in determining how much a country spends on health care services

Provincial governments in Ontario, Alberta, and British Columbia have initiated numerous such arrangements to build schools, highways, and hospitals. In addition, the federal government has publicly stated that these approaches are underutilized in Canada and provide a significant investment in infrastructure to be conducted via public-private partnerships (see Box 8.4). Critics have expressed concerns about the extent to which financial risk remains situated within the public sector in P3 arrangements, yet any profits accrue to the private sector (Rachlis, 2004). Some argue the primary purpose of P3s is to allow governments to remove expenses from public accounts.

P3s may not only lead to the creation of health markets, but also create a web of other markets and commodities such as those in the United States.

These markets represent a particular set of social relations that shapes how hospitals, doctors, and other health professionals provide care to patients (Armstrong & Armstrong, 2003, 2010; Leys, 2001). These potential new markets include the provision of laboratory tests, pharmaceuticals, and ambulatory care, among others.

Box 8.4: Public-Private Partnerships (P3s)

P3s generate "new" money only to the extent that they can generate a revenue stream from a source other than the government that would not otherwise be available to the government. For example, a private hospital operator might be able to generate revenue by offering medical services for sale that are not covered by medicare. Similarly, it may be that Highway 407 was worth more to the successful bidder, 407 International, because it expected to be able to charge higher tolls to highway users than the government would be able to get away with politically. Far from supporting the argument for P3s as a source of "new" money, however, these examples highlight the broader public policy accountability issues raised by P3s. The fact that P3s can, in principle, be used as a way to employ public assets for purposes that the public would not support or to generate revenue at levels that the public would not support is hardly a justification for the concept.

Source: Mackenzie, H. (2004). *Financing Canada's hospitals: Public alternatives to P3s* (p. 5). Ottawa: Canadian Health Coalition. Retrieved from www.healthcoalition.ca/wp-content/uploads/FULL-REPORT-October-2004.pdf.

In Canada, hospitals are private, not-for-profit facilities governed by their own boards of directors, but receive funds from the provincial or territorial government to provide health care services. Although all hospitals remain non-profit in Canada and in the United Kingdom, some hospitals in both countries contract out for services such as food provision and cleaning (Armstrong & Armstrong, 2003, 2010; Scott, 2001). This practice has increased as governments have limited transfers to hospitals, forcing hospital CEOs to make up gaps by contracting out some services to obtain them from the private sector. In the UK, hospital CEOs have reduced the number of registered nursing positions in order to save money. This change lowers the number of nurses available to care for patients on a hospital ward and has implications for the quality of patient care in hospitals.

In the United Kingdom, the National Health Service had a virtual monopoly on health care, similar to the single-payer system of medicare in Canada (Leys, 2001). In the late 1980s, however, initiatives such as pay-beds in public hospitals, car parking charges, and renting space to shops and businesses were introduced to bring in revenues to hospitals (Scott, 2001). Some Canadian hospitals have implemented similar measures to generate more revenues. With increased market-sector involvement, such activities can only increase. Health care will become an important area for investment.

Box 8.5: Public Private Partnerships in the United Kingdom
By Dr. Allyson Pollock

The policy of public private partnerships [PPPs] or private finance initiatives (PFIs) as they are called in the UK was a policy dreamed up by the then Conservative government in 1992 to bail out the failing construction industry.... I don't know exactly what models are being proposed for the P3s in Canada, but given that the same management consultants are advising, designing, evaluating, implementing and promoting the policies in Canada as in the UK, it seems likely there will be a remarkable overlap. The decision to rewrite the federal government's capital investment manual is a significant first step to reforming Canada along the UK lines of PPPs.

... PPPs are not a neutral financing mechanism. Neither are they a source of new money or investment. Private finance is debt financing. In other words it is a source of borrowing which has to be repaid—either out of the public purse or by giving the private sector a concession to raise user charges as in toll roads. It is not a neutral financing mechanism as we show in detailed studies of the National Health Services (NHS).

... Using PFI is more expensive for two reasons—the higher cost of borrowing (government borrowing is always cheaper) and the financing cost which can add up to 40% of the total costs of schemes. The financing costs are the rolled up interest that accrues by virtue of long repayment periods and borrowing money in advance. That adds a huge burden to the cost of PFI schemes. In addition PFI results in enormous cost escalation.

... Now coming to the public health concerns. The government can only justify the higher cost of the PFI and PPPs through the value for money analysis. But the real issue for public authorities is how private finance debts are to be repaid. In the UK, National Health Service (NHS) private finance is repaid from the revenue budgets of hospitals. This necessitated a massive change in our accounting systems as for the first time the UK NHS had to pay a charge on capital and this meant creating a stream in the revenue or operating budget to pay for new debt…. The repayment of these very expensive PFIs has put the NHS under enormous pressure. A number of subsidies had to be found. The first was land sales. The second was merging hospitals to release more land and buildings for sale. You might say it was sensible rationalization but it inevitably resulted in major service closure and the diversion of income to pay for the new smaller facility. The third was a diversion of capital grants in budgets intended for public facilities into paying off the debts of the new PFI hospitals.

Source: Excerpt from a presentation made by Dr. Allyson Pollack at a technical briefing on P3s for the Commission on the Future of Health Care in Canada. At the time, Dr. Pollack was head of the Health Policy and Health Services Research Unit at the School of Public Policy, University College London.

CUPE. (2002). *Experts tell Romanow commission that public-private partnerships are not the answer* (pp. 1–4). Ottawa: Canadian Union of Public Employees.

THE IMPACT OF MARKET FORCES AND DEREGULATION ON HEALTH CARE

There is little evidence to support the view that privatized health care provides better-quality care or is cost-efficient (Evans, 1997; Canadian Doctors for Medicare, 2015; Teeple, 2000). In fact, there is much evidence to support significant government intervention in order to ensure equal access to health care and lower health care costs.

A US study found that user fees at for-profit hospitals contributed to a 20 percent higher risk of death for people with high blood pressure, because they were less likely to see a doctor to get their blood pressure under control (Brook et al., 1983). The same study showed that user fees were as likely to deter the appropriate use of health care services as they were to deter the inappropriate use of health care services. Similarly, other studies have shown that user fees may deter the poor and elderly from using health care services that they may need (Rachlis & Kushner, 1995; Canadian Foundation for Health Care Improvement, 2012).

Another study involving a review and meta-analysis of studies compared mortality rates at private, for-profit hospitals and those at private, not-for-profit hospitals (Devereaux et al., 2002). Findings based on 15 observational studies, including more than 26,000 hospitals and 38 million adult patients, found that private, for-profit hospitals had a small but reliable 2 percent higher risk of death compared to private, not-for-profit hospitals. (Findings were adjusted for a number of possible confounders, such as severity of illness, etc.) The authors report that the single available study of infant mortality showed a 10 percent greater risk at for-profit hospitals. These higher mortality rates may be attributable to having fewer and less well-trained staff at private, for-profit hospitals (Rachlis, 2004). The authors concluded that:

> The Canadian health care system is at a crucial juncture with many individuals suggesting that we would be better served by private for-profit health care delivery. Our systematic review raises concerns about the potential negative health outcomes associated with private for-profit hospital care. Canadian policy-makers, the stakeholders who seek to influence them and the public whose health will be affected by their decisions should take this research evidence into account. (Devereaux et al., 2002, p. 1405)

A recent review examined the evidence on the impact of organizational and financial health system reforms on equity of health care (Bambra, Garthwaite, & Hunter, 2014). The authors found that private insurance and out-of-pocket expenses, and the marketization and privatization of health services, have either inconclusive or negative equity impacts.

Health care markets may also increase costs. For example, many studies have compared the administration costs of privatized health care to those of public health care systems. Consistently, private health care is associated with higher administration costs (Woolhandler, Campbell, & Himmelstein, 2003; Himmelstein, Miraya, Busse, Chevreul, & Geissler, 2014). Lower administration costs are associated with publicly financed health care.

Indeed, considerable evidence shows that the single-payer system is more cost-efficient because there is one place to send all the invoices and from which to receive payment (Yalnizyan, 2006; Canadian Doctors for Medicare, 2011). With a central location for paying and receiving payment, the single-payer system reduces administrative costs by not duplicating administration for different methods of payment. Moreover, as the single supplier and largest buyer of health care services, the government can negotiate better prices for products and drugs than may be the case for multiple purchasers.

Box 8.6: Health Costs: How the U.S. Compares with Other Countries

By Jason Kane

PBS News

How much is good health care worth to you? $8,233 per year? That's how much the U.S. spends per person. Worth it?

That figure is more than two-and-a-half times more than most developed nations in the world, including relatively rich European countries like France, Sweden and the United Kingdom. On a more global scale, it means U.S. health care costs now eat up 17.6 percent of GDP. A sizable slice of Americans—including some top-ranking politicians—say the cost may be unfortunate but the U.S. has "the best health care in the world."

But let's consider what 17 cents of every U.S. dollar is purchasing. According to the most recent report from the Organisation for Economic Co-operation and Development (OECD)—an international economic group comprised of 34 member nations—it's not as much as many Americans expect.

In the United States:

- There are fewer physicians per person than in most other OECD countries. In 2010, for instance, the U.S. had 2.4 practicing physicians per 1,000 people—well below below the OECD average of 3.1.
- The number of hospital beds in the U.S. was 2.6 per 1,000 people in 2009, lower than the OECD average of 3.4 beds.
- Life expectancy at birth increased by almost nine years between 1960 and 2010, but that's less than the increase of over 15 years in Japan and over 11 years on average in OECD countries. The average American now lives 78.7 years in 2010, more than one year below the average of 79.8 years.

There's a bright side, to be sure. The U.S. leads the world in health care research and cancer treatment, for instance. The five-year survival rate for breast cancer is higher in the U.S. than in other OECD countries and survival from colorectal cancer is also among the best, according to the group.

The concept is pretty simple: If waste is rooted out of the "assembly line process," the result will be better cars (or health outcomes, in this case) and lowered costs. At Virginia Mason Medical Center in Seattle, top officials decided that hospital "waste" can look like anything from unnecessary tests to elaborate waiting rooms to poorly designed floor plans. Tune in for the full report.

In the meantime, for a more detailed update on where the U.S. stands apart from its global peers, we spoke to Mark Pearson, head of Division on Health Policy at OECD.

NewsHour: Where does the U.S. health care spending stand relative to other OECD countries?

Pearson: Whether measured relative to its population or its economy, the United States spends by far the most in the world on health care.

The U.S. spent $8,233 on health per person in 2010. Norway, the Netherlands and Switzerland are the next highest spenders, but in the same year, they all spent at least $3,000 less per person. The average spending on health care among the other 33 developed OECD countries was $3,268 per person.

The U.S. is a very rich country, but even so, it devotes far more of its economy—17.6 percent of GDP in 2010—to health than any other country. The Netherlands is the next highest, at 12 percent of GDP, and the average among OECD countries was almost half that of the U.S., at 9.5 percent of GDP....

France and Japan demonstrate that it is possible to have cost-containment at the same time as paying physicians using similar tools to those used in the U.S. There are three key things that stand out when you compare these countries to the U.S.:

- They use a common fee schedule so that hospitals, doctors and health services are paid similar rates for most of the patients they see. In the U.S., how much a health care service gets paid depends on the kind of insurance a patient has. This means that health care services can choose patients who have an insurance policy that pays them more generously than other patients who have lower-paying insurers, such as Medicaid.
- They are flexible in responding if they think certain costs are exceeding what they budgeted for. In Japan, if spending in a specific area seems to be growing faster than projected, they lower fees for that area. Similarly, in France an organization called CNMATS closely monitors spending across all kinds of services and if they see a particular area is growing faster than they expected (or deem it in the public interest),

they can intervene by lowering the price for that service. These countries also supplement lowering fees with other tools. For example, they monitor how many generic drugs a physician is prescribing and can send someone from the insurance fund to visit physicians' offices to encourage them to use cheaper generic drugs where appropriate. In comparison, U.S. payment rates are much less flexible. They are often statutory and Medicare cannot change the rates without approval by Congress. This makes the system very inflexible for cost containment.

- There are few methods for controlling rising costs in private insurance in the U.S. In running their business, private health insurers continually face a choice between asking health care providers to contain their costs or passing on higher costs to patients in higher premiums. Many of them find it hard to do the former.

Source: Adapted from Kane, J. (2012, October 22). Health costs: How the U.S. compares with other countries. *PBS News.* Retrieved from www.pbs.org.

In support of this argument, the Organisation for Economic Co-operation and Development consistently shows that the US, with its market-driven system, spends more on health care than nations with public systems. Table 8.1 shows health spending for OECD member countries. These reports show that in 2012, the US spent almost 16.4 percent of its gross domestic product (GDP) on health compared to, for example, Canada at less than 10 percent.

Evans (1997) argues that that international experience over the last century has shown that increased reliance on the market tends to be "associated with inferior system performance—inequity, inefficiency, high cost, and public dissatisfaction" (p. 438). He cites the United States as a key example of allowing market forces to prevail in health care provision. Elsewhere, he has criticized the emergence of user fees as "zombies," bad ideas that keep coming back no matter how many times they are buried (Evans, Barer, & Stoddart, 1995).

DISTINGUISHING BETWEEN ALLOCATION AND DISTRIBUTION IN HEALTH CARE

As stated earlier, the economic theory on which neoliberalism is based calls for marketization in health care. Anyone who advocates market mechanisms

Table 8.1: Total Health Expenditure as a Share of GDP, 2012

Country	Public	Private	Total
Australia	5.9	2.8	8.7
Austria	7.7	2.4	10.1
Belgium	7.9	2.3	10.2
Canada	7.2	3.0	10.2
Chile	3.4	3.7	7.1
Czech Republic	5.9	1.1	7.0
Denmark	8.8	1.5	10.3
Estonia	4.6	1.2	6.8
Finland	6.4	2.1	8.5
France	8.5	2.3	10.8
Germany	8.2	2.6	10.8
Greece	6.2	2.9	9.1
Hungary	4.7	2.8	7.5
Iceland	7.0	1.7	8.7
Ireland	5.5	2.6	8.1
Israel	4.5	2.7	7.2
Italy	6.8	2.0	8.8
Japan	8.3	1.8	10.1
Korea	3.8	2.9	6.7
Luxembourg	5.5	1.2	6.7
Mexico	3.1	3.0	6.1
Netherlands	9.6	1.4	11.0
New Zealand	7.9	2.0	9.9
Norway	7.4	1.3	8.7
Poland	4.4	1.9	6.3
Portugal	6.1	3.2	9.3
Slovak Republic	5.5	2.1	7.6
Slovenia	6.3	2.5	8.8
Spain	6.4	2.5	8.9
Sweden	9.1	1.7	10.8
Switzerland	7.1	3.8	10.9
Turkey	3.9	1.0	4.9
United Kingdom	7.3	1.5	8.8
United States	7.9	8.5	16.4

Source: Organisation for Economic Co-operation and Development. (2015). *OECD health statistics.*
Retrieved from http://stats.oecd.org/index.aspx?DataSetCode=HEALTH_STAT.

in health care fails to consider whether this is a desirable objective for which governments should strive (Arrow, 1963; Rice, 1997; Hanoch & Rice, 2011). The much-claimed advantages of competitive markets cannot be fulfilled in health care (Rice, 1997; Bambra, Garthwaite, & Hunter, 2014; Canadian Doctors for Medicare, 2015) because economic theory treats allocation and distribution activities of the economy separately. Supply and demand are not sufficient to meet people's needs. Rice argues further that in health care and in other matters concerned with social welfare, a society must make allocation and distribution decisions simultaneously. These processes cannot be separated.

By way of illustration, Rice (1997) presents an example in which a very costly therapy is developed that has been shown to reduce the risk of developing a fatal disease, but its high cost means that only a few people can afford to pay for it. This means that it will increase the utility (welfare) of the few who can afford it, but it will probably reduce the utility of the larger group that knows that a life-saving technology is available, but not to them. Thus, reliance on markets may decrease social welfare for the society as a whole. If overall social welfare is to improve, it might therefore be preferable for the government to intervene to ensure that all citizens could have access to the life-saving technology.

Privatization in health care has returned in the health care debate because market mechanisms generate distributional advantages for some powerful interests in societies (Evans, 1997; Rice, 1997). This occurs in the following way: first, a more expensive health care system produces higher prices and incomes for providers, such as physicians, drug companies, and private insurers. Second, private payment delivers overall system costs on the basis of use or expected use of health care services. If people are charged for services at point of access, then the government contributes less. In effect, income is redistributed from low-income people to high-income people. Also, people with higher income can purchase better access or quality for themselves without having to support a publicly funded health care system for those with lower income to ensure they have access to quality health care services. Evans (1997) argues that there has thus always been "a natural alliance" (p. 427) of financial interests between service providers and high-income groups. These interests have a strong incentive to advocate market mechanisms in health care.

In addition, only those who can afford to pay for private care will jump the queue and go to the private system, while those who have low incomes will remain in the public system (Rachlis, 2004; Canadian Foundation for Health Care Improvement, 2012). Indeed, research evidence shows that user fees reduced the utilization of health care services when people needed care—

in short, they led to a reduced use of effective care. Research on the impact of user fees in Saskatchewan showed that they lowered the annual use of physician services by almost 6 percent. In particular, low-income families used physician services almost 20 percent less (Beck & Horne, 1980).

A further concern is that the private system could entice doctors in the public system to private health care with higher incomes and other benefits not provided in the public system (Rachlis, 2005; Canadian Foundation for Health Care Improvement, 2009). Allowing a parallel private system to coexist alongside the public system will not be in the best interests of most Canadians. Nor will it reduce the wait times in the public system, since those waiting for care in the public system cannot afford to consider private care.

FACTORS CONTRIBUTING TO MARKETIZATION

Since the postwar period, most industrialized countries have had a mix of public and private economic activity, in which a public sphere of economic activity coexists with a private sphere. The mixed economy is derived from a social-democratic conception of the economy that allows for both state and private involvement in public policy spheres such as health care. Leys (2001) argues that a flaw in the notion of a mixed economy was a failure to recognize the inherent instability of markets. When their survival is threatened, firms in the private sector seek strategies to increase their market and their market share. Firms in the public sector, or Crown corporations, do not contend with this imperative, since they are largely prohibited from behaving like private firms. Their mandate is to ensure access to a public good or service, not to increase market share. Leys notes that an important strategy for firms pressured to expand markets is to move into previously non-market spheres, such as health care. As Stone (1988, 2012) argues, the market distorts the notion of public service by making the focus the bottom line rather than achieving equity in access to quality care.

The rise in importance of the public sector as a site for investment has been attributed to the decline in manufacturing as a result of international competition (Price, Pollock, & Shaoul, 1999; Schrecker & Bambra, 2015). Thus, US and European corporations now see the service sector, including health care services, as an alternative source of profit. To increase the private services sector, however, requires opening up markets in areas in which the state has previously had responsibility. These areas include public services such as health care, education, and housing. By opening up the sector as a market, it allows domestic and foreign corporate entities to create private clinics or other for-profit health services. Thus begins the process of commodifying services that were once deemed public services as a matter of right to citizens of a country.

COMMODIFICATION AND DECOMMODIFICATION

While chapter 10 elaborates on commodification and decommodification, these concepts have relevance for understanding health care market issues. Esping-Andersen (1990) devised the concepts of decommodification and commodification to determine the extent to which individuals must depend on their market-derived incomes to obtain specific goods and services, such as health care. Decommodification refers to a state in which individuals are not reliant on their incomes to obtain a service, such as health care. In other words, health care is a public service provided on the basis of need, as it is in Canada and other countries with a public health care system.

Commodification means that individuals are reliant on their incomes and the market to obtain a service, such as health care. In the US, prior to the implementation of Obamacare, employer health benefits were the means to health insurance for most Americans; to obtain health insurance, they must have been employed, and the employer must have provided health benefits. As a result, many Americans did without health care because they were either not employed, had employers who did not provide health benefits, or were unable to afford either insurance or care. In short, health care in the US continues to be market-driven. As noted in previous chapters, Obamacare achieved "universal insurability" (Hall & Lord, 2014, p. 3). Americans must purchase health insurance from the private health insurance industry. Insurers cannot deny insurance to anyone or refuse to cover pre-existing conditions. Obamacare, or the Affordable Care Act, did not socialize health care or payment.

Increasing numbers of studies are finding growing dissatisfaction among providers, as well as consumers, with the health care market approach in the US. A recent interview study of local health care leaders in the US found that most doubted the capacity of market-based reforms to improve the efficiency and quality of US health care (Nichols, Ginsburg, Berenson, Christianson, & Hurley, 2004). Many of the respondents appeared to reluctantly accept that government intervention may be necessary to improve care. A recent survey of adults in the US and 10 comparison nations was carried out before the provisions of the Affordable Care Act came into effect (Schoen, Osborn,

Squires, & Doty, 2013). The results show that US adults were considerably more likely than their counterparts in other countries to do without needed health care because of the cost. American respondents were more likely to report difficulty paying for care, even with health insurance. This study found that costs have a larger role in deterring care and contributing to financial stress for those with chronic health conditions than for those without these conditions in Australia, Canada, and Switzerland, as well as the US. Still, the US responses are especially high; 43 percent of those with chronic illness do without care, citing costs. Also, two-thirds of respondents did not seek care because of high costs (Schoen et al., 2013).

In the Canadian context, allowing market forces into health care could very well violate the principles of medicare as specified in the *Canada Health Act*. In addition, as discussed in previous chapters, directing public revenues to private entities may violate not the letter but perhaps the spirit of medicare, particularly with regard to universality and public financing and administration of the health care system. All citizens, regardless of where they live in Canada, have a right to health care on the basis of need. Some argue this calls for health care services to have public financing and public administration (see Box 8.7).

Box 8.7: Wynne's Spin on Ontario Doctors Not Supported by the Facts
By Douglas Mark
The Globe and Mail

They say that truth is the first casualty in war. Take those comments made late last week by Dr. Eric Hoskins, Ontario's Minister of Health and Long-Term Care, suggesting that doctors' salaries have risen 61 per cent since 2003, when the Liberals took over. It is a claim so fundamentally misleading—OHIP billings do not equal salary—that it calls into question the minister's motives.

Or how about this one, from the ministry's own news release:

"The Ministry of Health and Long-Term Care will implement 10 changes to physician services payments. These include changes to fees and payments wherever possible so that Ontarians are paying the right amount for the right services. Doctors will still be able to provide any and all services for their patients that they feel are required."

Oh, really? And just how would that work, Mr. Hoskins? In my experience, less is never more. Less is always less. While you're at it, could you also explain how cutting $580-million from the health care budget—like you're threatening to do—is going to help improve the care our patients receive? If you can, you're better than Houdini.

Still, our beef isn't with Dr. Hoskins who, after all, is a colleague, and who clearly finds himself in a difficult spot. No, the real culprits here are Premier Kathleen Wynne and Treasury Board President Deb Matthews. No one with an ounce of common sense—not to mention years of medical training—could possibly have come up with such a harebrained scheme to manage our health care system.

No wonder our patients are so confused. Someone clearly isn't telling the truth. Time for a little reality check:

- There are approximately 12,600 general practitioners in Ontario, 14,500 specialists, 6,500 residents and 3,400 medical students;
- Breaking those numbers down by gender, there are almost 17,000 male and slightly more than 10,000 female doctors. Average age is 51.3 years;
- Tuition for students entering their first year of medical school is typically $21,863—a 339 per cent increase over tuition in 1997;
- On average, it takes eight to 12 years to become a doctor—a minimum of three years of undergraduate study at a university, three to four years of medical school, followed by two to five years in residency in a teaching hospital or clinic;
- Doctors must complete a minimum amount of continuing professional development courses and training throughout their careers, in order to maintain their license to practice medicine;
- Ontario's nearly 28,000 doctors treat 320,000 patients per day—to put this into context, that's almost the entire population of Iceland;
- Ontario's population grows by 140,000 patients per year—again, to put this into context, that's almost the entire population of Prince Edward Island;
- The number of seniors in our province is growing every year, putting even more pressure on an over-taxed health care system;
- Overhead—the cost of actually running a practice, including staff salaries, office space, medical supplies and office supplies—eats up approximately 30 per cent (or, on average, $130,000) of gross annual billings;
- Each doctor in Ontario contributes, on average, four full-time jobs in their community, $205,000 in GDP for Ontario's economy, and $50,000 in tax revenues, spread out over all three levels of government.

Those are the facts. An inconvenient truth for the Liberal government, I know. But the truth, nonetheless.

All of which brings us to the consequences.

Over the past 11 years, under Dalton McGuinty and Ms. Wynne, the Liberals have blown billions of our tax dollars, trying to dig their way out of one boondoggle—or cover up one scandal—after another. All this money adds up, and could've paid for a lot of healthcare.

Now, I'm sure I don't have to remind you what happens at the end of the month, when the rent is due and you've been reckless with your money. Because that's pretty much what we're facing here in Ontario. The landlord is knocking and we've got nothing for him, thanks to the Liberals.

So go ahead and blame the doctors. After all, the only thing we do is keep people healthy and save lives. To mention nothing of working overtime to shorten waiting lists, and generally keeping our leaky health care system afloat.

That's not spin. It's the plain truth. Something you won't get from either the Premier or Ms. Matthews.

Disappointing, to be sure. But hardly surprising.

Source: Mark, D. (2015, January 19). Wynne's spin on Ontario doctors not supported by the facts. *The Globe and Mail.* Retrieved from www.theglobeandmail.com.

THE IMPACT OF PRIVATE HEALTH CARE MARKETS ON POPULATION HEALTH

The creation of health care markets is consistent with an individualized approach to health care, as discussed in chapter 2. In tandem with the increasing commodification of health care services is an emphasis on individualized approaches to health, in which the individual must preserve her or his own health by making proper lifestyle choices, such as having a diet high in fruits and vegetables, consuming alcohol only moderately, and getting regular physical activity. The commodification of health reflects the influence of neoliberalism, a political ideology that posits the market as best for allocating and distributing resources.

In addition, as stated elsewhere, one of the primary concerns about creating private health care markets is that they reduce access to health care, particularly for vulnerable populations such as those with low income—the working poor—or those who are living in poverty. Such developments could accentuate unequal health outcomes.

Market approaches also have the potential to heighten inequalities in living conditions that are known to determine health. As background, during the 1980s, class-related differences in health outcomes in the UK were reported in the famous *Black Report* and revisited in *The Health Divide* (Townsend, Davidson, & Whitehead, 1992). Research—since replicated numerous times—has shown that social class is strongly related to health status (Coburn, 2000). That is, people with lower social class, occupational status, or income and wealth have poorer health status compared to those higher up on the class, occupational, or income ladder. This relationship is one of the most robust findings in the health and social sciences (Davey Smith, 2003; Romanow, 2002; Raphael, 2008; Gordon, Shaw, Dorling, & Davey Smith, 1999).

While it has been argued that all countries show socio-economic differences in health status, income and wealth gaps among Canadians have been widening since the 1980s (Yalnizyan, 2000; Broadbent Institute, 2014). Much of the cause of these growing social inequalities has been attributed to Canadian governments withdrawing from numerous programs that provide Canadians with income and employment security (Scarth, 2004; Stanford, 2004; Banting & Myles, 2013). These developments have been marked by the increasing influence of the market sector in Canadian society. And evidence from the United Kingdom indicates that such increases are good predictors of growing health inequalities (Shaw, Dorling, Gordon, & Smith, 1999).

In Canada, research into health inequalities has focused on how life expectancy and the incidence of various chronic diseases, such as heart disease and diabetes, as measures of population health differ among population groups. For example, a 16-year follow-up study in Canada found that for causes examined, age-standardized mortality was strongly correlated with income (Tjepkema, Wilkins, & Long, 2013). The lowest income quintiles had the highest mortality for all causes compared to high-income quintiles. Life expectancy for men who reside in the poorest of Montreal's health districts is 13 years less than for men residing in the richest districts of Montreal (Agence de la santé et des services sociaux de Montréal, 2007). Much of this is explained by the fact that approximately half of the population in the poorest health districts in Montreal have incomes below Statistics Canada's low income cut-off. Wilkins has documented profound differences in mortality rates from a variety of afflictions as a function of average neighbourhood income (Wilkins, Berthelot, & Ng, 2002).

There is little doubt that increasing the role of the market in Canadian society tends to be related to growing social and health inequalities (Raphael, 2000). Wilkins documents that income-related differences in mortality due to diabetes, suicide, and deaths from mental illness are increasing, while differences in heart disease are declining (Wilkins, Berthelot, & Ng, 2002).

Neoliberalism has been shown to foster higher income inequality (Kaplan, Pamuk, Lynch, Cohen, & Balfour, 1996; Coburn, 2000; Lynch, 2000; Schrecker & Bambra, 2015). This is because neoliberal policies weaken the welfare state by reducing the government's role in health and social services. Most industrial countries and many developing nations have introduced neoliberal policies that result in reduced social welfare and increased private sector involvement in social welfare provision.

Another way to think about the issue of markets and health is to consider the health status of nations whose political economies are dominated by the market rather than the state. Esping-Andersen (1990) argues that liberal political economies, such as Canada, the US, and the United Kingdom, are more receptive to market influence on public policy, while social democratic nations, such as Norway, Denmark, and Sweden, have greater state intervention in service provision. Do these nations differ in health status?

Navarro and Shi (2001) examined predictors of low infant mortality and higher life expectancy in a comparison of OECD countries from 1945 to 1980. Infant mortality has been identified as an important indicator of the general health status of a nation. Life expectancy is also an indicator of overall well-being in a population. The study found that countries with a social democratic tradition not only had more comprehensive health care systems, but were also more likely to have lower infant mortality rates and longer life expectancy. Liberal nations, such as Canada, showed opposite trends.

More specifically, infant mortality in Sweden improved from 16.6 per 1,000 in 1960 to 4.0 per 1,000 in 1996. In contrast, infant mortality in the United States was 26 per 1,000 in 1960 and fell to 7.8 per 1,000 in 1996. Canada's rate went from 27.3 per 1,000 to 6.0 per 1,000. These relationships are consistent with other international comparisons. Increased market influence is related to increases in social and health inequalities. Ultimately, Canadians have to decide whether they want markets to dominate in the organization and allocation of health care services and other health-related public policies. This was a landmark study that examined key health indicators among OECD nations. As will be discussed in chapter 9, the form that the welfare state assumes in different countries reflects both different political ideologies and different class structures.

IMPLICATIONS FOR HEALTH POLICY DEVELOPMENT

The dominance of neoliberalism in Canada and other industrialized countries has restructured domestic policies, which has implications for health policy and health provision. Its strength as the dominant political ideology reflects the influence of particular interests that stand to benefit from the shift to market-driven financing and delivery mechanisms. This can undermine the influence of other civil society actors that wish to preserve and improve medicare. It means that some perspectives may be shut out of the policy-development process. Indeed, governments sometimes undermine or ignore the voices that challenge the dominant perspective (Rochon & Mazmanian, 1993; Bryant, 2015). The restructuring may undermine the ability of national governments to set domestic policy and weaken democratic processes (Teeple, 2000). In fact, the commitment to market principles and practice exemplified in neoliberalism is opposed to those of democracy. It has been argued that this is because the market and democracy constitute two different approaches to resource allocation. The market signifies the social distribution of goods and services through an exchange between buyer and seller (Teeple, 2000), while democracy refers to a form of political organization in which citizens are deemed to have a role in political decision making. There is concern that neoliberalism undermines citizen participation and the democratic process. The requirements of economic globalization (to be examined in chapter 11) invest greater power in transnational corporations at the expense of civil society.

CONCLUSIONS

The creation of health care markets is the desired outcome of those advocating increased privatization of health care services. The creation of health care markets is driven by political ideology commitments to market-driven policies, buttressed by the economic interests of particular sectors. The establishment of these markets has implications both for access to health care for Canadians and for the allocation of political, economic, and social resources among the population. The intellectual support for such developments—neoliberalism—is based on economic theory that stresses the micro-economics of the individual, whereby self-advancement and self-interest are seen as the driving forces in human motivation.

The growth of health care markets has special implications for access to health care for specific groups in Canada, such as low-income populations.

As such, the advent of health care markets would shift care from being a right of citizenship to a commodity. Those who are the most disadvantaged—and therefore the most likely to need such services—would suffer the greatest consequences from such a shift.

Health care markets may increase costs and have been associated with generally inferior care as compared to care provided by public systems. Studies have found higher mortality rates in private, for-profit hospitals compared to public, not-for-profit hospitals. This may be due to use of less-experienced staff and reduced staff complements. Greater use of market approaches may also increase the burden on individual households to provide health care for family members (Armstrong & Armstrong, 2003, 2010). This burden tends to fall on women, who are usually the primary care providers in their families.

The creation of health care markets is not an isolated development, but is tied to government responses to the requirements of economic globalization. Later chapters explore how these forces shape health-related public policy as well as national politics (Leys, 2001; Teeple, 2000). Indeed, some critics argue that globalization interferes with and undermines national governments' capacity to set domestic policy and, in particular, to continue to provide public health care.

Recent international agreements that set forth the terms of trade between nations impose obligations on national governments. These terms may require changes to health care in Canada. Health care is a government monopoly, since provincial and territorial governments are the sole suppliers of health care services. Some of the private alternatives recommended by Mazankowski and Kirby (see chapter 7) could violate the terms of international trade treaties to which Canada is signatory (Grieshaber-Otto & Sinclair, 2004). In addition, Canada's treaty commitments could make it difficult to reverse commercializing reforms initiated by several provincial and territorial governments in future.

CRITICAL THINKING QUESTIONS

1. What is it about health care that does not make it a typical commodity?
2. What are some of the forces in favour of privatizing health care in Canada?
3. Why might the public be led to believe that markets in health care would improve the functioning of the health care system?
4. Why are governments apparently so willing to consider market solutions to health care problems?
5. What would be the result of bringing a market approach to health policy in general and to health care in particular?

FURTHER READINGS

Barer, M.L., Evans, R.G., Hertzman, C., & Johri, M. (1998). *Lies, damned lies, and health care zombies: Discredited ideas that will not die.* Vancouver: Centre for Health Services and Policy Research.

This report discusses how ideas related to the value of markets in health care are discredited yet refuse to die.

Esping-Andersen, G. (1990). *The three worlds of welfare capitalism.* Princeton, NJ: Princeton University Press.

Few discussions in modern social science have occupied as much attention as the changing nature of welfare states in Western societies. Gosta Esping-Andersen, one of the foremost contributors to current debates on this issue, provides a new analysis of the character and role of welfare states in the functioning of contemporary advanced Western societies.

Leys, C. (2001). *Market-driven politics.* London: Verso.

This book provides an original analysis of the key processes of the commodification of public services, the conversion of public-service workforces into employees motivated to generate profit, and the role of the state in absorbing risk.

Navarro, V. (2007). *Neo-liberalism, globalization, and inequalities: Consequences for health and quality of life.* Amityville, NY: Baywood Publishing Company.

This book assembles a series of articles that challenge neoliberal ideology. Written by well-known scholars, these articles question each of the tenets of neoliberal doctrine, showing how the policies guided by this ideology have adversely affected human development in the countries where they have been implemented.

Schrecker, T., & Bambra, C. (2015). *How politics makes us sick: Neoliberal epidemics.* Houndmills, UK: Palgrave Macmillan.

This book represents a new contribution to the literature on neoliberalism and its impact on health outcomes.

Stuckler, D., & Basu, S. (2013). *The body economic: Why austerity kills— Recessions, budget battles, and the politics of life and death.* Toronto: HarperCollins.

The Body Economic provides hard evidence on the often tragic human toll of the ongoing recession worldwide. From a rise in alcoholism in the UK to scores of suicides in California to HIV outbreaks and abandoned children in Greece, the book tells the stories of people who were not bailed out and who are now bearing the brunt of the 2007 stock-market crash. The book draws attention to recession medicine when the market runs amok and governments withdraw necessary supports.

RELEVANT WEBSITES

Canadian Centre for Policy Alternatives
www.policyalternatives.ca
   The Canadian Centre for Policy Alternatives produces many reports on health policy and on incomes in Canada.

The Canadian Foundation for Healthcare Improvement (CFHI)
www.cfhi-fcass.ca
   The CFHI supports the evidence-informed management of Canada's health care system by facilitating knowledge transfer and exchange, bridging the gap between research and health care management and policy. See especially their "Mythbusters" and "Evidence Booster" sections by using the site's search function.

National Coalition on Health Care in the United States
www.nchc.org
   This website provides information and insights on the state of health care in the United States, and regular reports on the impact of a privatized health care system.

UBC Centre for Health Services and Policy Research
www.chspr.ubc.ca
   The UBC Centre for Health Services and Policy Research stimulates scientific inquiry into population health and ways in which health services can best be organized, funded, and delivered. The centre's researchers and staff carry out a diverse program of research and development designed to deliver data, tools, and analysis useful to understand and renew health care, and improve the health of Canadians.

REFERENCES

Agence de la santé et des services sociaux de Montréal. (2007). *Atlas santé Montreal*. Montreal: Carrefour montrealais d'information sociosanitaire.

Armstrong, H., & Armstrong, P. (2003). *Wasting away: The undermining of Canadian health care*. Toronto: Oxford University Press.

Armstrong, H., & Armstrong, P. (2010). *Wasting away: The undermining of Canadian health care* (3rd ed.). Toronto: Oxford University Press.

Arrow, K.J. (1963). Uncertainty and the welfare economics of medical care. *The American Economic Review, 53*(5), 941–973.

Bakker, I. (1996). Introduction: The gendered foundations of restructuring in Canada. In I. Bakker (Ed.), *Rethinking restructuring: Gender and change in Canada* (pp. 3–25). Toronto: University of Toronto Press.

Bambra, C., Garthwaite, K., & Hunter, D. (2014). All things being equal: Does it matter for equity how you organize and pay for health care? A review of the international evidence. *International Journal of Health Services, 44*(3), 457–477.

Banting, K., Hoberg, G., & Simeon, R. (Eds.). (1997). *Degrees of freedom: Canada and the United States in a changing world*. Montreal & Kingston: McGill-Queen's University Press.

Banting, K., & Myles, J. (2013). *Inequality and the fading of redistributive politics*. Vancouver: UBC Press.

Beck, R.G., & Horne, J. (1980). Utilization of publicly insured health services in Saskatchewan before, during and after co-payment. *Medical Care, 18*, 787–806.

Broadbent Institute. (2014). *Gap between rich and poor greater than most Canadians think*. Retrieved from www.broadbentinstitute.ca.

Brook, R.H., Ware, J.E., Rogers, W.H., Keeler, E.B., Davies, A.R., Donald, C.A., et al. (1983). Does free care improve adults' health? *New England Journal of Medicine, 309*, 1426–1434.

Bryant, T. (2015). Implications of public policy change models for addressing income-related health inequalities. *Canadian Public Policy, 41*(2), S10–S16.

Bryant, T., & Raphael, D. (2015). Opening policy windows with evidence and citizen engagement: Adressing the social determinants of health inequalities. In G. Carey, K. Landvogt, & J. Barraket (Eds.), *Creating and implementing public policy: Cross-sectoral debates*. New York: Routledge.

Canadian Doctors for Medicare. (2011). *Neat, plausible, and wrong: The myth of health care unsustainability*. Toronto: Canadian Doctors for Medicare.

Canadian Doctors for Medicare. (2015). *For-profit health care: What does the evidence say about private, for profit health care?* Toronto: Canadian Doctors for Medicare.

Canadian Foundation for Health Care Improvement. (2009). *Myth: Most physicians prefer fee-for-service payment*. Retrieved from http://www.cfhi-fcass.ca/sf-docs/default-source/mythbusters/Myth-Fee-for-Service-E.pdf?sfvrsn=0.

Canadian Foundation for Health Care Improvement. (2012). *Myth: User fees ensure better use of health services*. Retrieved from www.cfhi-fcass.ca/sf-docs.

Coburn, D. (2000). Income inequality, social cohesion, and the health status of populations: The role of neo-liberalism. *Social Science & Medicine, 51*(1), 135–146.

Coburn, D. (2001). Health, health care, and neo-liberalism. In P. Armstrong, H. Armstrong, & D. Coburn (Eds.), *Unhealthy times: The political economy of health and care in Canada* (pp. 45–65). Toronto: Oxford University Press.

Davey Smith, G. (Ed.). (2003). *Inequalities in health: Life course perspectives*. Bristol: Policy Press.

Devereaux, P.J., Choi, P.T.L., Lacchetti, C., Weaver, B., Schunemann, H.J., Haines, T., et al. (2002). A systematic review and mcta-analysis of studies comparing mortality rates of private for-profit and private not-for-profit hospitals. *Canadian Medical Association Journal, 166*(11), 1399–1406.

Esmail, N., & Walker, M. (2005). *How good is Canadian healthcare? 2005 Report: An international comparison of healthcare systems*. Vancouver: The Fraser Institute.

Esping-Andersen, G. (1990). *The three worlds of welfare capitalism*. Princeton, NJ: Princeton University Press.

Evans, R.G. (1997). Going for the gold: The redistributive agenda behind market-based health care reform. *Journal of Health Politics, Policy, and Law, 22*(2), 427–465.

Evans, R.G., Barer, M.L., & Stoddart, G.L. (1995). User fees for health care: Why a bad idea keeps coming back. *Canadian Journal on Aging, 360*(8), 360–390.

Gordon, D., Shaw, M., Dorling, D., & Davey Smith, G. (1999). *Inequalities in health: The evidence presented to the Independent Inquiry into Inequalities in Health*. Bristol: The Policy Press.

Grieshaber-Otto, J., & Sinclair, S. (2004). *Bad medicine: Trade treaties, privatization, and health care reform in Canada*. Ottawa: Canadian Centre for Policy Alternatives.

Hale, S.M. (1990). *Controversies in sociology: A Canadian introduction*. Toronto: Copp Clark Pitman.

Hall, M.A., & Lord, R. (2014). Obamacare: What the Affordable Care Act means for patients and physicians. *British Medical Journal, 349*, g5376.

Hanoch, Y., & Rice, T. (2011). The economics of choice: Lessons from the U.S. health care market. *Health Expectations, 14*, 105–112.

Himmelstein, D.U., Miraya, J., Busse, R., Chevreul, K., & Geissler, A. (2014). Comparison of hospital administrative costs in eight nations: US costs exceed all others by far. *Health Affairs, 33*(9), 1586–1594.

Kaplan, G.A., Pamuk, E.R., Lynch, J.W., Cohen, J.W., & Balfour, J.L. (1996). Income inequality and mortality in the United States. *British Medical Journal, 312*(7037), 999–1003.

Leys, C. (2001). *Market-driven politics*. London: Verso.

Lynch, J. (2000). Income inequality and health: Expanding the debate. *Social Science & Medicine, 51*, 1001–1005.

Navarro, V., & Shi, L. (2001). The political context of social inequalities and health. *International Journal of Health Services, 31*(1), 1–21.

Nichols, L.M., Ginsburg, P.B., Berenson, R.A., Christianson, J., & Hurley, R.E. (2004). Are market forces strong enough to deliver efficient health care systems? Confidence is waning. *Health Affairs, 23*(2), 8–21.

Price, D., Pollock, A.M., & Shaoul, J. (1999). How the World Trade Organisation is shaping domestic policies in health care. *The Lancet, 354*, 1889–1892.

Rachlis, M. (2004). *Prescription for excellence: How innovation is saving Canada's health care system*. Toronto: HarperCollins.

Rachlis, M. (2005). *Public solutions to health care wait lists*. Ottawa: Canadian Centre for Policy Alternatives.

Rachlis, M., & Kushner, C. (1995). *Strong medicine: How to save Canada's health care system*. Toronto: HarperCollins.

Raphael, D. (2000). Health effects of new right policies. *Policy Options, 21*(8), 57–58.

Raphael, D. (Ed.). (2008). *Social determinants of health: Canadian perspectives* (2nd ed.). Toronto: Canadian Scholars' Press.

Rice, T. (1997). Can markets give us the health system we want? *Journal of Health Politics, Policy, and Law, 22*(2), 383–426.

Rochon, T.R., & Mazmanian, D.A. (1993). Social movements and the policy process. *Annals of the American Academy of Political and Social Sciences, 528,* 75–87.

Romanow, R.J. (2002). *Building on values: The future of health care in Canada.* Saskatoon: Commission on the Future of Health Care in Canada.

Savas, E.S. (2005). *Privatization and public-private partnerships.* Adapted from *Privatization in the city: Successes, failures, lessons.* Washington: CQ Press. Retrieved from www.cesmadrid.es/documentos/Sem200601_MD02_IN.pdf.

Scarth, T. (Ed.). (2004). *Hell and high water: An assessment of Paul Martin's record and implications for the future.* Ottawa: Canadian Centre for Policy Alternatives.

Schoen, C., Osborn, R., Squires, D., & Doty, M.M. (2013). Access, affordability, and insurance complexity are often worse in the United States compared to 10 other countries. *Health Affairs, 32*(12), 2205–2215.

Schrecker, T., & Bambra, C. (2015). *How politics makes us sick: Neoliberal epidemics.* Houndsmill, UK: Palgrave Macmillan.

Scott, C. (2001). *Public and private roles in health care systems.* Buckingham, UK: Open University Press.

Shaw, M., Dorling, D., Gordon, D., & Smith, G.D. (1999). *The widening gap: Health inequalities and policy in Britain.* Bristol: The Policy Press.

Stanford, J. (2004). Paul Martin, the deficit, and the debt: Taking another look. In T. Scarth (Ed.), *Hell and high water: An assessment of Paul Martin's record and implications for the future* (pp. 31–54). Ottawa: Canadian Centre for Policy Alternatives.

Stone, D. (1988). *Policy paradox: The art of political decision making.* New York: W.W. Norton and Company.

Stone, D. (2012). *Policy paradox: The art of political decision making* (3rd ed.). New York: W.W. Norton and Company.

Teeple, G. (2000). *Globalization and the decline of social reform: Into the twenty-first century.* Aurora, ON: Garamond Press.

Tjepkema, M., Wilkins, R., & Long, A. (2013). Cause-specific mortality by income adequacy in Canada: A 16-year follow-up study. *Health Reports, 24*(7), 14–22.

Townsend, P., Davidson, N., & Whitehead, M. (Eds.). (1992). *Inequalities in health: The Black Report and the health divide.* New York: Penguin.

Whiteside, H. (2009). Canada's health care "crisis": Accumulation by dispossession and the neoliberal fix. *Studies in Political Economy, 84,* 79–100.

Wilkins, R., Berthelot, J.-M., & Ng, E. (2002). Trends in mortality by neighbourhood income in urban Canada from 1971 to 1996. *Health Reports* (Stats Can), *13*(Supplement), 1–28.

Woolhandler, S., Campbell, T., & Himmelstein, D.U. (2003). Costs of health care administration in the United States and Canada. *New England Journal of Medicine, 349*(8), 768–775.

Yalnizyan, A. (2000). *Canada's great divide: The politics of the growing gap between the rich and poor in the 1990s.* Toronto: Centre for Social Justice Foundation for Research and Education.

Yalnizyan, A. (2006). Controlling costs: Canada's single-payer system is costly—but least expensive. In *Mending medicare: Analysis and commentary on Canada's health care crisis.* Ottawa: Canadian Centre for Policy Alternatives.

Chapter 9

HEALTH POLICY IN BROADER PERSPECTIVE: WELFARE STATES AND PUBLIC POLICY

INTRODUCTION

The form that health care policy and health-related public policy take in Canada is part of what has been termed the advanced welfare state (Myles, 1998; Banting & Myles, 2013). The advanced welfare state was a significant development in most developed political economies following the Second World War. The source of the Canadian welfare state as we know it today can be found in the insecurities and experiences of Canadians during the Depression and the Second World War (Teeple, 2000). In policy studies, the welfare state refers to a set of social reforms—such as public pensions, public health care, employment insurance, and social assistance—implemented by governments to provide citizens with various supports and benefits. These reforms are important because such policies have been shown to be important predictors of the overall health of a population (Raphael, 2007b).

Rather than seeing the advent of the advanced welfare state as a reasoned governmental response to perceived citizen need, it has been argued that in Canada it was actually a governmental concession to the significant and sustained calls for reforms by citizens and the labour movement (Teeple, 2000). The welfare state has been defined as "a capitalist society in which the State has intervened in the form of social policies, programs, standards, and regulations in order to mitigate class conflict and to provide for, answer, or accommodate certain social needs for which the capitalist mode of production in itself has no solution or makes no provision" (Teeple, 2000, p. 15).

Whatever the reason, as a result working families and individuals won some security against the unbridled operations of the economic system. A key guiding principle behind the welfare state is that the provision of public programs and services is an entitlement of citizenship rather than a commodity requiring purchase by earned income. These various programs and services enabled people to maintain a decent standard of living that was not totally dependent on their ability to earn market income. In essence, many programs and services come to be decommodified—that is, not subject to purchase in the open marketplace—a key concept in understanding the form and function of the welfare state in nations such as Canada.

In Canada, the welfare state also redistributes economic resources from high-income earners to low-income earners. As one example, the health care system is funded by general revenues received from citizen taxes (Teeple, 2006). High-income earners pay greater taxes in both absolute (dollars) and relative (tax rates) amounts (Murphy, Roberts, & Wolfson, 2007). Higher-income earners, however, are less likely to become ill and make use of the health care system (Raphael, 2007a). Thus, the public health care system is a very effective means of assuring health care provision to citizens as well as a means of economic redistribution. Whether this latter goal was an intention of its creation may be uncertain, but it clearly serves these dual purposes.

Canada has developed a more generous welfare state as compared to that of the United States, but evidence indicates that it shows greater similarity to the US version than it does to the more developed and generous European standard in being what is called a liberal welfare state (Saint-Arnaud & Bernard, 2003). In Europe, two alternatives to the liberal welfare state emerged during the late 19th and 20th centuries: the conservative and the social democratic (Esping-Andersen, 1990, 1999).

Esping-Andersen (1990) identifies clusters of social democratic (Sweden, Norway, Denmark, Finland), conservative (France, Belgium, Germany, Italy), and liberal economies (Canada, Ireland, United States, United Kingdom, Australia) that differ in their kind and degree of social provision. And these differences have been shown to be related to both the comprehensiveness of each nation's health care system as well as the health of their populations (Coburn, 2006; Navarro & Shi, 2001).

Yet in every case, economic globalization has exerted powerful pressures on governments, which has resulted in some weakening of the welfare state in most industrial countries (Banting, 1997; Banting & Myles, 2013; Teeple, 2000). In both Canada and the United States—both already with relatively undeveloped liberal welfare states—this has especially been the case. This chapter examines the nature of the Canadian welfare state. It considers how the three political economy typologies of the welfare state, theorized by Gosta Esping-Andersen (1990), help to make sense of how Canada develops and enacts health care and health-related public policy. The consequences of this public policy approach for the health and well-being of the Canadian population are also considered.

HISTORY OF THE WELFARE STATE

The welfare state refers to government intervention in the provision of supports and services that include education, social services such as employment insurance and training, public pensions, social assistance, and health care (Banting, 1997). In addition to providing citizens with various kinds of security, the creation of the welfare state also served as a vehicle to promote resource distribution and class harmony (Teeple, 2000).

The modern welfare state as it evolved in Canada and other developed nations is sometimes called the Keynesian welfare state, named after the economist John Maynard Keynes (Townsend, 1993). The main point of his work was that the state should intervene in the workings of the market economy in order to support societal functioning and citizen well-being (see Box 9.1).

Box 9.1: The Keynesian Welfare State

The modern welfare state is often referred to as the Keynesian welfare state (KWS), the name deriving in part from the economist John Maynard Keynes. The principal assumption in his work was the existence of a national economy in which, he argued, the State could intervene to influence levels of investment and domestic income, and thereby partially regulate unemployment through national "demand management" policies. Such intervention represented a certain socialization of the costs of production (with State credits, guarantees, grants, and concessions) and of working-class reproduction (through public works and forms of income support), as part of a political compromise with the working classes in an attempt to moderate the business cycle (to prevent a repeat of the unrest of the 1930s), to help rebuild the war-destroyed economies of Europe (to ensure the reconstruction of capitalism), and to contain or diminish a growing interest in socialism due to the experience of the 1930s and the devastation of the war. In an open letter to Roosevelt about the New Deal, Keynes wrote: "If you fail, rational change will be gravely prejudiced throughout the world, leaving orthodoxy and revolution to fight it out." Donald Winch argues that Keynesian policies were "an effective weapon for use against the Marxists on the one hand and the defenders of old style capitalism on the other; a real third alternative, the absence of which before the General Theory had driven many into the Communist camp."

Source: Teeple, G. (2000). *Globalization and the decline of social reform: Into the twenty-first century* (p. 9). Aurora, ON: Garamond Press.

The experiences of the Depression and the two world wars increased working-class demands for more security and protection from the downturns of the business cycle and the market's deleterious effects upon personal well-being. Many citizens came to believe that the dominance of the market economy had demonstrated that it benefitted one class—owners of business and the wealthy—at the expense of the majority. The welfare state emerged as a political compromise worked out by the state between the market sector and the working class to reconcile the negative effects of the business cycle, especially in its most extreme forms, such as the Depression of the 1930s (see Box 9.2).

Box 9.2: The Business Cycle

Definition

Business cycles are periodic swings in an economy's pace of demand and production activity. These cycles are characterized by alternating phases of growth and stagnation. A period in which real GDP is rising steadily is called an economic expansion, and a period in which it is falling steadily is called a recession. The early stage of an expansion, following a recession, is called an economic recovery. Although these cycles are part of the natural ebb and flow of economic activity, their length is difficult to predict.

How Does It Affect Canadians?

Business cycles have a direct impact on Canadians. Periods of economic boom bring jobs, growth, and economic prosperity. Slowdowns in the economy, on the other hand, hurt businesses and put people out of work.

Examples

The most serious economic contraction experienced in Canada in the last century was the Great Depression in the early 1930s. Canada has also had two serious recessions in more recent years—in 1982 and in the early 1990s. In the late 1990s and early 2000s, Canada experienced a period of healthy economic expansion and prosperity.

Source: Government of Canada (2008). *Economic concepts: The business cycle.* Retrieved from www. canadianeconomy.gc.ca.

The post–Second World War welfare state was also intended to help rebuild the war-damaged economies of Europe. By doing so, it repaired and preserved the capitalist economic system and restrained growing socialist activity that first arose during the Depression and continued to grow during the Second World War (Teeple, 2000). Thus, these social and economic reforms were meant to ameliorate the inequalities and insecurities created by the market economy, and at the same time preserve the market economic system that produced these insecurities.

The development of the welfare state—its specific social reforms and means of implementing them—differed among nations in time and circumstance. For example, Sweden, an exemplar of the social democratic approach, began to build its welfare state during the 1930s (Esping-Andersen, 1985). The German welfare state, an exemplar of the conservative approach, began as early as the 1870s. The liberal welfare state—always undeveloped compared to social democratic and conservative nations—showed its greatest development during the post–Second World War period. It was only during this period that Canada and the UK began to implement universal, publicly organized health care. In recent years, liberal welfare states have been particularly susceptible to market reforms (Swank, 2010). Chapter 8 explored the impact of markets on the health care system.

THEORIES OF THE WELFARE STATE

Various theoretical frameworks have been developed to understand the characteristics of different welfare states and the influences that shaped their development. Typologies arrange national welfare states into categories or clusters on the basis of one or more characteristics. A limitation of typologies is that they may mask important differences between nations that at first appear to be in the same category (Olsen, 2002).

One such typology is dichotomous. The dichotomous typology contrasts between the residual welfare state and the institutional welfare state (Olsen, 2002). The residual welfare states are less developed and provide a smaller range of social welfare measures. These include less generous benefits and lower income replacement rates on job loss or acquiring a disability. Overall, levels of social expenditures are lower as compared to welfare states characterized as institutional.

Residual states target benefits at the less well-off in a society. Eligibility criteria are stringent, and there are usually a multitude of rules and obligations that include means testing (Olsen, 2002). Means testing is a requirement in which applicants for income support such as social assistance must demonstrate that they have little or no other income. Once benefits are approved, there are waiting periods before they are provided, and these benefits are then provided for short entitlement periods. There is little state commitment to reducing poverty.

In contrast, an institutional welfare state does not treat public welfare programs as last resorts for emergencies or situations of urgent need (Olsen, 2002). Institutional welfare state social assistance benefits and services are seen as citizen-entitled social protections and social investments. The general approach is one of promoting well-being and preventing problems, rather than providing services and supports on a reactive or remedial basis. Benefits and services are more comprehensive, covering a wider range of contingencies, and are more generous, higher quality, and more easily accessed than benefits in a residual welfare system. The institutional approach sees allowing the free market to allocate resources as an inferior means of addressing many types of social need.

Olsen (2002) identifies a limitation with the binary residual-institutional approach, as it can lump very different kinds of welfare states into the same category. For example, the residual welfare states of southern Europe— Greece, Italy, Portugal, and Spain—differ from the English-speaking residual welfare states—Canada, the US, the UK, and Ireland. The binary typology has limited application, but it does provide a starting point for comparing different types of welfare states.

ESPING-ANDERSEN: THREE WORLDS OF WELFARE CAPITALISM

Esping-Andersen's three-welfare-state typology has been widely applied and is also the subject of much critique (Saint-Arnaud & Bernard, 2003). It also sheds light on why and how health care and health-related policies developed in Canada and how such policies can be influenced. Esping-Andersen (1990) considers whether the welfare state is best understood by analyzing a nation's social policies or by examining the institutional forces that shape these collections of a nation's social policies. Supporting the later approach, he argues that welfare state regimes are actually a complex of interrelated legal and organizational characteristics. In essence, the term *welfare state* in industrial capitalist societies signifies the set of features by which major institutions define

Box 9.3: Dichotomous Welfare State Typology: Residual versus Institutional

The first widely adopted typologies constructed to detail and classify the social policy orientation of various nations were often dichotomous, distinguishing between two major ideal types of welfare provision: a residual welfare state and a more comprehensive institutional welfare state.

... *Residual* welfare states are less comprehensive; they have a much narrower range of social welfare measures and cover far fewer social contingencies than institutional welfare states. They also provide more modest benefit levels and income replacement rates and, consequently, are characterized by considerably lower levels of social expenditure. And since residual welfare state programs are targeted at the poor or less well off, far fewer people are eligible for benefits. Allocating benefits largely on the basis of demonstrated need, these programs typically maintain other stringent eligibility conditions, rules, and obligations, including relatively long qualifying and waiting periods before benefits may be accessed, short periods of benefit entitlement, and a variety of grounds for disqualifying benefit recipients. Not surprisingly, there is also a very high social stigma attached to many of the benefits provided by residual welfare states. Best represented by the United States, the residual welfare state is premised on the notion that the market (and, to a lesser extent, the family) is the "natural" and best means for meeting the needs of citizens. Public measures are considered to be only supplementary, serving primarily as temporary substitutes when private welfare channels break down or are otherwise unavailable.

The *institutional* welfare state model, in contrast, does not treat public welfare programs primarily as a last resort to be activated during periods of emergency and urgent need (interruptions in earnings due to illness or unemployment, for example). Rather, they are embraced as an important first line of social protection, often emphasizing prevention rather than simply reactive or remedial measures. The free market, in turn, is considered to be a largely inferior way of addressing certain types of basic human needs. The character of institutional welfare states also stands in stark contrast to those categorized as residual; benefits and services cover a wider range of contingencies, are more generous and of a higher quality, and are more easily accessed.

Source: Olsen, G. (2002). *The politics of the welfare state* (pp. 69–70). Toronto: Oxford University Press.

social citizenship and provide welfare. The major institutions of the market economy, the state, and the family have unique interconnections that can take different forms (von Kempski, 1972).

At the time of his initial development of the three ideal welfare state types, Esping-Andersen recognized that while societies he included in the welfare state typology did not comprise a large number of cases, they did distinguish themselves into three distinct groups (Esping-Andersen, 1990). The distinguishing feature of these nations was their identification with three specific traditions of political mobilization and political philosophy: conservatism, liberalism, and socialism. These features were linked, he argued, to particular aspects of their contemporary social policy approach as well as their broader political and economic features (Arts & Gelissen, 2001). The form that welfare states assume in different countries is shaped by economic interests and political ideology.

Esping-Andersen does not explicitly discuss public health. It should be noted, however, that social democratic welfare states have embraced public concerns with health inequalities. Public health refers in this volume to addressing the social determinants of health by public policies that reduce poverty and social inequalities.

The result of this work was Esping-Andersen's *Three Worlds of Welfare Capitalism* (Esping-Andersen, 1990). His three welfare state typologies—liberal, conservative, and social democratic—classified nations on the basis of their established patterns of welfare provision. These patterns—based on the interrelationships of the state, the market, and the family—specified the mix each nation provided of public-sector, private-sector, and civil-sector social programs. Canada is squarely identified as a liberal welfare state.

Table 9.1: Examples of Members of Each Welfare State Regime

Liberal	Conservative	Social Democratic	Latin
Australia	Belgium	Denmark	Greece
Canada	France	Finland	Italy
Ireland	Germany	Norway	Portugal
UK	Netherlands	Sweden	Spain
US	Switzerland		

Sources: Adapted from Esping-Andersen, G. (1990). *The three worlds of welfare capitalism* (p. 52). Princeton, NJ: Princeton University Press; Saint-Arnaud, S., and Bernard, P. (2003). Convergence or resilience? A hierarchical cluster analysis of the welfare regimes in advanced countries. *Current Sociology*, *51*(5), 499–527.

Liberal Welfare States

The liberal welfare state is the most undeveloped form. It provides modest universal transfers and social-insurance plans to citizens, which is usually done with some form of means or income testing to determine eligibility (Esping-Andersen, 1990). As a result, social assistance is usually provided only to the least well-off. This type of regime provides basic social safety nets, minimal relief for individuals who are unable to compete successfully in the marketplace, and few benefits or programs as a right of citizenship or national residency. It is clearly a residual approach to social welfare based on the belief that when welfare benefits are too generous, recipients will prefer to depend on these benefits rather than seek out employment for earned income. For Esping-Andersen (1990), the liberal welfare state is exemplified by Australia, Canada, Ireland, New Zealand, the United States, and the United Kingdom.

The term *liberal* signifies its historical roots in 19th-century political economy, which embodies principles of a laissez-faire orientation associated with the early industrializing capitalist nations. It does not refer to the American usage as being somewhat more progressive than those who call themselves conservative. It can be argued that the conservative nations in Esping-Andersen's typology (see below) are actually more progressive in their provision of social security than liberal nations. Liberal nations are also rather more likely to take up policies considered to represent current neoliberal thought: emphasis on the marketplace as the arbiter of the distribution of resources among the population.

While even liberal welfare states redistribute economic resources from the well-off to the less well-off in a society through progressive income taxes and the operation of public health care systems, the extent of this redistribution is rather less than in other welfare state types (Navarro & Shi, 2001). Consistent with this, benefit levels tend to be low. The chief objective of this form of redistribution is to help address the needs of the least well-off, but there is little effort to compensate the disadvantaged for their past experiences or protect them from future hardships. Benefits are best seen as being of last resort, similar to the residual concept of the dichotomous typology.

Conservative Welfare States

Conservative regimes are characterized by either paternalist or sometimes authoritarian approaches that historically have had strong ties with the Church (Esping-Andersen, 1990). Examples are Germany, France, the Netherlands,

Belgium, Spain, and Italy. Esping-Andersen considers these nations as "corporatist" because of their "statist" and "organicist" traits (1990, p. 27). In other words, conservative welfare states are structured to maintain and reproduce the existing differences in status, income, and wealth among social classes and sectors. There is rather little commitment to creating an egalitarian society.

Conservative welfare regimes use a range of separate but state-mandated and state-directed social insurance programs for members of different sectors of the economy. These are financed primarily by employers and workers. The benefit levels provided vary by sector, with higher-paid employees receiving more generous payments. Conservative welfare states stress social insurance as opposed to social assistance or universal measures. They redistribute income over the life cycle of a single individual or family to ensure that support is available in old age or sickness, or during periods of unemployment.

The conservative welfare state is characterized as retaining status differences between social classes, but with less emphasis on the market and commodification as the providers of welfare. The Church has a prominent role in shaping the conservative or corporatist welfare regime, with emphasis on the family and promoting the traditional nuclear family. The emphasis is on the family providing social welfare. The state provides when the family has exhausted its own resources for taking care of family members. Family benefits promote traditional motherhood.

The conservative regime is also a corporatist welfare state (Esping-Andersen, 1990). In this sense, the word *conservative* relates to classical conservatism, which highlights community, authority, hierarchy, and tradition, together with a disposition to resist change and preserve traditions and societal values. Christian norms and traditional family roles are more central than the market.

Social Democratic Welfare States

Social democratic regimes have broad and extensive programs that provide economic and other forms of security to their citizens (Esping-Andersen, 1990). For example, many social-insurance programs are compulsory in the workplace, which, when combined with traditionally high employment levels, provides a very developed welfare state. Access to programs and benefit levels are based on a record of contributions made by employers and employees. Even when such contributions have not been made, benefits tend to be comprehensive. Coverage is strikingly more developed than that provided by liberal regimes.

The social democratic welfare regime comprises nations that emphasize universalism and the decommodification of social rights (Saint-Arnaud & Bernard, 2003). In other words, the state provides universal rather than targeted social welfare. The social democratic welfare states strive for far-reaching objectives closer to optimal conditions rather than providing the basic minimum characteristic of the liberal welfare states. The orientation of social democratic welfare regimes toward social problems is preventative. An important part of the approach is to promote equality and eliminate poverty through more equal distribution of economic resources, including income.

In social democratic regimes, full employment is a key priority, and active labour policies focused on employment training are extensive (Esping-Andersen, 1990). In contrast, liberal regimes such as Canada and the US have rather less commitment to active labour policies, the result of which is that workers with high education are more likely to have and take educational and training opportunities than those with less education (Myers & de Broucker, 2006). Liberal regimes have more insecure employment that provides few or no benefits.

The key feature, then, of social democratic regimes is the provision of basic citizen entitlements, such as access to a well-paying job, comprehensive health care, safe working environments, and secure retirements. Pensions are usually tied to inflation to keep older citizens well above the poverty line (Esping-Andersen, 1990). Social democratic regimes also tend to have strong active labour market policies that promote training and retraining programs for workers. Such regimes are similar to institutional welfare states that see citizen welfare as both a social right and social investment.

DECOMMODIFICATION AND STRATIFICATION

Esping-Andersen's typology is based in large part on the degree of decommodification and social stratification within a society (Arts & Gelissen, 2001; Esping-Andersen, 1990).

Commodification and Decommodification

Commodification refers to the degree to which citizens are dependent on the market and earned incomes for the provision of goods and services. Decommodification refers to the degree to which citizens are not dependent on their market incomes—or wages—to obtain these goods and services. When a service is decommodified, it is provided as a matter of right (Esping-Andersen, 1990). In other words, services such as education, child care, employment training, and health care are provided by the state in a "public economy" that coexists alongside the private capitalist market. These are powerful concepts that illuminate the role of the state versus the market in social welfare provision. These concepts and how they play out in a nation have strong implications for the development of health-related public policies in addition to traditional health care services.

Stratification

Esping-Andersen (1990) defined the welfare state as a "system of stratification" (p. 23): "Welfare states are key institutions in the structuring of class and the social order" (p. 55). This refers to the capacity of welfare states to reinforce or reduce existing patterns of inequality within a country, which occurs through shaping the kind and degree of social solidarity, class divisions, and status differences. For example, the liberal welfare state maintains and reinforces existing patterns of inequality, since there is rather little state intervention in the workings of the marketplace. There is little institutional or ideological commitment, for example, to reduce or eliminate poverty. Hence, social assistance programs are intended to meet the immediate needs of households. This contrasts with the social democratic regime, which has a deep commitment to reducing inequality and poverty. Similarly, the conservative regime is committed to preserving the family and socializing the costs of family by supporting families before they use up all of their own resources. This is not an approach conducive to reducing inequality, though it does blunt the rough edges associated with being on the lower end of the status hierarchy.

Health care, health-related policies, and their impacts therefore reflect differing national political ideologies: liberal, social democratic, or conservative. By highlighting political ideology, this typology provides a means for understanding not only national trajectories in health policy, but also the impacts of the resurgence of neoliberalism as a political ideology on some, but not all, welfare regimes. For example, it has been argued that liberal welfare regimes, already market-oriented, are more susceptible to the influence of neoliberalism and globalization on their policymaking (Raphael, 2003; Banting & Myles, 2013). And, as has been noted, health care policy is one area of increased market sector interest.

USEFULNESS OF THE ESPING-ANDERSEN WELFARE TYPOLOGY

Since the publication of *The Three Worlds of Welfare Capitalism*, debates have raged over: (1) the accuracy of Esping-Andersen's typology; (2) its sensitivity to issues of gender and diversity; and (3) the impact of economic globalization on the quality of these different forms of the welfare state (Kasza, 2002; Bambra, 2005, 2007).

Esping-Andersen responded to concerns about the role of gender in his 1999 volume, *Social Foundations of Post-industrial Economies* (Esping-Andersen, 1999) by exploring the issues of female employment and child care among the three welfare types. In her detailed examination of the relationship between decommodification and defamiliarization, Bambra (2004) identified much overlap between these concepts, concluding that much of the critique of Esping-Andersen as gender-blind was unfounded. Defamiliarization refers to the extent to which individual families are able to maintain a decent standard of living either through paid employment or an income-support program (Lister, 1994, cited in Kroger, 2009).

Esping-Andersen generally focuses on the nature of income and other related financial supports as an indicator of the form of a welfare state and does not relate the welfare state to health care. In many social democratic nations, health care developed as an integral component of the welfare state. In liberal nations such as the UK, national governments created a public health care system before developing the other service components of their welfare state.

WELFARE STATES AND HEALTH-RELATED PUBLIC POLICIES

Raphael (2010) recently compiled information on how Canada stacks up against other developed nations in terms of supports and benefits. His analysis sheds much light on where Canada stands as a member of the liberal welfare state club.

A key aspect of health-related public policy is degree of support for citizens. The Organisation for Economic Co-operation and Development (OECD) calculates the percentage of each country's gross domestic product that is transferred to its citizens. Transfers refer to governments taking fiscal resources generated by the market economy and distributing them to the population as services, monetary supports, or investments in social infrastructure. Such infrastructure includes education, employment training, social assistance or welfare payments, family supports, pensions, health and social services, and other benefits.

Nations may choose to transfer relatively small amounts, allowing the marketplace to decide how economic resources are distributed. Or, a nation may choose to intervene to control the marketplace and give itself decision-making authority concerning these allocations. As it turns out, the nations that transfer a greater proportion of resources are more likely to have less income inequality, lower poverty rates, and generally better health status among the population compared to those countries that transfer less (see Box 9.4).

Box 9.4: Taxes and Services

Cost of cutting taxes not worth the savings
By Elaine Power and Jamie Swift
Toronto Star

Two of the major political parties in the upcoming election are promising tax cuts to "put more money in taxpayers' pockets."

"Great," we think. Who wouldn't want more money in their pockets, especially as the post-holiday credit-card bills arrive?

There are two important questions we need to consider before jumping to the conclusion that tax cuts are a good thing: a) will tax cuts really put more money in our pockets? and b) what are the costs of those tax cuts?

The first problem is that tax cuts at the federal level mean, in part, reduced income transfers to the provinces, which then download the problem to municipalities.

We've already lived through a decade of decreased federal funding to the provinces, compounded by provincial tax cuts and downloading of services. So Ontario's city governments must make tough decisions: Raise taxes. Cut services. Impose user fees for services that were once free. Or all of the above.

It's a new version of the old "trickle-down" theory of economics. Some people, especially the more affluent, may end up with more money because of Ottawa's tax cuts. But it is not a sure thing.

More important are the costs of tax cuts.

What doesn't get funded—or is inadequately funded—because "we can't afford it"? Tax cuts affect programs that Canadians value: education, health care, public health, the environment, income support programs, and so on. They erode "public goods" such as clean air and water that are impossible to produce for profit.

Tax cuts already have a proven track record: The Walkerton water disaster. An ongoing crisis in health-care funding. Aboriginals living in Third World conditions. Inadequate funding for education. A growing gap between the rich and the poor. Reduced help for marginalized groups like "high-risk" youth and victims of domestic abuse. One in six children living in poverty, and double that rate for Indian, immigrant and visible minority children. A deplorable lack of affordable housing.

The simple fact is that tax cuts undermine the government's ability to act. And this is exactly what the tax cutters intend. Tax cuts are an integral component of a particular ideological position, often called neo-liberalism, which argues—without supporting evidence—that the market can always provide goods and services better than government.

But can the market provide health care for all?

Evidence from the American experience suggests not. Can the market provide affordable housing for the alarming number of workers who do not earn a living wage? Evidence from the past 10 years of tax-cutting in Ottawa and Queen's Park, combined with a retreat from social housing programs, suggests not.

Downloading onto municipal governments also underpins the neo-liberal worldview. Our cities have the least fiscal capacity and are least able to regulate a market dominated by a small number of ever more powerful corporations.

Canadians are not overtaxed. The Organisation for Economic Co-operation and Development ranks Canada among the lowest taxed industrialized nations: 21st among 30 industrialized nations, and fifth among the seven largest.

We wove our social safety net after World War II, when Canadians saw themselves as nation-builders. In the wake of the events of the 1930s and 1940s, we had a collective sense that no one should ever again have to suffer the humiliations of unemployment and poverty experienced during the Great Depression.

Canadians believed then—as we do now—that we could look after each other and work together to achieve whatever national goals we set for ourselves. We could build a better future for all Canadians. We still can.

Taxes are the price we pay for a decent, caring, and civilized society.

When a candidate promises you tax cuts, ask him or her what the real cost will be. Instead of gazing down at the bottom line, let's start asking ourselves what kind of Canada we want to build together. And let's demand that our politicians work for the public good.

Elaine Power teaches in Queen's School of Physical and Health Education and Jamie Swift teaches in Queen's School of Business.

Source: Power, E., & Swift, J. (2006, January 19). Cost of cutting taxes not worth the savings. *Toronto Star*, A17.

Among the 34 developed nations of the OECD, the average public social expenditure in 2012/13 was 21.9 percent of gross domestic product (GDP) (OECD, 2014a). There is great variation among countries. Belgium, Denmark, Finland, and France all spent 30 percent or more of GDP on social expenditures. Sweden spent 28.4 percent of its GDP on social expenditures. It had been the leader in social spending until recently, but France is the highest social spender at 32.8 percent of GDP. Canada ranks 26th of 34 developed industrialized nations, spending just 18.3 percent of GDP on public social expenditures. This is below the US which spent 19.8 percent on social expenditures.

How do these differences in spending translate into specific policy areas? Figure 9.1 shows how Canada compares to a number of OECD nations in transfer of resources to its citizenry as indicated by the percentage of GDP allocated to public expenditures on health, old age benefits, incapacity-related benefits, and families.

Canada's health expenditures were at 10.2 percent of GDP in 2013, down from 11.2 percent in 2011 (OECD, 2013a). It ranked 22nd in health expenditures among 34 wealthy countries. As noted in previous chapters, public spending on health care in Canada represents about 70 percent of total health spending. The US ranks low on public health care, spending 48 percent of GDP, as more of its spending (52 percent) comes from private sources.

It is in the other areas of benefits and supports to citizens—that is, health-related policy—that Canada provides limited support compared to other developed economies. Old-age poverty rates in Canada remain among the 10 lowest observed in OECD countries, with 7.2 percent of seniors aged 65 and over living in poverty. Canada's old-age benefits rate falls below the OECD average of 12.8 percent, with 4.5 percent of GDP spent on old-age pensions (OECD, 2013b). Canada is also among the lowest spenders on incapacity- or disability-related issues, allocating less than 1 percent of its GDP. Canada also ranks very low on family benefits, at 28th of 29 developed economies, spending just 1.43 percent of its GDP on families. The OECD average for spending on family benefits is 2.55 percent of GDP.

Income support to other age groups in the population comprises family benefits, wage subsidies, and child support paid by governments to help keep low-income individuals and families out of poverty. Social services include counselling, employment supports, and other community services. Consistent with its spending on other social and health policy areas, Canada spends 0.6 percent of GDP on unemployment benefits and 1 percent on social services, below the OECD average of 2.4 percent (OECD, 2014a). It spends 2.9 percent of GDP on income supports to the working-age population (rank 27th of 30), and 2.2 percent on social services (rank eighth of 30).

Figure 9.1a: Public Expenditure on Health as Percentage of GDP, 2011 (or nearest year)

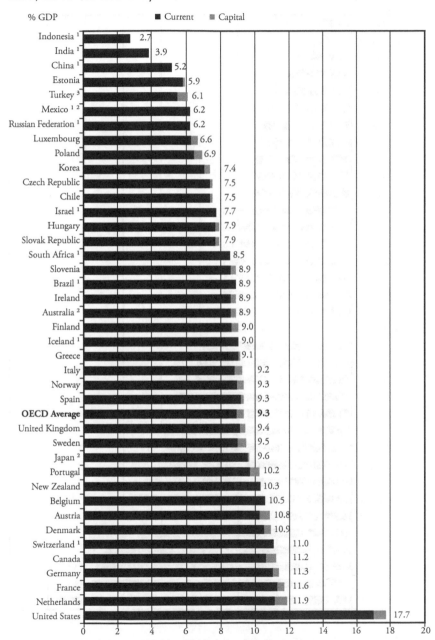

1. Total expenditure only; 2. Data refers to 2010; 3. Data refers to 2008.

Figure 9.1b: Public Expenditure on Old Age as Percentage of GDP, 2009

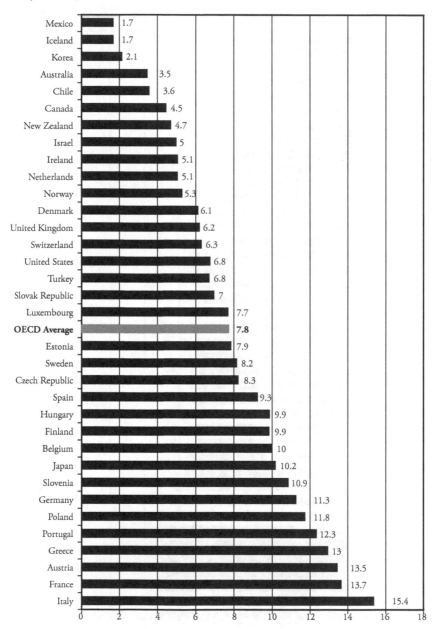

Figure 9.1c: Public Expenditure on Incapacity as Percentage of GDP, 2011

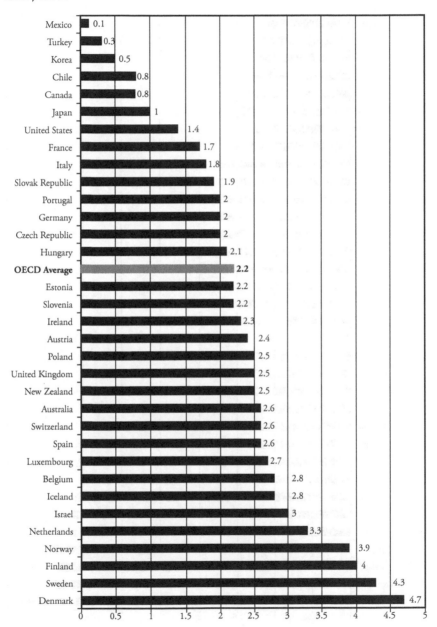

Figure 9.1d: Public Expenditure on Family as Percentage of GDP, 2011

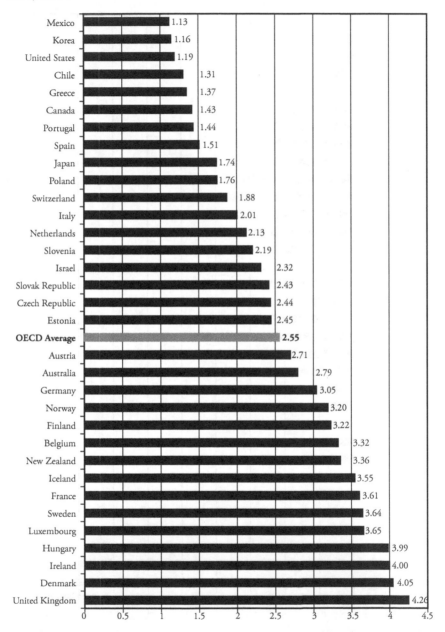

Source for Figures 9.1a–d: Organisation for Economic Co-operation and Development. (2013b). *OECD health statistics. Social expenditure database,* www.oecd.org/els/social/expenditure. http://dx.doi. org/10.1787/888932918833.

Box 9.5: Hurricane Katrina Reflects the Lack of Social Infrastructure in the United States

Inequalities in the US have long been associated with race. Hurricane Katrina exemplified racial inequalities and the lack of public supports for people who lost everything they owned and were too poor to leave New Orleans before the storm hit.

"Racial disparities are leading indicators of trouble, and just like canaries gasping for air, the marginalized are signaling that this democracy is in trouble because injustices are reproducing themselves and structural arrangements are benefiting a few at the expense of the many. Without a doubt, the greatest burdens in this country are shouldered by poor people of color, but they are not the only ones who are suffering. The uneven way we fund schools harms white students as well as students of color. The way our institutions perpetuate and increase wealth disparities has shrunk the middle class. Slashing social safety net programs in the name of increasing personal responsibility has added millions of people to the ranks of the working poor. Consequently, we can use the Katrina crisis as a launching pad not only for investigating the way we think and talk about race in this country, but also for developing a new discourse on race and class that highlights how the public and private are related, how democracy and structural arrangements that produce disparate outcomes are incompatible, and why institutional inequality concerns us all. In this way, our discussion about race can become transformative; instead of dividing people, it can bring them closer together in a collective reimagining of a just society" (p. 68).

Source: Powell, J.A., Kwame Jeffries, H., Newhart, D.W., & Stiens, E. (2006). Towards a transformative view of race: The crisis and opportunity of Katrina. In C. Hartman & G.D. Squires (Eds.), *There is no such thing as a natural disaster: Race, class, and Hurricane Katrina* (pp. 59–84). New York: Routledge.

Active labour policy is another area of government spending, concerned with support for training and other policies that promote employment for workers who have lost their jobs through restructuring. Canada contributed just 0.8 percent of its GDP to this area in 2013 (OECD, 2015a).

IMPLICATIONS FOR PUBLIC POLICY AND HEALTH

How do public policy commitments affect differing living conditions, which are known to be key determinants of health? Some of the issues examined here are resources available to the unemployed, the level of social assistance benefits, minimum wages, and pension benefits. These can mean the difference between having income, employment security, and good health, and living in poverty and having poor health.

Unemployment Benefits

Figure 9.2 shows the percentage benefit replacement for individuals—at the average production worker level—unemployed over a five-year period for initial and long-term unemployment (OECD, 2014a). Most Canadians can collect employment insurance (EI) for about 50 weeks. After exhausting these benefits, a family with liquid assets would need to spend them in order to be eligible for social assistance benefits. Canada provides 73 percent replacement income during periods of initial unemployment. This is higher than the OECD average of 68.9 percent. Most nations provide lower replacement coverage for long-term unemployment. Canada provides 49 percent coverage, just above the OECD average of 48.9 percent.

Social Assistance or Welfare

The OECD considers social assistance and welfare support as "benefits of last resort" (OECD, 2014a, p. 114). On average, most countries generally spend more on cash benefits than on social and health services. Ostensibly, the aim of social assistance is to reduce or avoid poverty. In a number of countries, benefit levels fall well below the poverty line.

On the whole, countries with more general social assistance benefits also provide a housing benefit, which pushes the benefit closer to the median income. Japan, Netherlands, Ireland, Denmark, United Kingdom, Switzerland, Finland, Sweden, Iceland, and Luxembourg all provide a housing benefit in addition to more generous social assistance benefits. Most of these countries are social democratic and conservative welfare states, with the exception of Ireland and the United Kingdom, which are liberal welfare states. The support level provided is less than the relative poverty level, measured as 50 percent of median income in international comparisons.

Figure 9.2: Average Percentage of Net Replacement Rates over 60 Months of Unemployment, 2011

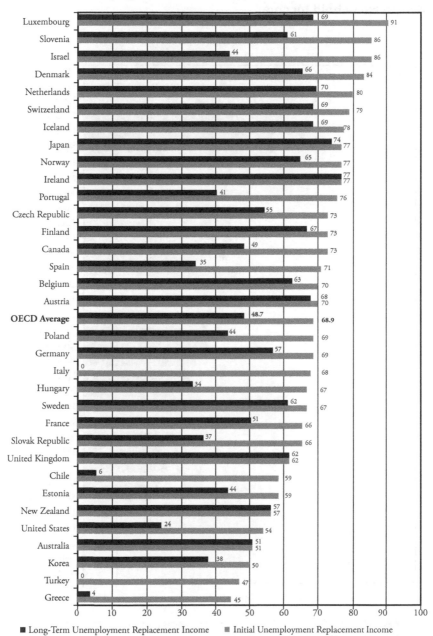

■ Long-Term Unemployment Replacement Income   ■ Initial Unemployment Replacement Income

Source: Organisation for Economic Co-operation and Development. (2014a). *Society at a glance: OECD social indicators 2014*. Paris: OECD. Retrieved from www.oecd.org/els/social/workincentives.

Figure 9.3: Net Income Level Provided by Cash Minimum-Income Benefit, Including Housing Assistance or Not, in Percentage of Median Household Income

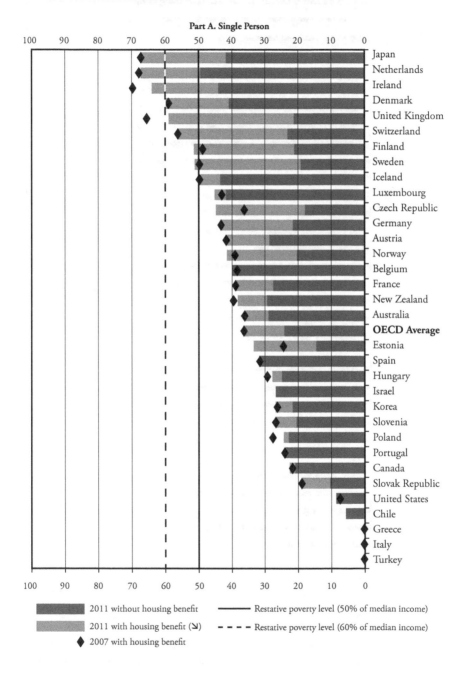

Figure 9.3: Net Income Level Provided by Cash Minimum-Income Benefit, Including Housing Assistance or Not, in Percentage of Median Household Income (cont.)

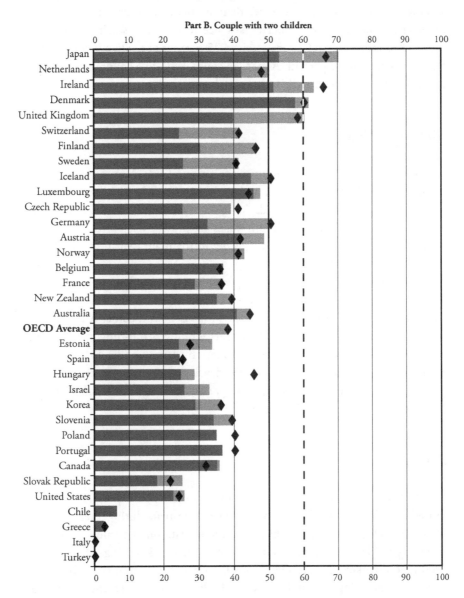

Part B. Couple with two children

Source: OECD. (2014b). *Tax-benefit models.* Retrieved from www.oecd.org/els/social/workincentives.

In contrast, non-European and non-Anglo-Saxon countries tend to provide means-tested benefits and less generous benefits overall (Esping-Andersen, 1990). The aim of such benefits is not to address the long-term situation of recipients, but to meet their immediate needs. In Canada, the housing benefit provided to social assistance recipients is small. In 2011, an unattached individual in Canada received 25 percent of median income with a housing benefit of 1.2 percent. A married couple with two children received 35 percent of median income with a housing benefit of 0.6 percent.

Minimum Wages

Canada ranked ninth on minimum wage among OECD countries in 2007, before the 2008 economic crisis, and in 2013 (OECD, 2015b). Figure 9.4 provides data that show how Canada compares with other nations on minimum wages. The concern is that minimum wages are provided at a level that enables people to obtain what they require in order to maintain their health and keep them above the poverty line.

Canada's minimum wage is 45 percent of the median wage (OECD, 2015b). A Canadian family with two children and one full-time minimum wage earner is at 47 percent of the median household income. A two-parent family with two children and both parents employed full-time at minimum wages receives 45 percent of median income. This family is therefore identified as a low-wage-earning family. Of 15 developed industrialized countries, Canada ranks ninth for benefits for lone-parent working families and 10th for benefits for two-parent working families.

Pensions

The Canada Pension Plan (CPP) is an income benefit program paid to retired individuals who have contributed to the plan during their working lives (OECD, 2015b). The OECD compares data on the value of pension benefits provided by each nation in relation to the gross earnings of an average production worker. Canada spends less than 5 percent of GDP on pensions. For a worker earning median income, the CPP provides 51 percent of earnings. Canada's replacement levels are among the lowest of OECD member nations.

Figure 9.4: Minimum-Wage Levels before Taxes: Percentage of Median Wage, Pre-crisis and Latest

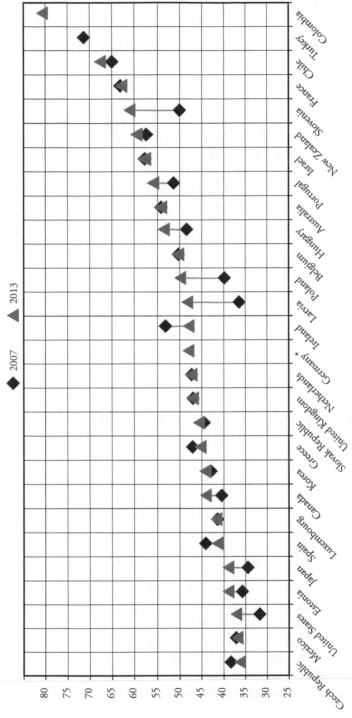

Notes: Levels refer to full-time workers. Panel (b) also shows data for Colombia and Latvia, who are currently seeking OECD membership.

* Germany: Minimum-wage level 2015 is expressed in percentages of the projected 2015 median wage. Projections are based on earnings data from the OECD Economic Outlook database.

Source: Organisation for Economic Co-operation and Development. (2015b). *Focus on minimum wages after the crisis: Making them pay* (p. 3). Paris: OECD.

Support for People with Disabilities

Canada allocates less than 1 percent of GDP toward disability benefits (OECD, 2015a). This means that Canada ranks 30th among 34 industrialized nations. This allocation has remained unchanged since 2003.

IMPLICATIONS FOR HEALTH POLICY AND THE CANADIAN WELFARE STATE

Canada's approach to health-related public policy appears to be rather undeveloped as compared to other industrialized nations, which include both social democratic and conservative welfare states. These findings become understandable when Canada is recognized as a liberal welfare state, in which the primary governmental ideological inspiration is one of minimizing government intervention (Saint-Arnaud & Bernard, 2003; Banting & Myles, 2013). The implications of this for developing and implementing health and health-related public policy are that there are formidable ideological and societal barriers to such action. The means by which these barriers can be overcome may involve the same processes discussed in terms of maintaining the public health care system in Canada: building political and social movements in support of health.

WELFARE STATES AND HEALTH OUTCOMES

The relationship between welfare state regime and health outcomes can be succinctly summarized: population health tends to be better in social democratic nations and worse in liberal nations. Navarro and Shi (2001) related the welfare state typology to health policy and health outcomes. Specifically, they examined the social democratic, Christian democratic/conservative, liberal, and formerly fascist regimes of Europe and North America, and compared their health and social spending patterns and the impact on population health status in four main areas: (1) the primary determinants of income inequalities; (2) the levels of public expenditures and health care benefit coverage; (3) public support of services for families; and (4) infant mortality as a measure of population health status for the period 1946 to 1990. They found that political traditions committed to the redistribution of economic and social resources and full-employment policies, such as those found in the social democratic parties, tended to be more successful in enhancing population health status.

Between 1960 and 1990, social democratic regimes had the largest public expenditures on health care, followed by the Christian democratic regimes. In contrast, the liberal Anglo-Saxon regimes tended to have the lowest expenditures in this area. Social democratic countries had the lowest infant mortality rates for the period 1960 to 1996 (Navarro & Shi, 2001). These findings have been replicated in more recent analyses (Navarro et al., 2004; Coburn, 2006).

Table 9.2 shows public expenditures on health in welfare state regimes between 1985 and 2010 (OECD, 2015c). Christian democratic regimes have surpassed social democratic regimes. Christian democratic regimes had the highest coverage. This differs from Navarro and Shi's (2001) findings on health expenditures. The reasons for this difference are not clear. The ideological commitments of governments affect public policy choices. Consistent with Navarro and Shi's (2001) findings, liberal welfare states have the lowest health expenditures. Among the liberal Anglo-Saxon political economies, the United States continues to have the highest health expenditures compared to the other liberal welfare states. Also consistent with Navarro and Shi's (2001) findings, social democratic regimes have the lowest infant mortality rates compared to Christian democratic and liberal regimes (OECD, 2015a). Infant mortality is a good indicator of overall population health.

POLITICAL IDEOLOGY AS AN INFLUENCE

Political ideology and its manifestation in public policy is a key influence on health and social expenditures, health-related public policies, and ultimately population health outcomes. Esping-Andersen's (1990) typology is therefore relevant to understanding how health policy is made and implemented in Canada. Given that Canada has a public health care insurance system, is it appropriate for Canada to be lumped in with the United States in the liberal cluster? Initially it would appear not, but the similarities between Canadian and US public policies on a range of health-related public policy approaches appear to support this placement (Bernard & Saint-Arnaud, 2004). This has especially been the case recently, as differences between the two countries may have narrowed as a result of closer integration of their economies during the 1980s and into the 1990s as a result of free trade treaties, specifically the Free Trade Agreement and the North American Free Trade Agreement.

In spite of trade agreements linking the two political economies, the US has a private health care system for most of the population, while Canada still has a public system to which all citizens have access on the basis of

Table 9.2: OECD Public Expenditures on Health, 1985 to 2010

	1985	1990	2000	2005	2010
Social democratic political economies					
Sweden	7.4	7.3	7.4	8.3	8.5
Denmark	8	8	8.1		
Norway	5.5	7.1	7.7	8.3	8.9
Finland	6.7	7.2	6.7	7.7	8.2
Mean	6.9	7.4	7.5	8.1	8.5
Christian democratic (conservative) political economies					
Austria	6	7.7	9.2	9.6	10.1
Belgium	6.9	7.1	8	9	9.9
Germany	8.5	8	9.8	10.3	11
Netherlands	6.7	7.1	7	9.5	10.4
France	7.6	8	9.5	10.2	10.8
Switzerland	7	7.4	9.3	10.3	10.5
Mean	7.5	7.6	8.8	9.8	10.5
Liberal Anglo-Saxon political economies					
United Kingdom	5.1	5.1	6.3	7.4	8.6
Australia	6.1	6.5	7.6	8	8.5
United States	9.5	11.3	12.5	14.6	16.4
Canada	7.6	8.4	8.3	9.1	10.6
Mean	7.1	7.8	8.7	9.8	11.0
Latin (former fascist dictatorships)					
Greece		6	7.2	9	9.2
Italy		7	7.6	8.4	8.9
Portugal	5.4	5.5	8.3	9.4	9.8
Spain	5	6.1	6.8	7.8	9.1
Mean	3.0	5.2	7.5	8.7	9.3

Source: OECD. (2015c). Health expenditure and financing: Health expenditure indicators. *OECD Health Statistics (database)*. DOI: http://dx.doi.org/10.1787/data-00349-en.

need, not income. Although about 30 percent of health care costs in Canada are not covered by the public system—a very high figure in international comparison—and there is increasing privatization of parts of the Canadian health care system, Canada still scores higher than the US in terms of access for low-income populations (Sanmartin & Ng, 2004). Neoliberalism, a political ideology of the market discussed in previous chapters, has contributed to this shift to economic globalization and the intense marketization that has occurred in some service sectors in Canada.

And while low-income populations in both Canada and the US are more likely to report poor or fair health than high-income populations, a greater percentage of low-income Americans (31 percent) do so compared to low-income Canadians (23 percent). In addition, the primary reasons for unmet health care needs differ between nations. In Canada, wait times for care have become the most frequently given reason, whereas in the United States, it is cost or lack of health insurance that deters Americans from seeking the health care services they need.

And while social inequalities, including income inequalities, have been growing in Canada, it continues to emerge as more egalitarian compared to the United States in terms of redistributive health and social policies (Siddiqi & Hertzman, 2007; Broadbent Institute, 2014). Figure 9.5 shows the Gini coefficient for OECD member countries in 2010. The Gini coefficient measures the distribution of income and varies between 0 and 1. A Gini coefficient of 0 means there is no income inequality. A value of 1 means one person owns all the wealth. Canada's Gini coefficient is .32, compared to the United States at .38. These values are much higher than those of social democratic and Christian democratic regimes, which all have Gini coefficients less than the OECD average of .31.

Whether these specific differences between the Canadian and US health care systems and health-related public policies will maintain these different profiles remains uncertain. Since these figures came out, Canada has negotiated free trade agreements with the European Union (in September 2014) and other countries (Global Affairs Canada, 2015). It is anticipated that finalizing the agreement with the European Union may take a few more years. Most such agreements tend to promise "opening new markets" and job creation. It is unclear what impact this agreement and other new free trade agreements will have on the Canadian economy, the environment, or the health of the population. Chapter 11 considers the potential impact of the Comprehensive Economic and Trade and Trans-Pacific Partnership agreements.

Figure 9.5: Income Inequality (Gini Coefficient), 2010

Source: OECD. (2014). *Income distribution database.* Paris: OECD. Retrieved from www.oecd.org/social/inequality.htm.

THE WELFARE STATE IN DECLINE

Chapter 1 noted how Canada and other Western, developed political economies have reduced health and social spending in response to global economic pressures. This has been done, it is stated, to enhance national competitiveness in the global economy. Studies indicate that less developed welfare states have negative effects on health, as illustrated by higher infant mortality rates and shorter life expectancies (Navarro et al., 2004). In other words, the more governments invest in social and economic resource redistribution, the better population health outcomes tend to be. In addition, liberal—which are also Anglo-Saxon—economies appear to be more susceptible to the policy-influencing effects of neoliberalism and globalization (Hemrijck, 2002; Banting & Myles, 2013). Banting and Myles (2013) argue that Canada's economy "depends heavily on international trade" (p. 12), and is more open compared to other OECD countries. Why has neoliberalism penetrated the Anglo-Saxon liberal economies to a greater degree than in social democratic or conservative regimes? Why are some welfare states more resilient than others?

As with other issues, many explanations have been posited to account for such globalization-resistant resiliency. Swank (1992, 1998) argues that the same class and political institutions that mediated and shaped the welfare state in the age of expansion now shape domestic responses to internationalization. He thus concludes:

> Where institutions of collective interest representation—social corporatism and inclusive electoral institutions—are strong, where authority is concentrated, and where the welfare state is based on the principle of universalism, the effects of international capital mobility are absent, or they are positive in the sense that they suggest economic and political interests opposed to neoliberal reforms.... [In these countries, these interests] have been successful in defending the welfare state. (Swank, 1998, p. 44)

In contrast, where political institutions fragment representation and political authority, as in the Anglo-Saxon democracies, the ability of investment capital to move from place to place exerts downward pressure on social provision.

A related explanation is to consider the political organization of society, and specifically the electoral process. In *Fighting Poverty in the US and Europe*, Alesina and Glaeser (2004) address this very issue with regard to differences in the size of the welfare state. While they agree with Swank that institutions and political ideology are important influences, they add that the European wars of the 19th and 20th centuries fuelled a variety of grievances among the working classes that provided fertile ground for socialist and communist parties to build support.

In response to these organized movements, many European nations instituted some form of proportional representation, in which the percentage of legislative seats is determined on the basis of the percentage of votes that a political party receives in an election. This means that smaller—and usually not dominant—political parties can gain influence in policymaking to a much greater extent than is the case in first-past-the-post systems, which are typical of liberal political economies. Left or social democratic parties have been able to use this mechanism to further their goals of more comprehensive welfare states, such that the presence of proportional representation is an excellent predictor of the size and depth of welfare states.

Canada does not have proportional representation, but has had periods of minority federal governments, when the left party (the Co-operative Commonwealth Foundation and later the NDP) have held the balance of power. It was during these times, especially during the 1960s, that progressive changes such as public pensions and Canada's health care system were established. In Canada, the establishment of proportional representation would enable smaller political parties like the New Democratic Party and the Green Party to gain more seats and more influence on the political system and public policy outcomes. The arguments for proportional representation raise interesting issues with respect to the welfare state. This is an area rich for further research into its value in furthering the welfare state and the development of health care and health-related public policy.

CONCLUSIONS

This chapter has examined the form and function of the welfare state. It examined how and why Canada fits into Esping-Andersen's liberal welfare state group. Being a liberal welfare state has shaped the Canadian approach to health and social programs, and this approach has implications for population health and well-being. More developed welfare states show increased public health and social expenditures and better population health.

Social democratic regimes have the highest investment in health and social spending and the best population health outcomes, while liberal welfare states have the lowest spending and worse outcomes. In addition, Canada's spending in these areas has declined since the 1980s. Already at a disadvantage, the Canadian response to the economic pressure associated with increasing economic globalization has further weakened the Canadian welfare state.

Much of this has to do with Canada already being a liberal welfare state. In addition, the absence of proportional representation makes it more difficult for left-leaning political parties, such as the NDP and the Green Party, to influence public policy. The liberal political economies appear to be more susceptible to neoliberal-influenced responses to the demands of economic globalization, an issue further addressed in the next chapter.

CRITICAL THINKING QUESTIONS

1. What was your reaction upon finding out that Canada is considered a liberal welfare state?
2. How do business interests dictate health policy in Canada?
3. Should the Canadian approach to provisions of citizen benefits and supports be reoriented to be more like those seen in European nations? What would be the arguments in favour of this? What arguments could be used to oppose this shift?
4. What public policies would need to be changed to improve the economic security of Canadians, thereby improving their health and quality of life?
5. What are some of the barriers to having Canadians become aware of the importance of public policies addressing economic and social security as determinants of health and quality of life?

FURTHER READINGS

Bambra, C. (2007). Going beyond the three worlds of welfare capitalism: Regime theory and public health research. *Journal of Epidemiology and Community Health*, *61*(12), 1098–1102.

In this analysis, Bambra reviews the original Esping-Andersen typology of welfare states and provides the range of related conceptualizations. Most of these find Canada to be a firm exemplar of a liberal welfare state.

Banting, K., & Myles, J. (Eds.). (2013). *Inequality and the fading of redistributive politics*. Vancouver and Toronto: UBC Press.

This volume contains contributions on various aspects of the changing welfare state and changing approaches to social provision in Canada. The introduction by the editors discusses how changing politics—neoliberalism—shape the shift away from redistribution in Canada.

Eikemo, T., & Bambra, C. (2008). The welfare state: A glossary for public health. *Journal of Epidemiology and Community Health, 62*, 3–6.
        This article provides background information on welfare states for those working in the health field.

Esping-Andersen, G. (1990). *The three worlds of welfare capitalism*. Princeton, NJ: Princeton University Press.
Esping-Andersen, G. (1999). *Social foundations of postindustrial economies*. Toronto: Oxford University Press.
        These two books provide a typology of Western welfare states that takes into account a range of social policies and links these with variations in the historical development of Western countries. The author describes how profound differences that exist among liberal (e.g., the US, Canada, the UK), conservative (e.g., Germany, France, Italy), and social democratic (e.g., Sweden, Norway, Denmark) political economies translate into widely differing lived experiences among citizens of these nations.

Organisation for Economic Co-operation and Development. (2013). *Health at a glance: OECD indicators 2013*. Paris: Organisation for Economic Co-operation and Development.
Organisation for Economic Co-operation and Development. (2014). *Society at a glance: OECD social indicators 2014*. Paris: Organisation for Economic Co-operation and Development.
        These reports provide a wealth of data that put Canadian social and health indicators within an international perspective.

RELEVANT WEBSITES

Clare Bambra's website at the University of Durham, UK
www.dur.ac.uk/geography/staff/geogstaffhidden/?id=2991
        Dr. Bambra's research focuses on public policy and health inequalities; work and health; comparative social policy, politics, and health; and urban regeneration and health. She has many articles listed on welfare states and social and health indicators.

Innocenti Research Centre (IRC)

www.unicef-irc.org

The IRC works to strengthen the capacity of UNICEF and its co-operating institutions to respond to the evolving needs of children and to develop a new global ethic for children. It promotes the effective implementation of the Convention on the Rights of the Child in both developing and industrialized countries, thereby reaffirming the universality of children's rights and of UNICEF's mandate.

Organisation for Economic Co-operation and Development

www.oecd.org

This site provides a wealth of reports, publications, and statistics about every aspect of society in modern industrialized states. Many of its contents are free or available electronically through a university's library.

An Introduction to Social Policy

www.spicker.uk

This module on social policy examines social welfare and its relationship to politics and society. It focuses on the social services and the welfare state.

Wolfson Research Institute, Durham University

www.dur.ac.uk/wolfson.institute

The Wolfson Research Institute for Health and Wellbeing aims to foster and disseminate the wide range of research undertaken at Durham University to improve human health and well-being. Its work spans research across anthropology, biological and biomedical sciences, business, classics, education, engineering, geography, medicine and medical humanities, pharmacy, philosophy, psychology, social and community work, sociology, sport, and theology. The institute's research includes well-established strengths in research on primary care, public health, child development, cognitive neuroscience, medical anthropology, health geography, social work, and medical humanities as well as exciting new developments in medical imaging, cardiology, health in the Global South, and mental health.

REFERENCES

Alesina, A., & Glaeser, E.L. (2004). *Fighting poverty in the US and Europe: A world of difference*. Oxford: Oxford University Press.

Arts, W., & Gelissen, J. (2001). Welfare states, solidarity, and justice principles: Does the type really matter? *ACTA Sociologica, 44,* 283–299.

Bambra, C. (2004). The worlds of welfare: Illusory and gender blind? *Social Policy and Society, 3*(3), 201–211.

Bambra, C. (2005). Worlds of welfare and the health care discrepancy. *Social Policy and Society, 4,* 31–41. doi:10.1017/S1474746404002143.

Bambra, C. (2007). Going beyond the three worlds of welfare capitalism: Regime theory and public health research. *Journal of Epidemiology and Community Health, 61*(12), 1098–1102.

Banting, K. (1997). The social policy divide: The welfare state in Canada and the United States. In K. Banting, G. Hoberg, & R. Simeon (Eds.), *Degrees of freedom: Canada and the United States in a changing world* (pp. 267–309). Montreal & Kingston: McGill-Queen's University Press.

Banting, K., & Myles, J. (2013). *Inequality and the fading of redistributive politics.* Vancouver: UBC Press.

Bernard, P., & Saint-Arnaud, S. (2004). *More of the same: The position of the four largest Canadian provinces in the world of welfare regimes.* Ottawa: Canadian Policy Research Networks.

Broadbent Institute. (2014). *Gap between rich and poor greater than most Canadians think.* Ottawa: Broadbent Institute. Retrieved from www.broadbentinstitute.ca.

Coburn, D. (2006). Health and health care: A political economy perspective. In D. Raphael, T. Bryant, & M. Rioux (Eds.), *Staying alive: Critical perspectives on health, illness, and health care* (pp. 59–84). Toronto: Canadian Scholars' Press.

Esping-Andersen, G. (1985). *Politics against markets: The social democratic road to power.* Princeton, NJ: Princeton University Press.

Esping-Andersen, G. (1990). *The three worlds of welfare capitalism.* Princeton, NJ: Princeton University Press.

Esping-Andersen, G. (1999). *Social foundations of post-industrial economies.* New York: Oxford University Press.

Global Affairs Canada. (2015). *Trade.* Retrieved from www.international.gc.ca.

Hemrijck, A. (2002). The self-transformation of the European model. In G. Esping-Andersen (Ed.), *Why we need a new welfare state* (pp. 173–214). Oxford: Oxford University Press.

Kasza, G. (2002). The illusion of welfare regimes. *Journal of Social Policy, 31*(2), 271–287.

Kröger, T. (2009, August). Dedomestication and childcare policy: A comparison of care service provisions of fifteen welfare states. Paper presented at the International Sociological Association RC19 Conference, Social Policies: Local Experiments, Travelling Ideas. Montreal, Canada. Retrieved from http://www.cccg.umontreal.ca/rc19/PDF/Kroger-T_Rc192009.pdf.

Lister, R. (1994). "She has other duties": Women, citizenship, and social security. In S. Baldwin & J. Falkingham (Eds.), *Social security and social change: New challenges* (pp. 31–44). Hemel Hempstead: Harvester Wheatsheaf.

Murphy, B., Roberts, P., & Wolfson, M. (2007). High-income Canadians. *Perspectives on Labour and Income, 8,* 1–13.

Myers, K., & de Broucker, P. (2006). *Too many left behind: Canada's adult education and training system.* Ottawa: Canadian Policy Research Networks.

Myles, J. (1998). How to design a "liberal" welfare state: A comparison of Canada and the United States. *Social Policy and Administration, 32*(4), 341–364.

Navarro, V., Borrell, C., Benach, J., Muntaner, C., Quiroga, A., Rodrigues-Sanz, M., et al. (2004). The importance of the political and the social in explaining mortality differentials among the countries of the OECD, 1950–1998. In V. Navarro (Ed.), *The political and social contexts of health* (pp. 11–86). Amityville, NY: Baywood Press.

Navarro, V., & Shi, L. (2001). The political context of social inequalities and health. *International Journal of Health Services, 31*(1), 1–21.

Olsen, G. (2002). *The politics of the welfare state*. Toronto: Oxford University Press.

Organisation for Economic Co-operation and Development. (2013a). *Health at a glance 2013: OECD indicators*. Paris: Organisation for Economic Co-operation and Development.

Organisation for Economic Co-operation and Development. (2013b). *OECD health statistics: Social expenditures database*. Retrieved from dx.doi.org10.1787/88932918833.

Organisation for Economic Co-operation and Development. (2014a). *Society at a glance 2014: OECD social indicators, 2014 edition*. Paris: Organisation for Economic Co-operation and Development.

Organisation for Economic Co-operation and Development. (2014b). *Tax-benefit models*. Retrieved from www.oecd.org/els/social/workincentives.

Organisation for Economic Co-operation and Development. (2015a). *Health at a glance 2015: OECD indicators*. Paris: Organisation for Economic Co-operation and Development.

Organisation for Economic Co-operation and Development. (2015b). *Focus on minimum wages after the crisis: Making them pay*. Paris: Organisation for Economic Co-operation and Development.

Organisation for Economic Co-operation and Development. (2015c). Health expenditure and financing: Health expenditure indicators. *OECD health statistics (database)*. DOI: http://dx.doi.org/10.1787/data-00349-en.

Raphael, D. (2003). Addressing the social determinants of health in Canada: Bridging the gap between research findings and public policy. *Policy Options, 24*(3), 35–40.

Raphael, D. (2007a). Interactions with the health and service sector. In D. Raphael (Ed.), *Poverty and policy in Canada: Implications for health and quality of life* (pp. 173–199). Toronto: Canadian Scholars' Press.

Raphael, D. (Ed.). (2007b). *Social determinants of health: Canadian perspectives* (2nd ed.). Toronto: Canadian Scholars' Press.

Raphael, D. (2010). Canadian public policy and poverty in international perspective. In D. Raphael (Ed.), *Poverty and policy in Canada: Implications for health and quality of life* (pp. 335–364). Toronto: Canadian Scholars' Press.

Saint-Arnaud, S., & Bernard, P. (2003). Convergence or resilience? A hierarchical cluster analysis of the welfare regimes in advanced countries. *Current Sociology, 51*(5), 499–527.

Sanmartin, C., & Ng, E. (2004). *Joint Canada/United States survey of health, 2002–03*. Ottawa: Statistics Canada.

Siddiqi, A., & Hertzman, C. (2007). Towards an epidemiological understanding of the effects of long-term institutional changes on population health: A case study of Canada versus the USA. *Social Science & Medicine, 64*(3), 589–603.

Swank, D. (1992). Politics and the structural dependence of the state in democratic capitalist nations. *American Political Science Review, 86*(1), 38–54.

Swank, D. (1998). *Global capital, democracy, and the welfare state: Why political institutions are so important in shaping the domestic response to internationalization*. Berkeley: Centre for German and European Studies, University of California at Berkeley.

Swank, D. (2010). Globalization. In F.G. Castles, S. Leibfried, J. Lewis, and H. Obinger (Eds.), *The Oxford handbook of the welfare state* (pp. 318-330). Oxford: Oxford University Press.

Teeple, G. (2000). *Globalization and the decline of social reform: Into the twenty-first century.* Aurora: Garamond Press.

Teeple, G. (2006). Foreword. In D. Raphael, T. Bryant, & M. Rioux (Eds.), *Staying alive: Critical perspectives on health, illness, and health care* (pp. 1–4). Toronto: Canadian Scholars' Press.

Townsend, P. (1993). *The international analysis of poverty.* Milton Keynes, UK: Harvester Wheatsheaf.

von Kempski, J. (1972). Zur Logik der Ordungsbegriffe, besonders in den Sozialwissenschaften. In H. Albert (Ed.), *Theorie und Realitat. Ausgewahlte Aufsatze zur Wissenschaftslehre der Sozialwissenschaften* (pp. 115–138). Tubingen: J.C.B. Mohr (Paul Siebeck).

Chapter 10

CANADIAN FEDERALISM, THE CANADIAN SOCIAL UNION, AND HEALTH POLICY

INTRODUCTION

Canadian federalism has been both a support and an impediment to the development of health policy in Canada (Prince, 2003). On one hand, it initially provided a vehicle for the federal government to use its spending power to finance health and social programs. On the other hand, federalism has come to be a continuing source of conflict between the two levels of government, as provincial and territorial governments demand more and more federal dollars to support health and social programs. Until recently, it seemed that federalism could not be restored to the state of co-operation between the two levels of government that was seen during the 1950s and 1960s, when the Canadian welfare state as we know it came about (Noel, St-Hilaire, & Fortin, 2003).

The era of co-operative federalism, in which the two levels of governments participated in cost-sharing many health care and health-related public policy programs, came to an apparent end in the 1980s (Cameron & Simeon, 2002). By 1980, increasing concern with reducing budget deficits led to health care and various social programs becoming the targets of governmental restructuring and retrenchment. Rather than seeing budget deficits as resulting from policies that shrank revenues, health care and other program spending were seen as the culprits (Banting, 1997). The "politics of fiscal deficits" (Cameron & Simeon, 2002, p. 53) began to shape not only intergovernmental relations, but also public perceptions as to the causes of and solutions to the growing public-sector deficits.

In recent years, the federal and provincial/territorial governments have hammered out different agreements in an attempt to renew the spirit of co-operation in social provision that had prevailed during the creation of the welfare state. The Social Union Framework Agreement (SUFA) was the product of such negotiations in 1999. It was followed by the health accords of 2000,

2003, and 2004. These agreements represent a collaborative federalism, in which the federal and provincial/territorial governments work together in these policy areas (Facal, 2005). This chapter examines SUFA and the health accords of 2000, 2003, and 2004, and considers their impact on the development and implementation of health policy in Canada. The chapter also considers the prospect for continued collaborations between the federal and provincial/ territorial governments in these efforts, and the potential for constructive intergovernmental relations under the Justin Trudeau–led majority Liberal government elected in the 2015 general election.

A BRIEF HISTORY OF CANADIAN FEDERALISM

The literature identifies three primary periods of Canadian federalism: (1) co-operative federalism; (2) executive federalism; and (3) collaborative federalism (Prince, 2003; Simmons & Graefe, 2013). Although broadly descriptive categories, they can help locate different intergovernmental initiatives in health and social policy.

Co-operative Federalism: 1950s to Early 1960s

The first period in the history of federalism is the 1950s to the early 1960s, which is characterized as co-operative federalism (Teeple, 2000; Banting & Myles, 2013). This was the stage in which the two levels for government cost-shared social programs to ensure universal access to them. Both levels of government generally recognized and accepted their obligations for social provision. For many, this was the golden age of Canadian welfare that saw the creation of the Canadian health care system and the general growth of social programs and services.

Executive Federalism: Mid-1960s to 1990s

The second period, from the mid-1960s to the 1990s, is described as executive federalism, a term coined by Doug Smiley (1980). Smiley argues that during this period Canada drifted away from what he termed "classical federalism," in which each order of government carried out the responsibilities assigned to it by the Constitution. He defines executive federalism "as the relations between elected and appointed officials of the two levels of government in federal-provincial interactions and among the executives of the provinces in inter-provincial interactions" (p. 91). Smiley argues that the institutions and processes of executive federalism became more oriented toward conflict rather than consensus.

Box 10.1: The Social Union Framework Agreement

The "social union" initiative is the umbrella under which governments will concentrate their efforts to renew and modernize Canadian social policy. It focuses on the pan-Canadian dimension of health and social policy systems; the linkages between the social and economic unions; and the recognition that reform is best achieved in partnership among provinces, territories, and the government of Canada. The primary objective of the social union initiative is to reform and renew Canada's system of social services and to reassure Canadians that their pan-Canadian social programs are strong and secure. In working to build a strong social union, the government of Canada and the provinces and territories have reached a broad consensus that the first priorities should be children living in poverty and people with disabilities.

Source: Canada Customs and Revenue Agency. (n.d.). *National child benefit.* Retrieved from http://www.nationalchildbenefit.ca/eng/06/links.shtml.

Collaborative Federalism: Mid-1990s into 2000s

Finally, the current era of federalism reflects a recognition by both levels of government of a crisis in Canadian federalism, to the point of its being almost dysfunctional. Simeon and Willis (1997) describe a "widespread sense of policy and institutional failure" (p. 150). It is also essentially considered to be driven by an agenda of reparation (Prince, 2003). This reparation has occurred in the face of demands by the provinces and territories for stable, predictable, and sufficient funding of social transfers and programs. Canadian spending reached its height at 18 percent of GDP in 1990, and then fell to 16.9 percent in 2007 (Banting & Myles, 2013). The reinstatement of previously frozen and reduced federal funding was apparent in the restored federal funding levels in the Health Accord of 2003 under the Canada Health and Social Transfer, and is also evident in transfers to the provinces and territories for programs aimed at people with disabilities.

IMPLICATIONS OF RECENT DEVELOPMENTS FOR HEALTH POLICY

Related to these phases of Canadian federalism are the actual policy processes that took place. Prince (2003) identifies four principal phases of recent national policy change and spending from the 1980s through the 1990s. Prince's phases refer to public policy orientations rather than focusing on the nature of intergovernmental relations and include an attempt to make sense of the types of policies that emerged at each phase.

1980–1984: Maintaining Governmental Roles

The period from 1980 to 1984 saw the maintenance of the important role that governments play in social provision. This occurred in spite of economic shocks as globalization began to take hold (Myles, 1998).

1984–1988: Restraining Social Program Costs

Governmental commitments to the maintenance of health and social programs began to weaken during the mid-1980s. Upon election of his party to power in Ottawa in 1984, Conservative Prime Minister Brian Mulroney initiated a number of actions that increased provincial spending requirements for health and other programs. Mulroney froze federal transfers to the provincial and territorial governments for health care and post-secondary education (Banting, 1997). In the health care field, this development represented the first retreat by the federal government in meeting its obligations to health care under the Canada Health Act.

This phase also marked the beginning of the rise of global economic pressures on nation-states that culminated in the free trade era. The 1988 election became a referendum on free trade, which the Conservatives won in spite of significant opposition to free trade during the lead-up to the election. In 1989, Canada and the US signed the Free Trade Agreement.

Much of the opposition to free trade agreements centred on their potential threat to medicare and other social programs. Opponents believed that the requirements for open investment contained in these agreements made it difficult for nations to pass laws that protect publicly provided health care and other services from being open to private investment and potential takeover. As such, these agreements could be seen as threatening the ability of governments to set domestic policy. National sovereignty in numerous policy areas could be weakened. These issues are taken up in the following chapter.

1988–1997: Restructuring the Role of Government

From 1988 to 1997, the federal government—both Conservative and Liberal—began to restructure the role of government in social provision. This was associated with significant curtailing of federal—and in some cases provincial and territorial—health care and other program spending. The term *restructuring* can be seen as a euphemism for significantly reduced governmental social spending.

By the time the Free Trade Agreement came into effect in 1989, then–Prime Minister Mulroney reduced federal transfers to the provinces and territories, forcing them to bear a greater proportion of health and other social program costs. The federal government spared few social programs. For example, in 1995, the new federal Liberal government of Jean Chrétien replaced the Established Programs Financing Act (1977) with the Canada Health and Social Transfer (CHST) (Brooks & Miljan, 2003). Under the CHST, the federal government began to retreat from its commitment to match provincial and territorial spending on health. From then on, the federal contribution to health would be based on the previous year's level of provincial or territorial spending, adjusted to take into account any change in a province's or territory's gross provincial product. As a result, Ottawa's share of public health care spending fell steadily.

Also, prior to the CHST, the provinces and territories had been provided with separate funding envelopes for health care, social services, and post-secondary education. Under the CHST, only one funding envelope was provided, such that provinces and territories came to decide how CHST monies would be allocated. Since health care was seen as the main priority by most provincial and territorial governments, funds were made available for this budget area at the expense of the other funding areas. This led to profound reductions in many provinces and territories to social assistance funding, which adversely affected the less well-off.

1997–Present: Repairing the Social Union

By 1997, governments of all stripes began to recognize that the social infrastructure was deteriorating and that there was a need to reinvest in social programs. Hence, the federal, provincial, and territorial governments decided to redefine the social union. Prince (2003) notes that the social union is a broad term that refers to three separate issues.

> ### Box 10.2: The Social Union Framework Agreement (SUFA) and the Social Union
>
> Prince (2003) distinguishes between SUFA and the social union. SUFA is one agreement. Prince defines the social union as referring to three different issues. The first is a sequence of processes and structures instigated by the annual premiers' conference in 1995, and thereafter by the Provincial/ Territorial Council on Social Policy Renewal. The second is policy decisions and intergovernmental relations, such as action plans, budget allocations, and program changes that emerged. And the third is perspectives on federalism and social policy. Prince argues that this latter issue also exemplifies belief systems about the appropriate roles of and relationships between the state, the economy, families, and communities. In short, the social union "refers to the long-term ideas and infrastructure of Canadian social policy" (Prince, 2003, p. 126).

THE SOCIAL UNION FRAMEWORK INITIATIVE AND AGREEMENT (SUFA)

The "social union" initiative refers to government efforts to renew and modernize Canadian social policy. Its aims were to strengthen the role of government vis-à-vis social provision as citizen entitlement. The focus was national health and social policy systems, the linkages between the social and economic unions, and the recognition that reform is best managed co-operatively among the provincial, territorial, and federal governments (see Box 10.3). The concept of a social union is that a unified nation shares a set of norms, standards, and objectives concerning the basic elements of social citizenship (Cameron & Simeon, 2002).

The restructuring of government since 2000—and largely under Stephen Harper's Conservative government in Ottawa—has been anything but collaborative, and certainly not benign in its implications for health and social policy (Noel et al., 2003; Simmons & Graefe, 2013). Critics suggest that this renewed collaborative federalism ostensibly intended by SUFA was hierarchical rather than non-hierarchical, as implied by the term *collaborative* (Simmons & Graefe, 2013).

For example, SUFA and other social policy initiatives, such as the National Child Benefit and the National Children's Agenda of the late 1990s, manifest hierarchy implicit in new governance arrangements, "with the federal government steering while the provinces rowed" (Simmons & Graefe, 2013, p. 28).

Three criteria for assessing the extent of collaboration have been devised (Simmons & Graefe, 2013). First, collaboration between the federal and subnational governments must be grounded in new or changed institutions to provide lasting impact. Second, the collaboration must be sufficiently productive in facing challenges and developing remedies for difficult issues. Finally, real or true collaboration necessitates that all parties to the collaboration are equals, and their "working together" is founded on consent and voluntary cooperation.

In 2011, then Minister of Finance Jim Flaherty (now deceased) announced to the provincial and territorial governments that the federal government would scale back its health transfers. Federal transfers would increase by 6 percent until 2016/17. After 2017, increases would be tied to economic growth— including inflation—at about 4 percent, but would never dip below 3 percent. Indeed, many have argued that this change threatens medicare, gradually reducing the capacity of the federal government to enforce the Canada Health Act. It also demonstrates a lack of federal leadership in health (Walkom, 2011; Picard, 2011).

SUFA and other social policy initiatives, such as the National Child Benefit and the National Children's Agenda of the late 1990s, reflect a hierarchy implicit in a number of new governance arrangements, with the federal government taking the lead (Simmons & Graefe, 2013, p. 28). The Harper government's approach to health policy is consistent with other unilateral actions by previous federal governments.

Prior to the signing of SUFA, the federal government used the 1995 budget to bring down the federal deficit primarily through spending reductions (Facal, 2005) It reviewed spending programs in its own areas of jurisdiction, but also radically reduced its transfer payments to the provinces and territories. With the introduction of the Canada Health and Social Transfer (CHST), actual federal funding cuts of $6 billion occurred over a two-year period. These cuts took place in health care, social services, and post-secondary education. In addition to its lofty stated aims, SUFA was also an attempt to placate the provincial and territorial governments by sketching out controls over federal actions.

Box 10.3: The Purpose of SUFA

Alain Noel and others at the Institute for Research on Public Policy (Noel et al., 2003) argue that the purpose of the Social Union Framework, formulated in 1999, and the health accords that followed in 2000 and 2003 were to provide the basis for more constructive and co-operative intergovernmental relationships, or more collaborative/co-operative federalism in social policy (Facal, 2005). SUFA was intended to provide common guiding principles and a code of conduct for interactions between the federal, provincial, and territorial governments in health care, post-secondary education, training, social assistance, and social services. Its objectives were to:

- help governments work together to address the needs of Canadians
- establish adequate, stable, and sustainable funding for social programs
- undertake efforts to avoid administrative overlap and duplication
- mediate and resolve intergovernmental disputes
- improve public accountability and transparency

SUFA itself is a non-constitutional yet formal agreement intended to clarify the roles of the two levels of government in public policy (Fortin, Noel, & St-Hilaire, 2003). The federal, provincial, and territorial governments (with the exception of Quebec) signed the document in February 1999. SUFA was intended to renew the social union and make explicit the obligations and commitments of the two levels of government in the health, social services, post-secondary education, social assistance, and training policy domains.

In practice, SUFA was an attempt to specify the means by which the federal government could exercise—yet be under some provincial and territorial control—its power in public policy areas that the Canadian Constitution identifies as exclusive provincial jurisdiction (Facal, 2005; Cameron & Simeon, 2002). The agreement prohibits the unilateral use by the federal government of its spending power.

The first ministers stated that SUFA provided a template for fostering more constructive and co-operative relations between the federal, provincial, and territorial governments in health and social provision (Fortin et al., 2003). First ministers are the heads of the federal and the provincial and territorial governments—that is, the prime minister and the premiers of the provinces and territories. One of the first sets of agreements to emerge from SUFA has been concerned with health care. Concerns have been raised about the elitist nature of SUFA (see Box 10.4).

Box 10.4: Concerns with SUFA

Policy analysts have criticized the document as an exemplar of "elite accommodation" (Cameron & Simeon, 2002, p. 57). Others argue that SUFA fails to define the social union and to resolve the disputes that brought it into being (Noel et al., 2003). In short, it is considered little more than rhetoric on paper. Another concern was that Quebec had not signed on to the agreement. Quebec had not participated actively in interprovincial meetings from 1995 to mid-1998 (Facal, 2005). The Quebec government refused to endorse SUFA because the other provinces did not appear ready to support its demand for recognition of the unconditional right to opt out with full financial compensation from the federal government for any province prepared to assume full responsibility in areas of exclusive provincial jurisdiction. A similar rationale led to the development of the health accords of 2000 and 2003.

THE HEALTH ACCORDS OF 2000, 2003, AND 2004

The first focus of federal and provincial/territorial government meetings under SUFA was to consider health care issues. As a result of these meetings, the federal health minister and his provincial and territorial counterparts produced health accords in 2000, 2003, and 2004. The agreements were focused on health care.

The Health Accord of 2000

The 2000 health accord increased federal transfer payments to the provinces and territories for health care and other programs through the Canada Health and Social Transfer by $21.1 billion over five years (Noel et al., 2003). The short title for this first health accord agreement was the "Accord on Health Care Renewal." This sum also included $2.2 billion for early childhood development within the CHST. The health care–related funds entailed:

- $1 billion over two years to the provinces and territories to shore up necessary diagnostic and treatment equipment;
- $800 million to the provinces and territories for innovation and reforms in primary care; and

- $500 million to Canada Health Infoway to help expedite the
  adoption of modern information technologies in order to ensure
  better health care.

The Canada Health Infoway is an independent, non-profit agency with a
membership comprising 14 federal, provincial, and territorial deputy ministers
of health (Canada Health Infoway, 2007). Its mandate is to facilitate the use of
electronic health information systems and electronic health records across Canada.

Some considered the 2000 accord to be a pre-election stopgap initiated
by the federal government to defuse the health care issue (Fortin et al.,
2003). While transfer payment increases announced at the same time were
considerable—$21.1 billion over five years—they have not to date had a
significant impact on health services (Fortin et al., 2003).

Health Accord 2003

Three years later, in 2003, the first ministers returned to the bargaining table
to negotiate a new health accord (Facal, 2005). This followed the release of
the health reform reports of Senator Michael Kirby and Commissioner
Roy Romanow (Kirby, 2002; Romanow, 2002). The 2003 accord provided
more federal funding for primary health care, home care, and catastrophic
drug coverage. It also appeared to be a response to the recommendations of
the Kirby and Romanow reports. The accord also created an independent
Health Council of Canada, whose membership would consist of health care
experts, representatives from both levels of government, and members of the
public, with the goal of monitoring and reporting on health care and broader
population health issues. As indicated in chapter 6, the Harper government
abolished the Health Council in 2013.

Like the previous health accord of 2000, the 2003 health accord increased
federal funding. The first ministers established an "enhanced accountability"
framework (Canada Department of Finance, 2008). Under the framework, the
first ministers committed to providing comprehensive and regular reports to
the public based on comparable indicators pertaining to health status, health
outcomes, and quality of services. Governments agreed to establish the Health
Council, as recommended by Romanow, to monitor and provide annual public
reports on the implementation of the accord.

The accord was also intended to improve wait times for care and access
to home and community care, as well as to provide catastrophic drug

coverage. These provisions were consistent with Kirby's recommendations, so the 2003 accord may have been seen as a way of satisfying some requirements Kirby and Romanow identified. The 2003 health accord was intended, like the SUFA before it, to bring about "more constructive and cooperative federalism" (Noel et al., 2003, p. 1). Following its implementation, however, the premiers expressed dismay about what they considered to be less than adequate levels of federal funding.

Health Accord 2004

The first ministers met again in 2004 and added to the commitments made in the 2003 Health Accord (Health Canada, 2006). The 2004 Health Accord— also known as the 10-Year Plan to Strengthen Health Care—promises to sustain and renew the health care system, and assures long-term funding to achieve these goals. The 2004 accord also promises to reduce wait times for care and improve access, with a focus on cancer care and heart treatments, diagnostic imaging, joint replacements, and sight restoration. The federal investments of $41 billion over 10 years specified in the 2004 accord enabled governments to plan ahead with the assurance of enhanced federal funding. The first ministers also committed to regular reports on the performance of the health care system to the Canadian public.

The concern remains as to whether these commitments to renewal and improved funding levels are merely words on paper. The next sections consider the impacts of the 2000, 2003, and 2004 health accords in particular, and the SUFA in general.

EVALUATION OF THE IMPACT OF SUFA AND THE HEALTH ACCORDS

SUFA and the 2000, 2003, and 2004 health accords are intended to foster more co-operative relations between the two levels of government in the health and social policy fields (Noel et al., 2003). To date, it is unclear what impact any of these agreements have had on health and social service provision by either level of government.

While SUFA provided the federal, provincial, and territorial governments some room to manoeuvre in their health reform efforts, it has provided little fostering of political debate over two critical issues on the health policy agenda

(Maioni, 2000). These are: Who should be allowed to set the rules in health care? and, What should the rules be? Perhaps the most critical issue is what role the federal government should play in the health care sector with respect to setting the rules.

And concerning these rules, a primary question, which appears to be a focus of provincial and territorial concern, is: What should be the boundaries between the public sector and private markets in provincial health care systems? A key issue underlying this question is whether private markets should have a role in health care delivery at all (see Box 10.5).

Box 10.5: Privatized Medical Care No Cure for Waiting Lists
By Colleen M. Flood and Meghan McMahon
Toronto Star

A constitutional challenge to Ontario legislation that prohibits the purchase of private health insurance for medically necessary health care services (dubbed the "Ontario Chaoulli") was announced on Sept. 5.

It's another call for increased privatization, based on the misinformed notion that an expanded role for private insurance will remedy wait times in Canada.

Just last month, the outgoing president of the Canadian Medical Association, Dr. Colin McMillan, put forward Medicare Plus, the CMA's solution for sustaining our health care system. It proposed expanding the role for private insurance and private payment, and allowing physicians to work for the public system and treat private patients, too.

After a stream of backlash from the Canadian Healthcare Association, the Registered Nurses Association of Ontario, Canadian Doctors for Medicare, and others, the CMA responded by saying that it is time to examine the nature of the public versus private health care debate.

Indeed it is. Will the CMA's recommendations make medicare better? The evidence says no.

Currently, Canadian regulations prevent doctors who are paid by public Medicare from also providing medically necessary care for private payment. But doctors can "opt out" of the public system and "go private" (except in Ontario).

Why do we have this regulation? Because if we didn't, doctors would naturally want to spend much more of their time than they presently do treating private patients—as these patients often have easier conditions to treat and they (or their insurer) will pay more.

A doctor, like any normal person, will be attracted to working for more and doing less—who can blame them? So it is not surprising that some members of the CMA like the idea of Medicare Plus.

But from the public's perspective, and from the perspective of most patients, it's a bad idea. If you are a patient wealthy enough to pay privately or you have private insurance, then you may fare better under Medicare Plus. But lines for treatment in the public hospitals will grow longer and longer.

The CMA's recommendation also ignores the simple fact that, in the absence of an increase in the number of doctors (where will we get them from?), the introduction of a parallel private system must mean that the doctors we do have will be distributed between both public and private patients.

Private patients will pay more to have their medical needs met on a preferential basis, leaving public patients on ever-growing waiting lists. Evidence suggests that allowing doctors to practise in the public and private sectors will not, as Medicare Plus states, "improve access for the entire population."

Other countries that allow doctors to work on an unregulated basis in the public and private sectors—like New Zealand, the UK, and Ireland—currently have, or have had, chronic problems with long waiting lists.

The evidence doesn't seem to indicate that having parallel private health insurance or "Medicare Plus" has cured waiting lists in these countries. Where waiting lists have been wrestled down—as in the UK—it has been through a huge infusion of public money and improvements in the management of public hospitals. The cure has not come from more private money or private insurance.

And countries like France that appear to have a large private sector actually heavily regulate doctors who work privately—including the price they can charge and the amount of time they can spend treating private patients. So what looks on the surface to be "private" is not really: it's quasi-public because of such heavy regulation.

So we could follow the European route—and heavily regulate doctors who "go private"—or we can stick with the cleaner and simpler approach of requiring doctors who are paid by public Medicare to be paid only by Medicare but still allow doctors to "go private" if they are prepared to work completely within the private payment sector.

But we have to recognize that even with European-style regulation we would be embracing the idea that it's fine for folks with more money to jump queues and get preferential treatment from doctors.

This is in direct opposition to the principle of equity that has historically guided the Canadian Medicare system, which was created in part to eliminate distinctions between the rich and poor in access to medically necessary health-care.

Canada's healthcare system needs reform—but reform based on the best available evidence and guided by Canadian values. On the issue of waiting times, for example, the Institute of Health Services and Policy Research—part of the Canadian Institutes of Health Research—funded research that helped establish the first-ever national benchmarks for waiting times in December 2005. CIHR-IHSPR is committed to providing evidence-based solutions that will improve the health care system. Let us not make the mistake of misusing the wealth of evidence that strongly supports a public health-care system like Canadian Medicare.

Source: Flood, C.M., & McMahon, M. (2007, September 18). Privatized medical care no cure for waiting lists. *Toronto Star*, p. AA8.

Although federal, provincial, and territorial governments have all welcomed an expanded private sector role, some have argued that involving the private sector runs counter to the spirit, if not the letter, of the *Canada Health Act* (Rachlis, 2004; Canadian Doctors for Medicare, 2011). Others argue that private sector financing and delivery of health care services jeopardizes the sustainability of public health care itself (Canadian Health Coalition, 2008). Rather than addressing the problems of the public health care system, private sector involvement may worsen the situation.

SUFA, HEALTH CARE, AND HEALTH-RELATED PUBLIC POLICY

Some question the "privileged" position of health care in the debate on SUFA (McIntosh, 2000). Specifically, McIntosh cautions that other aspects of the social union—much of it concerned with health-related public policy—could be abandoned in the process. Further, he argues that labour market policies are especially important in that they lie at the centre of social and economic policies, which "makes their overall direction a crucial component of a re-created social union" (McIntosh, 2000, p. 48).

Yet, McIntosh agrees that the "crisis" in the health care system is real and requires the attention of policy analysts and governments. But labour market policy is also about health and clearly constitutes an important health-related public policy area. As an important social determinant of health employment (Jackson, 2004; Tremblay, 2004, 2008), McIntosh (2000) notes that secure attachment to the labour market in "well-paid, meaningful employment" is critical to human health and well-being (p. 48).

Indeed, McIntosh highlights the obsession of Canadian politicians with health care and the failure to consider promoting human health and well-being as a critical health policy outcome. He also notes the lack of an overarching vision for labour market policy or any other public policy, and little consideration of the potential consequences of continuing in such a manner.

The federal, provincial, and territorial governments renewed the Social Union Framework Agreement in 2002, but even then it was apparent that it was becoming peripheral to the actual functions and ongoing negotiations taking place in intergovernmental relations. The document said much about building for the future, but as Pat and Hugh Armstrong (2003, 2010) and others have argued, it does nothing to prevent further erosion of health care. The health accords lack enforcement mechanisms. They are statements of commitment, but provide little direction for governmental action.

IMPLICATIONS OF THE NEGLECT OF SUFA

The Social Union Framework Agreement was intended to assure the Canadian public of the willingness and ability of Canadian governments to co-operate. Gibbins (2003), of the Canada West Foundation, argues that some perceived SUFA as representing a fundamental transformation of the Canadian federal system that would usher in an "unprecedented level of cooperation, formality and civility to intergovernmental relations" (Gibbins, 2003, p. 31). It had also assured increased citizen participation in the previously exclusive world of intergovernmental relations. Others noted that SUFA excluded Quebec, which was seen as a major flaw, but the health accord struck in the fall of 2000 at least brought Quebec into the SUFA framework in health care.

Lazar (2000) argues that SUFA is primarily about process rather than outcomes. It is primarily concerned with how governments should relate to one another and to citizens in making social policy, and says rather less about developing new social policy commitments (Lazar, 2000). SUFA calls for joint federal-provincial/territorial planning and coordination in social policy, more citizen and stakeholder participation in decision making, and increased accountability and transparency. Lazar (2000) concludes that

SUFA is potentially "a major departure in Canadian social policy and in the management of the federation" (p. 11). He notes that it is difficult to assess its impact because most of its activities have occurred behind closed doors. In other words, the process has neither increased transparency nor increased citizen involvement, a key component of the agreement.

SUFA has failed to change the politics of social policy or health reform (Maioni, 2000). The warring between the two levels of government continues. This is particularly so since the federal government has tended to focus on particular health care issues, such as wait times, which seems to exacerbate tensions between the federal and provincial/territorial governments. The intent was to renew the collaborative federalism that had characterized the 1950s and 1960s when the two levels of government cost-shared social and health programs. There was a commitment to ensure that all citizens had access to necessary health care and social programs. Governments were cognizant of their obligations to ensure universal access to social programs.

What is also significant is that none of the health accords even refer to the Social Union Framework Agreement (Noel et al., 2003). It is therefore questionable how much impact SUFA has had on the health accords. The agreements outline commitments to public accountability, transparency, and joint planning specified in SUFA. What they appear to have excluded are agreements on key issues such as the level of the federal financial commitment to health care and the appropriate level to ensure sustainable funding, and how the provinces and territories are to report on how they spend this contribution. At best, the 2004 health accord enhanced the mandate and scope of the new Health Council. In the end, the documents spout much rhetoric, but mandate no action or commitment on the part of any government to health care and its sustainability into the future.

In addition, the Social Union Framework Agreement and the health accords provide promises with respect to health care, such as upholding the principles enshrined in the Canada Health Act. They do not specify, however, how these principles will be ensured. Nor do they address the issues of privatization and increased commercialization of health care that commentators such as the Canadian Centre for Policy Alternatives, various provincial and territorial governments, and others consider to be key issues.

The federal government has a role to play in preventing the further commercialization of health care. As Maioni (2000) argues, the agreement neither addresses nor offers means to address the continuing dispute over who should set the rules in the health sector, or what rules should govern the Canadian health care system.

ABSENCE OF QUEBEC

What is notable is Quebec's absence from SUFA. The federal, provincial, and territorial governments, with the exception of Quebec, affirmed federal spending in areas of provincial jurisdiction and specified the rules for intergovernmental relations in social policy. Trying to make sense of Quebec's absence, Noel (2001) asks, "If the situation is so one-sided, why did all provincial and territorial governments except Quebec accept the agreement?" (pp. 58–59). Quebec may have objected to affirming federal spending power and, by extension, its authority in exclusive provincial jurisdiction. At first ministers' meetings, Quebec asserted its right to opt out of national programs and receive federal compensation.

Noel (2001) suggests that SUFA brought together a process that was already underway, which he attributes to federal fiscal and social policies—and perceived pressures to reduce government deficits and constrain government spending. He adds that initiatives on the Social Union by the provinces and territories did not emanate from a wish to collaborate on social policy. Rather, they emanated from a desire on the part of these governments to rail against the CHST and the reduced federal cash transfers that it brought. This does not mean that the provinces and territories are more socially progressive and enlightened than the federal government. On the contrary, the provinces and territories wanted limits on the federal spending power that would be consistent with the decreasing value and reliability of federal transfers—in short, increasing decentralization, which would enhance the independence of the provincial and territorial governments. Noel (2001) suggests that the Quebec government, under then Premier Lucien Bouchard, united with the other provinces and territories after the federal government implemented the National Child Benefit. In the end, the provinces and territories acted to protect themselves. This provided yet another opportunity for Quebec to also oppose federally imposed requirements.

Noel (2001) concludes that a more constructive stance for the provinces and territories would be to change the course of events by taking advantage of the SUFA review and renewal process to re-establish a common position and advocate simple but forceful demands (Facal, 2005). These demands would include increases in social transfers and repairing the fiscal imbalance. In the same vein, they could also attempt to insert an enforcement mechanism in the form of a statement of principle in SUFA for "adequate, affordable, stable and sustainable funding for social programs" (Facal, 2005, p. 3).

SUFA has failed to protect social programs such as medicare from further commercialization. The framework and health accords reflect governments' general tendency to develop social policy in a vacuum. The processes that led to SUFA and the health accords of 2000, 2003, and 2004 reflect an unwillingness by both levels of government to address the key issues and to arrive at an agreement on what contributes to health, how it can be maintained, and the role of governments in promoting the health and well-being of the population.

Moreover, these processes are almost entirely concerned with health care to the exclusion of other key issues that are known to contribute to health, such as labour market policy, housing, income, and other issues. Fundamentally, governments lack the vision to do what is necessary to improve and maintain the health of the population. There are many ways to do this, as demonstrated by the actions and policies of governments in western Europe, where public spending on health and social programs far exceeds the commitments of Canadian governments. The penchant of Canadian governments to commercialize health care reflects a drift toward an American model of social provision.

There was little evidence during the Harper government's term in office that they would provide a more constructive approach than those of previous federal governments. The Harper government promised 6 percent more toward health care until 2016–2017 (Bailey & Curry, 2011). The health transfer would thereafter be tied to economic growth, but transfers would not fall below 3 percent per year.

Public policy organizations, such as the Canadian Centre for Policy Alternatives, monitor federal, provincial, and territorial public policy issues and propose alternative public policies to address key health and social policy issues. They specifically oppose commercialization strategies in health and social provision to address the problems of the health care system.

For example, in an editorial prepared for the Canadian Centre for Policy Alternatives, Colleen Fuller (2000) argues that "private health care is not the solution" (p. 1). She cites research that shows for-profit hospitals are 3 to 11 percent more costly than not-for-profit hospitals. Fuller adds that the shift of services from the hospital to the community was in the right direction, but notes that

> if people cannot get services in their communities on the same terms and conditions they get them in the hospital, they are going to head for a growing line-up for a hospital bed. This is how user fees act as a barrier to access, and this is how people respond. (Fuller, 2000, p. 1)

Fuller concludes that the first ministers should have agreed to interpret the *Canada Health Act* more generously and progressively than they did. She means that they should clearly define home care, long-term care, and out-patient rehabilitation as services covered by the no-user-fee rules of the legislation.

As far as increasing accountability, as raised in the health accords and in the Social Union Framework Agreement, the *Canada Health Act* requires regular provincial and territorial reporting on their health care spending. The act states very clearly that if provinces and territories fail to report to the federal health minister how they are complying with national standards, they will not receive any federal money. Fuller (2000) argues that reporting is essential to ensure that the principles of the CHA are enforced, and that user fees are not erecting a barrier to access. The absence of enforcement mechanisms to ensure the compliance of all parties to the terms of SUFA and the health accords shows that these documents are merely platitudes to preserving medicare. It reflects a lack of political leadership and commitment to do what is necessary to improve the health of the population and preserve an important social program that defines Canada.

The accords and other measures may be well intentioned in attempting to reaffirm the commitments of the federal, provincial, and territorial governments to social and health provision. Without commitments backed up by action by both levels of government, these agreements are merely words to show the Canadian public that governments are still thinking about health care.

During the 2015 general election, the Liberal Party promised to renew the 2004 Health Accord. Specifically, it promised to renegotiate a health accord with the provincial and territorial governments (Liberal Party of Canada, 2015). This would include a long-term funding agreement. Since the Liberal Party won a majority government on October 19, 2015, federal Minister of Health Jane Philpott has met with her provincial and territorial counterparts, but as of the time of writing, no commitments on the accord have yet been made.

CONCLUSIONS

SUFA and the health accords of 2000, 2003, and 2004 can be understood as efforts to renew a collaborative federalism between the two levels of government. The federal, provincial, and territorial governments recognized the decline in cordial relations between them and the general decrease in social provision. Although these agreements have shown little impact to date in improving relations between governments, they have initiated an important national discussion about the appropriate role of government in social provision— albeit behind closed doors and without consultation with civil society actors.

These agreements may signify more in terms of altering and perhaps improving intergovernmental relations and processes to assure the Canadian public that the two levels of government are communicating. As discussed, the restructuring of institutional arrangements between the federal and subnational/regional governments seems to have further impaired the possibility of intergovernmental collaboration on health and social policy.

Fundamentally, the agreements do not articulate a clear vision with respect to what both levels of government wish to achieve in these important policy areas—health and social policy. Moreover, the primacy of health care in the agreements may lead to the exclusion of other fundamental public policy issues that are germane to health, such as income and employment security, housing security, and labour policy, as McIntosh (2000) and others suggest. Discussion has failed to move much beyond health care and the appropriate roles of the federal, provincial, and territorial governments in health policy, and in public policy areas that research has shown are more critical to human health than health care. It also reflects the shift to neoliberalism discussed in chapter 9, which has contributed to a diminished federal role and the weakening of the Canadian welfare state, and by extension, medicare.

CRITICAL THINKING QUESTIONS

1. How does Canadian federalism shape the health care reform process?
2. How aware were you of the various health care accords prior to reading this text?
3. Do you think there is a chance these health care accords will save the medicare system? Why?
4. What do you make of SUFA and the 2000, 2003, and 2004 health accords? How many Canadians do you think are aware of these agreements and their implications for health and social policy in Canada?
5. Considering that very few young Canadians vote, do you think that Canadian governments will be required to respond to their needs in the future?

FURTHER READINGS

Bakvis, H., & Skogstad, G. (Eds.). (2007). *Canadian federalism: Performance, effectiveness, and legitimacy* (2nd ed.). Toronto: Oxford University Press.

The second edition of *Canadian Federalism: Performance, Effectiveness, and Legitimacy* is a collection of 18 original essays casting a critical eye on the institutions, processes, and policy outcomes of Canadian federalism. It is divided into three parts: (1) The Institutions and Processes of Canadian Federalism; (2) The Social and Economic Union; and (3) Persistent and New Challenges to the Federation.

Fortin, S., Noel, A., & St-Hilaire, F. (Eds.). (2003). *Forging the Canadian Social Union: SUFA and beyond*. Montreal: Institute for Research on Public Policy.

This volume provides a severe assessment of the 1999 Social Union Framework Agreement. It brings together assessments of various dimensions of SUFA from seven leading experts in social policy and intergovernmental relations.

Health Council of Canada. (2007). *Annual report: Why health care renewal matters: Learning from Canadians with chronic health conditions*. Retrieved from http://www.healthcouncilcanada.ca/tree/2.20-Outcomes2FINAL.pdf.

Although the Health Council of Canada no longer exists, its first annual report to Canadians focuses on access. In its second report, the council focuses on quality. Its final reports examine the collective capacity to measure the performance of health care systems across the country and suggest ways to strengthen transparency and accountability in health care.

RELEVANT WEBSITES

Canadian Federalism and Public Health Care: The Evolution of Federal-Provincial Relations
www.mapleleafweb.com/features/canadian-federalism-and-public-health-care-evolution-federal-provincial-relations

This website has a discussion of the basic division of powers in health care, Canadian federalism and the introduction of public health care, and shifts in this federal-regional relationship since the 1950s.

Caledon Institute of Social Policy
www.caledoninst.org

Established in 1992, the Caledon Institute of Social Policy is a private nonprofit organization with charitable status. It carries out rigorous research and analysis on poverty and social policy. It develops and promotes action for social policy reform at all levels of government.

First Ministers' Accord on Health Care Renewal 2003
www.hc-sc.gc.ca/hcs-sss/delivery-prestation/fptcollab/2003accord/index_e.html
First Minister's Meeting on the Future of Health Care 2004
www.hc-sc.gc.ca/hcs-sss/delivery-prestation/fptcollab/2004-fmm-rpm/
index_e.html

These websites provide details of the first ministers' health accords of 2003
and 2004.

Institute for Research on Public Policy
www.irpp.org

IRPP seeks to improve public policy in Canada by generating research,
providing insight, and sparking debate that will contribute to the public
policy decision-making process and strengthen the quality of the public policy
decisions made by Canadian governments, citizens, institutions, and organizations.

Institute of Intergovernmental Relations, Queen's University
www.queensu.ca/iigr/home

The Institute of Intergovernmental Relations at Queen's University
is Canada's premier university-based centre for research on all aspects of
federalism and intergovernmental relations, both in Canada and in countries
around the world.

REFERENCES

Armstrong, H., & Armstrong, P. (2003). *Wasting away: The undermining of Canadian health care*. Toronto: Oxford University Press.
Armstrong, H., & Armstrong, P. (2010). *Wasting away: The undermining of Canadian health care* (2nd ed.). Toronto: Oxford University Press.
Bailey, I., & Curry, B. (2011, December 19). In surprise move, Flaherty lays out health-spending plans til 2024. *The Globe and Mail.* Retrieved from http://www.theglobeandmail.com/news/politics/in-surprise-move-flaherty-lays-out-health-spending-plans-til-2024/article4247851.
Banting, K. (1997). The social policy divide: The welfare state in Canada and the United States. In K. Banting, G. Hoberg, & R. Simeon (Eds.), *Degrees of freedom: Canada and the United States in a changing world* (pp. 267–309). Montreal & Kingston: McGill-Queen's University Press.
Banting, K., & Myles, J. (2013). *Inequality and the fading of redistributive politics.* Vancouver: UBC Press.
Brooks, S., & Miljan, L. (2003). *Public policy in Canada: An introduction.* Toronto: Oxford University Press.
Cameron, D., & Simeon, R. (2002). Intergovernmental relations in Canada: The emergence of collaborative federalism. *Publius: The Journal of Federalism, 32*(2), 49–71.

Canada Department of Finance. (2008). *Investing in Canada's health care system*. Retrieved from www.fin.gc.ca/budget03/bp/bpc3-eng.asp.

Canada Health Infoway. (2007). *Infoway: Establishing electronic health records for Canadians*. Retrieved from www.infoway-inforoute.ca/en/WhoWeAre/Overview.aspx.

Canadian Doctors for Medicare. (2011, February). *Neat, plausible, and wrong: The myth of health care unsustainability*. Toronto: Canadian Doctors for Medicare.

Canadian Health Coalition. (2008). *Grading the government*. Ottawa: Canadian Health Coalition.

Facal, J. (2005). *Social policy and intergovernmental relations in Canada: Understanding the failure of SUFA from a Quebec perspective*. Regina: The Saskatchewan Institute of Public Policy.

Fortin, S., Noel, A., & St-Hilaire, F. (Eds.). (2003). *Forging the Canadian Social Union: SUFA and beyond*. Montreal: Institute for Research on Public Policy.

Fuller, C. (2000). *Health accord is welcome, but national standards still in jeopardy*. Ottawa: Canadian Centre for Policy Alternatives.

Gibbins, R. (2003). Shifting sands: Exploring the political foundations of SUFA. In S. Fortin, A. Noel, & F. St-Hilaire (Eds.), *Forging the Canadian Social Union: SUFA and beyond* (pp. 31–46). Montreal: Institute for Research on Public Policy.

Health Canada. (2006). *Healthy Canadians: A federal report on comparable health indicators 2006*. Ottawa: Health Canada.

Jackson, A. (2004). The unhealthy Canadian workplace. In D. Raphael (Ed.), *Social determinants of health: Canadian perspectives* (pp. 79–94). Toronto: Canadian Scholars' Press.

Kirby, M.J. (2002). *The health of Canadians: The federal role*. Ottawa: Standing Senate Committee on Social Affairs, Science, and Technology.

Lazar, H. (2000). *The Social Union Framework Agreement: Lost opportunity or new beginning?* Kingston: School of Policy Studies, Queen's University.

Liberal Party of Canada. (2015). *A new health accord*. Ottawa: The Liberal Party of Canada. Retrieved from www.liberal.ca/realchange/a-new-health-accord.

Maioni, A. (2000). Assessing the Social Union Framework Agreement. *Policy Options*, *21*(3), 39–41.

McIntosh, T. (2000). Is the Social Union too "healthy"? Re-thinking labour market policy. *Policy Options* (April), 48–49.

Myles, J. (1998). How to design a "liberal" welfare state: A comparison of Canada and the United States. *Social Policy and Administration*, *32*(4), 341–364.

Noel, A. (2001). Power and purpose in intergovernmental relations. *Policy Matters/Enjeux publics*, *2*(6), 1–28.

Noel, A., St-Hilaire, F., & Fortin, S. (2003). Learning from the SUFA experience. In S. Fortin, A. Noel, & F. St-Hilaire (Eds.), *Forging the Canadian social union: SUFA and beyond* (pp. 1–29). Montreal: Institute for Public Policy Research.

Picard, A. (2011, August 23). When even Dr. Optimism is losing faith in medicare, it's time to fix it. *The Globe and Mail*. Retrieved from www.theglobeandmail.com/life/health-and-fitness/when-even-dr-optimism-is-losing-faith-in-medicare-its-time-to-fix-it/article626869.

Prince, M.J. (2003). SUFA: Sea change or mere ripple for Canadian social policy? In S. Fortin, A. Noel, & F. St-Hilaire (Eds.), *Forging the Canadian Social Union: SUFA and beyond* (pp. 125–130). Montreal: Institute for Research on Public Policy.

Rachlis, M. (2004). *Prescription for excellence: How innovation is saving Canada's health care system*. Toronto: HarperCollins.

Romanow, R.J. (2002). *Building on values: The future of health care in Canada*. Saskatoon: Commission on the Future of Health Care in Canada.

Simeon, R., & Willis, E. (1997). Democracy and performance: Governance in Canada and the United States. In K. Banting, G. Hoberg, & R. Simeon (Eds.), *Degrees of freedom: Canada and the United States in a changing world* (pp. 150–186). Montreal & Kingston: McGill-Queen's University Press.

Simmons, J., & Graefe, P. (2013). Assessing the collaboration that was "collaborative federalism" 1996–2006. *Canadian Political Science Review, 7*(1), 25–36.

Smiley, D.V. (1980). *Canada in question: Federalism in the eighties* (3rd ed.). Toronto: McGraw-Hill Ryerson Limited.

Teeple, G. (2000). *Globalization and the decline of social reform: Into the twenty-first century.* Aurora, ON: Garamond Press.

Tremblay, D.G. (2004). Unemployment and the labour market. In D. Raphael (Ed.), *Social determinants of health: Canadian perspectives* (pp. 53–66). Toronto: Canadian Scholars' Press.

Tremblay, D.G. (2008). Unemployment and the labour market. In D. Raphael (Ed.), *Social determinants of health: Canadian perspectives* (2nd ed.) (pp. 75–87). Toronto: Canadian Scholars' Press.

Walkom, T. (2011, April 20). Harper and the subtle erosion of medicare. *Toronto Star*, np. Retrieved from www.thestar.com/news/canada/2011/04/20/walkom_harper_and_the _subtle_erosion_of_medicare.html.

Chapter 11

GLOBALIZATION AND FREE TRADE

INTRODUCTION

The late 20th century witnessed radical changes to the world economy related to globalization, the liberalization of trade, the removal of barriers to the flow of investment capital, and greater integration with the American economy (Banting, Hoberg, & Simeon, 1997a; Teeple, 2000; Banting & Myles, 2013). National governments in Canada and other advanced economies have responded to these changes by restructuring their economies. In some nations such as Canada, this has also involved significant reductions in governmental spending on health care and social services. What has been most evident is the decline of the welfare state which was discussed in chapter 9. In Canada, beloved social programs such as medicare have been the targets of restructuring and retrenchment. The drastic reduction of the welfare state, however, did not take place in all nations. Nor has it occurred in a vacuum. This reflects national differences in policy priorities (Organisation for Economic Co-operation and Development, 2014, 2015; Swank, 2010).

What is driving these global changes? In a nutshell, the answer is neoliberal policies that reflect an ongoing commitment to the free movement of goods and services across the globe, as articulated in free trade agreements (Teeple, 2000). These global changes influence and are influenced by nations' domestic policies. Previous chapters have touched on the implications of neoliberalism and international trade treaties for the Canadian health care system and for population health. This chapter further examines how these developments are influencing health policy. The primary focus is the impact of globalization on health care, health-related public policies, and health outcomes. This includes an examination of how these forces may be influencing the democratic process in Canada and other nations.

ECONOMIC GLOBALIZATION

Economic globalization refers to the integration of world economies (Banting, Hoberg, & Simeon, 1997b). More specifically, economic globalization is "a process of greater integration within the world economy through movement of goods and services, capital, technology and (to a lesser extent) labour, which lead increasingly to economic decisions being influenced by global conditions" (Jenkins, 2004, p. 1). The process of integration can also involve the internationalization of health care services through liberalization or deregulation, as directed by provisions found in trade agreements between countries (Bakker, 1996; Teeple, 2000).

The process of economic globalization requires that national governments accept freer markets and global economic integration as the foundation(s) for national macroeconomic policy (Labonte & Schrecker, 2007c). Such changes are frequently presented by governmental and business authorities as inevitable and necessary to ensure economic competitiveness (Bakker, 1996). National governments open up their domestic markets and services to global competition by means of procurement agreements, establishing dispute-settlement mechanisms, and allowing investment by global financial institutions.

Box 11.1: The First Glimpse of Economic Globalization

Karl Marx wrote the following passage in *The Communist Manifesto* more than 160 years ago:

> The need of a constantly expanding market for its products chases the bourgeoisie over the entire surface of the globe. It must nestle everywhere, settle everywhere, establish connections everywhere.... The bourgeoisie has, through its exploitation of the world market, given a cosmopolitan character to production and consumption in every country. To the great chagrin of reactionaries, it has drawn from under the feet of industry the national ground on which it stood. All old-established national industries have been destroyed or are daily being destroyed. They are dislodged by new industries, whose introduction becomes a life and death question for all civilized nations, by industries that no longer work up indigenous raw material, but raw material drawn from the remotest zones; industries whose products are

consumed, not only at home, but in every quarter of the globe. In place of the old wants, satisfied by the production of the country, we find new wants, requiring for their satisfaction the products of distant lands and climes. In place of the old local and national seclusion and self-sufficiency, we have intercourse in every direction, universal inter-dependence of nations. And as in material, so also in intellectual production. The intellectual creations of individual nations become common property. National one-sidedness and narrow-mindedness become more and more impossible, and from the numerous national and local literatures, there arises a world literature.

Source: Marx, K. (1848). *The communist manifesto* (pp. 223–224). New York: Penguin Classics.

As suggested by its definition, economic globalization is complex and consists of numerous, interrelated policy dynamics (Labonte & Schrecker, 2007a). These dynamics have implications for health care organization and delivery as well as population health outcomes. As noted in previous chapters, neoliberal ideology has been applied to justify these changes. In reality, the ideology appears to benefit those whose economic interests lie within the business sector (Langille, 2004, 2008).

Capital is more likely to generate larger profits when it can span the globe than when it is limited to one nation. For example, many companies have already experienced increasing profits associated with shifting factories and service industries to lower-wage nations such as India and China. Capital, therefore, seeks freedom from national regulation or other state intervention (Teeple, 2000). Corporate interests are now global or international in scope, although they continue to act on national jurisdictions and local domestic policies. These corporations pressure governments to open up more and more goods and services to the market sector.

As a result of these economic and political pressures, achieved through a variety of lobbying and other processes, national governments manage and adjust domestic policies to meet the imperatives of these transnational, or multinational, market forces (Leys, 2001). Some have suggested that economic globalization, in fact, marks the political demise of the nation-state (Cerny, 1993, 2014; Teeple, 2000) because it appears that multinational corporations, not elected governments, have a central role in determining public policy. The ability of national governments to set domestic policy and manage their economies is effectively undermined in the face of commitments to meet international business interests (see Box 11.2).

Box 11.2: The Development of the Global Economy

The development of globalization must be examined in historical context. Its origins can be traced to the Second World War, when the foundations for a world economy were established. The shift to a globalized economy occurred alongside the development of the welfare state in Canada, the UK, the US, and the countries of western Europe. The formation of the global economy began toward the end of the Second World War at the United Nations Monetary and Financial Conference held in Bretton Woods, New Hampshire, in 1944 (Leys, 2001; Teeple, 2000). At the conference, the delegates established an international trading regime and the foundation of an international monetary system to enable the development of global trade, with a view also to avoid global depressions like the Great Depression of the 1930s.

The focus of Bretton Woods was the formation of a global economy. The principal components of a framework for a supranational regime of capital accumulation and trade liberalization were formed (Teeple, 2000). These components comprised the principles of liberal democracy that were entrenched in the United Nations, the Marshall Plan for reconstruction, the International Monetary Fund (IMF), the World Bank, and the General Agreement on Tariffs and Trade to control and liberalize trade around the world. All of these dimensions for a postwar world order were achieved and were up and running by the end of the 1960s.

Observers describe the Bretton Woods conference as a US-led process that culminated in the formation of political and economic structures and policies under the control of the US (Teeple, 2000). The US was seen as the logical world leader at the end of the war. It had not suffered the devastation European powers endured during the war. The US therefore emerged as the only power that could assume a dominant role in global politics and economics. Indeed, Teeple (2000) describes the US as the "pre-eminent capitalist power at the end of the war" (Teeple, 2000, p. 53) and it was therefore well placed to restructure and redefine the postwar world economy in its interests. In addition, of all the countries, the US had the largest economy and was eager to identify new markets for trade and investment. Thus, the delegates established an exchange-rate mechanism by setting equivalences of national currencies to be compared with the US dollar.

From this process, the IMF and the World Bank emerged. Among its purposes, the IMF was established to regulate international trade balances and promote international monetary co-operation, exchange stability, and orderly exchange arrangements; to foster economic growth and high levels of employment; and to provide temporary financial assistance to countries to help ease the balance of payment adjustments (Articles of Agreement of the International Monetary Fund, adopted at the United Nations Monetary and Financial Conference, Bretton Woods, New Hampshire, July 22, 1944). The purpose of the World Bank was to provide and manage an international fund for economic development.

The General Agreement on Tariffs and Trade (GATT) was formulated in 1947. It was to serve as the institutional means for a negotiated removal of all national barriers to world trade and to develop universal regulations to enable freer commerce (Leys, 2001; Teeple, 2000). At this time, the United Nations was also created as a supranational, quasi-government and political foundation for the new internationalism. The UN assumed responsibility for peacekeeping operations. It has also been characterized as a vehicle to control the expansion of socialism in Korea, the Congo, Greece, and Indonesia; propagate the principles of liberal democracy and the rights of private property as a political system supporting and consistent with the promotion of capitalism; and develop international laws based on private rights for the "world community" (Teeple, 2000).

Teeple and others argue that the intention of the US was to establish the framework for a single world economy of competing capitals (Leys, 2001; Teeple, 2000). Before the war, capital was essentially national in character and corporate interests were national interests, protected at home and abroad by means of armed forces, tariff barriers, currency controls, and nationalism and citizenship, and with other national laws and policies. The Bretton Woods agreement facilitated the expansion of global trade. Ultimately, the GATT provided an institutional vehicle for a negotiated lifting of all national barriers to world trade. It also paved the way for the development of global regulations for freer trade.

Indeed, the creation of the welfare state occurred in tandem with the new era of global capitalism. The welfare state was intended to ameliorate the effects of the market economy, such as unemployment, by providing income and other support programs during periods of unemployment. The aim was unimpeded capital accumulation and mobility. The welfare state appeased the working class while still enabling the capitalist economy to function. All was well until the oil crisis of 1973.

National governments become unable to initiate certain economic and social strategies because they were forced to adopt policies consistent with trade treaty requirements. These policy directions may weaken the welfare state. Cerny (1993) notes:

> The interaction of changing financial market structures on the one hand and states on the other has done more than production, trade or international cooperative regimes to undermine the structures of the Keynesian welfare state and to impose the norms of the competition state. (pp 79–80) (see Box 11.3)

In other words, governmental programs associated with the welfare state become incompatible with the requirements of the global market economy. These changes, as one can imagine, may have profound implications for democratic processes. Some critics predict the demise of the nation-state, since the requirements of economic globalization have impeded the capacity of national governments to set domestic policy.

Box 11.3: NHS Privatization: A Step Too Far

Private-sector incursion into the NHS is not new: previous Labour governments used private–public partnerships to fund the building of NHS infrastructure. But now the momentum for privatisation is increasing to an unsustainable level. Last year the Financial Times reported that government tenders worth about £5 billion were available to provide many NHS services. Current tenders include catering or provision of health care in prisons; however, a recent tender proposal by four general practitioner clinical commissioning groups (CCGs) in Staffordshire and Stoke would see external contractors manage entire clinical cancer-care pathways for patients with bladder, lung, prostate, and breast cancer. Including end-of-life care, the contract is valued at £1.2 billion. The proposed removal of an entire care pathway to the private sector is a concerning development, partly because it suggests further dismantling of the NHS, and partly because it is indicative of how little thought has gone into the consequences.

There are several issues with the Staffordshire and Stoke proposal. How can an entire pathway be excised wholesale from the rest of health care? Cancer diagnoses and treatment often rely on several departments and use of costly technologies. Presumably, the contractor will not be expected to run departments peripherally involved in cancer care, or to invest in all of the attendant technologies, and, since the tender is only for 10 years, there would be little financial incentive to do so. Thus, the contractor will most likely rely on existing NHS resources, creating a supply and demand problem for access between public and private use. Where will the specialists employed by the contractors come from? Again, it is probable that the contractor will source them from within the existing NHS structure. These measures will erode the NHS, leading to a failure to invest in staffing and long-term infrastructure—as seen in other sectors that have undergone partial privatisation. This scenario will become particularly acute over successive tenders, and especially damaging if winning bids are chosen predominantly on financial grounds, or if a contractor fails and the government has to step in to handle the costly repercussions.

Source: Crawford, S.M. (2014). NHS privatization: A step too far. *The Lancet Oncology, 15*(9), 905.

As noted elsewhere in this volume, the nation-state was essential to the creation of the welfare state in developed Western political economies. It set national standards to ensure equal access to and quality of services for all citizens, regardless of where they lived. This was the basis of the welfare state. Such services were provided on the basis of need, not income or ability to pay. The welfare state was intended to protect workers from the negative effects of market forces. Its creation signified the recognition that the market could not deliver necessary goods such as health care or income support.

The requirements of the global economy for free market conditions and lack of governmental "interference" seem to clash with the collectivist orientation of the welfare state. As noted above, one of the critical tasks of national governments was to mitigate the adverse effects of the market through social provision via the welfare state (Leys, 2001; Banting & Myles, 2013; Cerny, 2014). But these governmental processes have become increasingly market-driven in response to global pressures for deregulation, freer trade, and capital mobility. Indeed, Cerny (2014) argues that the state's welfare responsibilities have been "reduced politically and socially ... to propping up the international competitiveness of domestic economic activities within a more open world" (p. 361).

National governments, however, have not been deemed totally obsolete. Rather, the process of economic globalization constrains and redefines the powers of national governments to further the process of commodification (Cerny, 2014; Leys, 2001). Commodification refers to the transformation of relationships, formerly untainted by commerce, into commercial relationships of exchange, of buying and selling. The process has also facilitated the growth and mobility of international capital such that national economies become open to foreign investment. Economic globalization effectively comes to increase the power of transnational corporations.

Much research shows that liberal welfare states such as Canada, the United States, and the United Kingdom are especially susceptible to globalization and its imperatives (Banting & Myles, 2013). Studies on the impact of political factors on welfare spending between 1962 and 2000 found that left-party government effects on the welfare state diminish under intense globalization when labour power diminishes (Cao, Prakash, & Ward, 2007; Navarro, 2004). In contrast, in jurisdictions with strong and stable labour power, left political parties seem better able to mediate the negative effects of economic globalization (Swank, 2002). The rapid growth of capital markets was found to be strongly related to welfare retrenchment in liberal welfare states.

ECONOMIC GLOBALIZATION AND NEOLIBERALISM

Neoliberalism has become an influential, if not the dominant, political ideology that both justifies and drives economic globalization. As an ideology, it is committed to the market economy as the best allocator of resources and wealth in a society (Coburn, 2000). It perceives individuals as motivated chiefly by material and economic considerations, and competition as the primary market instrument for innovations.

Broadly speaking, neoliberalism seeks to transfer control of the economy from the public to the private sector. This has tremendous policy implications. Williamson (1990) has created a short list of policy implications under neoliberalism:

- trade liberalization—that is, liberalization of imports, with particular emphasis on the elimination of quantitative restrictions (licensing, etc.), and any trade protection to be provided by tariffs
- liberalization of inward foreign direct investment
- privatization of state enterprises

- deregulation—abolition of regulations that impede market entry or restrict competition, except for those justified on safety, environmental, and consumer protection grounds, and prudent oversight of financial institutions
- redirection of public spending away from subsidies
- tax reform—broadening the tax base and adopting moderate marginal tax rates
- interest rates that are market-determined

Economic globalization therefore requires that politics and policy-making be market driven (Labonte & Schrecker, 2007a, 2007b, 2007c; Leys, 2001; Teeple, 2000). Neoliberalism justifies the marketization of politics and public policy decisions. It also effectively justifies the marketization of everyday life. As Coburn (2000) argues: "The essence of neoliberalism, in its pure form, is a more or less thoroughgoing adherence, in rhetoric if not in practice, to the virtues of a market economy, and, by extension, a market-oriented society" (p. 138).

The impact of economic globalization and neoliberal policies on health care organization and delivery and on health-related public policy has been gradual but consistent. In the late 1960s and into the early 1970s, world trade grew at an unprecedented rate, as evidenced by an over 800 percent increase in commodity exchange (Cypher, 1979). The world market in commodities surpassed national markets, thereby enabling global commodity production. Between 1950 and 1975, foreign direct investment by the United States alone increased substantially, and the returns from abroad grew from 7 percent to more than 25 percent over the same period (Cypher, 1979). As a result of this economic activity, multinational corporations gradually became the primary forces in economic relations between nations (Teeple, 2000), yet there was still interest in human development issues, as evidenced by both the creation and the general maintenance of the welfare state in most advanced economies in the postwar era.

The 1980s changed that. Teeple (2000) identifies the 1980s as the critical decade during which the welfare state began to decline. This decline coincided with the rise of the global economy and the adoption of neoliberal policies in countries around the world. For Teeple, the principle behind these policies is unrestricted economic power of private property and capital accumulation. These policies harmonize national capitals, accumulated national wealth, and nation-states in order to build a global system of internationalized capital and "supranational" institutions. They provide a solid foundation for market forces to play out and, conversely, reduce the role the state plays in regulating the market economy. These policies may come to influence the organization and delivery of health care services in Canada.

GLOBALIZATION AND CANADIAN HEALTH POLICY

Specific policy areas within the jurisdiction of national governments, such as health care, are particularly vulnerable to global forces. The modern form of the global economy that began after the end of the Second World War saw its resurgence during the 1970s and has some formidable strengths: (1) a wide selection of locations for capital investment; (2) the weight and ubiquity of global financial markets; and (3) the importance to national economies and societal functioning of transnational manufacturing and service corporations.

In his case study on the impact of market forces on British politics and society, Leys (2001) argues that "capital mobility has not just removed the 'Keynesian capacity' of national governments—their ability to influence the general level of demand. It has made all policy-making sensitive to 'market sentiment' and the regulatory demands of TNCs [transnational corporations]" (p. 2).

The Impact of Globalization on Health Care

Leys's (2001) groundbreaking case study on the impact of economic globalization on politics and government policy in the UK can provide insights into the potential transformation of medicare in Canada. In his study, Leys describes the increasing privatization of the National Health Service (NHS).

Background

The NHS was the sole provider of medication, equipment, and other medical supplies in the UK. It negotiated prices with suppliers. Most Britons received good-quality care at NHS hospitals and, as a result, the NHS was an extremely popular social program. Yet, with demographic changes, medical advances, and other developments, the NHS required constant budget increases—so much so that by late 1970s, the NHS represented 11 percent of total government expenditures, and these costs seemed destined to rise. During the 1980s, Prime Minister Margaret Thatcher saw the NHS as a drain on the economy, and she sought to privatize many of its components. The results were disheartening (see Box 11.3).

Armstrong and Armstrong have documented similar changes occurring in Canadian hospitals (Armstrong & Armstrong, 2003, 2010; Armstrong et al., 2002). For example, many hospitals have contracted out ancillary hospital services, such as cleaning and food services. They have also reduced the number of nurses on wards. All of these changes can have serious implications for quality of patient care. In particular, increased privatization increases the burden of care on individual households as a result of the failure of hospitals and other health care facilities to provide essential care. The changes that occurred in Ontario in the mid-1990s provide good examples of this.

In a development similar to what happened in the UK during the Thatcher years, Premier Mike Harris's Conservative provincial government (elected in 1995) embarked on an extensive program to reduce public spending in several public policy areas in health, finance, social services, and other ministries. While the Conservatives' attempts to introduce significant private sector involvement in mainline delivery of professional health care services were resisted and eventually dropped for fear of electoral reprisal from voters, the government centralized control of the health budget and privatized some ancillary health care services in the province (Bryant, 2003). The Conservative government established community care access centres and required all home care service providers to compete for service contracts. For the first time in history, long-time community health care providers such as the Victorian Order of Nurses saw themselves competing with for-profit agencies for service contracts.In recent years, the shift to privatization has been somewhat insidious. For example, provincial and territorial governments cover most public healthcare costs. The federal and subnational (i.e., provincial and territorial) governments seek measures to reduce health spending. Indeed, some provincial and territorial governments tend to ignore private clinics that develop in their jurisdictions (Walkom, 2011). Under the terms of the *Canada Health Act*, private clinics cannot receive any public funds. In terms of quality of care, these market-oriented reforms can result in reduced access to long-term care for populations with low income who are therefore unable to pay for care. By taking the responsibility away from state-provided hospital support mechanisms, it shifts the burden to ill-equipped and ill-prepared family members (see Box 11.4).

GLOBALIZATION AND HEALTH EQUITY

Privatizing health care services can reduce access for vulnerable populations. Research has shown that user fees and other market-based strategies tend to mean that people with low income may do without care (Evans, 1997; Rachlis, 2004; Canadian Doctors for Medicare, 2011).

In addition, health-related public policies that draw upon neoliberal concepts can also contribute to increased social and health inequalities (Coburn, 2000, 2001, 2004; Raphael et al., 2001; Bryant, Raphael, Schrecker, & Labonte, 2011). A substantial research literature now documents exactly how governmental responses to economic globalization have been influencing the social determinants of health, leading to both increased social inequalities and increased inequalities in health outcomes (Broadbent Institute, 2014; Raphael & Bryant, 2006a; Raphael, 2008). This has especially been the case in nations with liberal political economies, such as Canada and the United States (Raphael & Bryant, 2006b; Raphael & Bryant, 2015).

Box 11.4: Gender and Globalization

Much of the globalization literature focuses on the impact on developing and developed nations, but fails to consider globalization's toll on women (Labonte & Schrecker, 2007c). Women, who tend to be the caretakers of both the old and the young of the family, are often consigned to labour that is low paying and without health benefits. Women's health is jeopardized as a result of working in environments with poor conditions and low pay. Women in developing countries, which experience high levels of absolute and relative poverty, are particularly vulnerable to such conditions (Alarcon-Gonzalez & McKinley, 1999; Sparr, 2000).

Trade Liberalization, Economic Growth, and Poverty Reduction

Some proponents of globalization claim that economic globalization is not necessarily bad for population health. World Bank studies suggest that economies of "globalizers" expand faster than those of "non-globalizers." (The so-called high "globalizers"—China, India, Malaysia, Thailand, and

Vietnam—were defined as nations whose trade-to-GDP ratio had increased since 1977; "non-globalizers"—primarily countries in Africa and Latin America—were those whose ratios declined.) The studies linked globalization with trade liberalization. The World Bank associated this growth with increased resources for delivering health services and access to other social determinants, as evidenced by the reduction of extreme poverty. This argument, however, is somewhat flawed. As Labonte and Schrecker (2007b) note, the World Bank studies measured change and not absolute levels of globalization or trade. Moreover, the nations identified as "globalizers" were less global than those nations considered "non-globalizers." Labonte and Schrecker add that the economic difficulties of non-globalizers can be partly linked to global issues beyond the control of national economic policy decision makers (see Box 11.5).

Box 11.5: Absolute and Relative Poverty

Absolute poverty is defined as living without the most basic resources for survival such as food, shelter, and clothing. Starvation is the basic measure in this definition. For families living in absolute poverty, the sole daily preoccupation is the struggle to find enough food and water to survive another day. The tendency has been to maintain that absolute poverty is exceedingly rare in a country like Canada. Yet, the number of people living on the streets is growing and while it is known that people are dying from starvation and inadequate shelter, especially during Canadian winters, the number of these casualties remains unknown.

Relative poverty is defined as families and individuals whose income and other resource levels are scant in comparison to the majority of people in Canadian society. The number of people living in relative poverty fluctuates with economic conditions. The measure of relative poverty is the number of people living below a certain percentage of the average income level of the rest of the country. This arbitrary measure can mask the real circumstances in which many "poor" people are living because income is not an accurate indicator of quality of life. While low income may not result in starvation, it can negatively affect development and future opportunities, barring impoverished people from full participation in society.

Source: Ryerse, C. (1990). *Thursday's child. Child poverty in Canada: A review of the effects of poverty on children* (p. 3). Ottawa: National Youth in Care Network.

Labonte and Schrecker (2007c) argue that while reducing absolute poverty is an admirable goal, several issues must be considered before concluding that globalization leads to poverty reduction. To the extent that globalization is related to growth, it seems to enhance population health *only if* growth reliably reduces poverty without triggering other negative outcomes (Deaton, 2004; Labonte & Schrecker, 2007c). In the real world, the presumed relationship between globalization and poverty reduction is weak, with more evidence showing that growth without equitable distribution is generally ineffective in reducing poverty (Woodward & Simms, 2006). This is because the increases in national wealth associated with globalizing may not be distributed equitably among the population. This has clearly been the case in Canada, where the economic growth over the past two decades—supposed outcomes of increased trade associated with NAFTA—has primarily accrued to the most well-off (Statistics Canada, 2004).

Conversely, trade liberalization has been shown to weaken many people's economic circumstances (Labonte & Schrecker, 2007c). In a nutshell, globalization has been found to benefit the wealthy while failing to assist the poor. A wide range of measures shows inequality between regions, and ratios and comparisons of incomes of rich and poor groups in nations consistently show that inequality continues to increase (Sutcliffe, 2004; Organisation for Economic Co-operation and Development, 2014). It may very well be that the gap between the rich and the poor in Canada will continue to increase as well, unless Canadian governments initiate efforts to protect the population from the negative effects of economic globalization.

LABOUR MARKETS AND GLOBAL RESTRUCTURING OF PRODUCTION

Labour markets and global restructuring constitute another way in which economic globalization may influence the social determinants of health (Labonte & Schrecker, 2007c). An important aspect of economic globalization is the restructuring of production and service provision across numerous national borders by transnational corporations (Dicken, 2003; Millen & Holtz, 2000; Millen, Lyon, & Irwin, 2000).

Research on globalization and markets identifies several trends that appear to be related. For example, the most important trend with respect to health care and health equity is this: competition for foreign direct investment and outsourced production leads governments to lean favourably toward private corporations. These corporations then attempt to influence public policy to favour business interests. Policy changes that favour business include lowering labour practice standards, reducing health and safety regulations, and weakening policies that redistribute income and wealth (Cornia, 2005). Cerny (1993) argues that globalization forces the convergence of national social and economic policies toward the ideal of the competition state, directed to the "promotion of economic activities, whether at home or abroad, which will make firms and sectors located within the territory of the competitive in international markets" (p. 136). Because these changes are economically driven—that is, for the benefit of businesses, not necessarily people's health— they can, in effect, increase health inequities.

The related restructuring of labour markets affects men and women in different ways (Elson, 2002; Elson & Cagatay, 2000; Petchesky, 2003). In addition to increasing the insecurity of work for both men and women, restructured work can have particularly negative health effects for women. For example, work in the garment industry (where women are the majority of workers) can be dangerous. Poor working conditions and long work hours are acceptable due to the lack of alternatives for many women in developing countries with few economic opportunities. Similarly, changes in working conditions in the health care sector can affect women who constitute the majority of health workers (Armstrong, 2006; Armstrong & Armstrong, 2002, 2010; Armstrong et al., 2002). In conclusion, globalization may lead to new economic opportunities, but these opportunities may be available only at "the price of exposure to hazardous working conditions" (Labonte & Schrecker, 2007c, p. 11).

Debt Crises: The Market under Pressure

Via the International Monetary Fund (IMF), the World Bank has lent funds to many developing nations. These loans have helped countries to restructure their economies with a view to enabling them to pay external creditors (Labonte & Schrecker, 2007c). With these loans, Labonte and Schrecker (2007c) argue that the World Bank and the IMF "promoted multiple, more or less coordinated domestic policies of integrating national economies into the global marketplace" (p. 14). Debt crises, however, have severely limited the capacity of developing countries to address basic needs in public health, education, water, sanitation, and nutrition.

Studies on the health impacts of debt crises are unable to isolate the effects of structural adjustment (namely, debt) from the effects of globalization-related economic difficulties (Labonte & Schrecker, 2007c). In over 76 studies, the Commission on Macroeconomics and Health noted predominantly negative effects, particularly in Africa. However, this commission de-emphasized the case against structural adjustment (or debt), which was attributable to incomplete sampling of the literature. Labonte and Schrecker argue that the authors of this commission carried out a limited review of country cases, and excluded ethnographic studies and country-level participatory evaluations that can explicate the negative impact of adjustment policies (or debt) on population health. They thus conclude that debt affects social determinants "both directly and indirectly" (p. 15). For example, reductions in food subsidies, government wages, and employment have direct negative effects on access to nutrition and household income. Labonte and Schrecker further suggest that the major impacts on social structure are related to poverty, income inequality, and changing gender relations, such as the unequal impact on women's incomes and their household responsibilities. Poverty and economic insecurity have significant impacts on exposure and vulnerability offset by housing and working conditions, among other considerations. Health systems were also affected via decreased health spending and the use of cost-recovery measures.

Summary: Globalization and the Social Determinants of Health

All of these issues linked to neoliberalism can adversely affect the social determinants of health—namely, employment and access to nutritious food, education, and housing (Labonte & Schrecker, 2007c). They can also impede access to health services. This means that the working poor and unemployed may lack the financial resources to pay for care.

GLOBALIZATION, TRADE AGREEMENTS, AND THE CANADIAN HEALTH CARE SYSTEM

In Canada, the federal government has tried to protect health care from the free market. Successive Canadian federal governments have promised to protect health care in trade treaty negotiations and have assured that the health care system cannot be touched by free trade treaties, in particular NAFTA and the

General Agreement on Trade in Services (Grieshaber-Otto & Sinclair, 2004). In virtually all recent trade negotiations, Canada has tried to ensure its ability to preserve existing health measures and to enact new ones.

The 2001 Mazankowski Report on Health Care outlined a broad range of themes and recommendations to reform health care in Alberta. The Kirby Report, discussed in chapter 7, also stressed the need for co-operation among all stakeholders to reduce problems of maldistribution, undersupply, and jurisdictional competition (Mazankowski, 2001; Kirby, 2002). Both reports recommended market-based reforms. There is particular concern that these recommendations, if implemented, could lead to challenges relating to potential profit: health care presents a huge and tempting commercial opportunity for the private sector (Mazankowski, 2001; Kirby, 2002).

Concern about the lure of profit is indeed justified. Both Mazankowski and Kirby espouse market values and discipline as necessary to improve health care. Mazankowski advocated a larger role for private financing and for-profit delivery of health care. Kirby supported public financing and enlarging the medicare monopoly to include new services. He also called for incorporating market-based methods and a larger private sector role in health care delivery.

Current federal, provincial, and territorial government policies are contributing to the erosion of the public health care system through under-resourcing and increasing privatization of elements of the system (Grieshaber-Otto & Sinclair, 2004). Importantly, there is no going back: once an area is privatized, international trade treaties—to which governments are bound—can potentially lock in these market-based health care reforms (see Box 11.6).

NAFTA, GATS, AND THE CANADIAN HEALTH CARE SYSTEM

Canada participated in both NAFTA and the General Agreement on Trade in Services (GATS), although it may very well be that medicare, a cherished social program in Canada, might come to be incompatible with the terms of these treaties (Grieshaber-Otto & Sinclair, 2004). Like other nations, Canada declared its commitment to uphold the health care system, and reserved the right to implement new health care measures. NAFTA, however, contained a number of exemptions, exceptions, and reservations to allowing health care issues to fall outside trade treaty rules. Some of these procedures applied to all nations, and others only to Canada.

Box 11.6: The Impact of Expanding Private Sector Involvement in Health Care

1. Cutbacks in health insurance will be difficult and costly to reverse. Canada listed health insurance as one of its specific commitments in GATS. This means that the GATS National Treatment and Market Access rules will apply to this sector. Trying to bring delisted services back into the realm of publicly insured services could limit international service providers' commercial opportunities. They, in turn, could urge their own governments to launch trade challenges against Canada.
2. Delisting health care services from publicly insured services would impede efforts to regulate aspects of privately insured services within Canada (Grieshaber-Otto & Sinclair, 2004).

The scope of NAFTA was far-reaching. Its services and investment chapters covered all measures in all sectors, with the exception of those for which national governments negotiated specific exclusions or exemptions. GATS is equally broad, and pertains to all provisions by governments that can have an impact on services, including the ways in which these services are delivered. The only area outside of GATS regulation is that provided "in the exercise of governmental authority" (Grieshaber-Otto & Sinclair, 2004, p. 23). This means that those services provided within the jurisdiction of government could continue.

NAFTA had two reservations—that is, country-specific exceptions that shelter government policies in health care. Annex I was a general reservation against some of NAFTA's terms that allowed each of the three NAFTA countries (Canada, the US, and Mexico) to retain all nonconforming provincial, territorial, and state government programs and policies that were in place when NAFTA came into effect on January 1, 1994. The Annex I reservation was bound. This meant that existing public policy programs and policies could only be adjusted to make them more consistent with NAFTA provisions. If a program or policy is abolished, it cannot be later reinstated and remain outside NAFTA regulations. Understandably, a major concern about the protection provided by the Annex I reservation is that once it ceases, it cannot be reinstated.

Canada negotiated a second reservation in NAFTA. Annex II, also referred to as the NAFTA social services reservation, is unbound. It protects existing policies and programs that are not consistent with NAFTA and also allows the Canadian government to implement new policies and programs that are not

NAFTA consistent. These programs are protected if they are health related and established as a social service for a public purpose. According to Grieshaber-Otto and Sinclair (2004), these terms are somewhat ambiguous, and the US and Canadian governments have interpreted them differently. This lack of clarity contributes to uncertainty about the range of the Annex II reservation.

The concerns raised by these trade agreements are enough that the safeguards did not fully protect the Canadian health care system (Grieshaber-Otto & Sinclair, 2004). NAFTA's very broad provisions against "expropriation"— that is, usurping an established enterprise without compensation—cover all sectors, including health. Grieshaber-Otto and Sinclair suggest that even where safeguards protect health services, they may at the same time enhance the commercial element in financing or delivery.

Similarly, GATS does not apply to services provided by governments. It applies only if the services are provided as not-for-profit. One difficulty with this is that the Canadian health care system comprises both public and private financing and delivery. This means that the governmental authority exclusion may not provide sufficient protection of the Canadian health care system from GATS rules that "do not fully exclude the Canadian health care system" (Grieshaber-Otto & Sinclair, 2004, p. 25). Of particular concern is that trade treaties have the potential to lock in privatization and proposed market-oriented strategies to reform medicare.

The Comprehensive Economic and Trade Agreement and the Trans-Pacific Partnership

As stated in earlier chapters, the federal government is negotiating the Canada-European Union Comprehensive Economic and Trade Agreement (CETA) as of 2013 and the Trans-Pacific Partnership agreement. The primary objective of international trade agreements, including CETA and TPP, is to liberalize trade by reducing trade barriers between countries (McBane, 2014). They can also limit how governments and societies regulate themselves democratically. Both agreements—still to be ratified—have implications for health.

With respect to CETA, the Canadian government agreed to the European Union demand to discontinue the general reservation in NAFTA Annex I, which provided a modicum of protection for health services (McBane, 2014). As a result of this concession, provincial and territorial governments will need to negotiate exemptions for specific non-conforming measures in the health care sector or rely on the Annex II reservation in NAFTA. Annex II provides a limited and qualified reservation that protects a health service only if it is identified as "a social service established or maintained for a public purpose" (McBane, 2014). CETA has not yet been ratified.

The TPP presents other challenges to the Canadian health care system, particularly prescription medications. Many critics consider it a harmful agreement that will increase drug costs and undermine access to medicines, particularly in poorer nations (Sinclair, 2015; Schram, Labonte, & Khatter, 2014). Of greater concern to Canada, it will bind Canada to a regulatory system that would entrench high drug costs.

Box 11.7: Pacific Trade Deal Not Quite What it Seems
By Thomas Walkom, National Affairs

The Trans-Pacific Partnership is essentially a reworked NAFTA plus Japan, with a couple of low-wage countries thrown in. The Trans-Pacific Partnership deal is both more and less than it seems. It is less in that Canada already has trade and investment deals with four of the 12 nations that make up the TPP—including the all-important United States.

Of the remaining seven, only Japan is a major economic player. The fact that Canadian goods will eventually be able to enter that country duty-free is significant. The fact that Brunei, New Zealand, Vietnam, Malaysia, Australia and Singapore are also opening their doors to Canadian exports is less so.

When Prime Minister Stephen Harper boasts that Canada is now part of a trade zone with a combined gross domestic product of $28.5 trillion, he neglects to mention that roughly $20 trillion of that is accounted for by countries with which Ottawa already has deals.

But the TPP is also more than it seems.

First, it is not just a trade pact. Ottawa boasts that because of the new deal, Canadian two-by-four lumber will enter Japan duty-free. That seems to be true (although the real barrier to Japan importing Canadian lumber is not the tariff; it is the fact that the Japanese don't use two-by-fours in house construction). But modern trade pacts are about far more than trade. They invariably include clauses designed to protect foreign investors from government regulations that might interfere with profit-making.

The North American Free Trade Agreement between Canada, the U.S. and Mexico was a trail blazer in this regard. U.S. firms successfully used the so-called investor-state dispute settlement clauses of that pact to overturn Canadian laws and regulations, including those designed to protect public health.

In 1997, for instance, the federal government was stymied in its efforts to ban the use of toxic MMT in gasoline after the additive's U.S. manufacturer challenged Ottawa before a NAFTA panel. Does the Trans-Pacific Partnership expand these corporate rights? Does it constrain them? Since the text of the agreement is secret, it's hard to answer these questions.

The Canadian government says only that the new pact will establish "strong rules" to treat foreign investors "in a fair, equitable and non-discriminatory manner."

The U.S. government goes farther. It says the entire NAFTA dispute settlement process will be "upgraded" to make it more difficult for corporations to make frivolous claims.

In particular, according to the office of the U.S. trade representative, the TPP will not allow dispute settlement panels to overturn laws. Instead they will be limited to issuing what are, in effect, stiff fines.

In some situations, according to U.S. documents, public-interest groups will be permitted to argue before dispute settlement panels. The hearings, which under NAFTA are held in camera, will be open to the public.

Interestingly, the TPP—unlike NAFTA—will allow governments that fail to live up to environmental or labour standards to be challenged before dispute settlement panels.

We do know from U.S. press accounts that the pact specifically exempts anti-smoking laws from corporate challenge. What we don't know is whether other government health and safety regulations are up for grabs.

Ottawa says the TPP does not remove the right of governments to "legislate and regulate in the public interest." That's what was said about NAFTA originally. But those claims proved to be false. With the TPP, as with NAFTA, all will depend on how the final text is worded and how the dispute settlement panels interpret this wording. In the end, the new Trans-Pacific deal is essentially a renegotiated NAFTA with Japan and a couple of cheap-labour countries (Vietnam, Malaysia) thrown in. We know it will hurt workers in Canada's auto industry. That's one reason why Tom Mulcair's New Democrats have belatedly criticized it. It's also why the Conservative government is promising $1 billion in subsidies to auto firms over the next decade.

We also know that it will hurt, but not cripple, dairy and poultry farmers, which is why the Conservatives are offering them $4.3 billion in compensation. But we won't know much else about this deal until its secret details become public—well after the Oct. 19 election.

Source: Walkom, T. (2015, October 7). Pacific trade deal not quite what it seems. *Toronto Star*. Retrieved from www.thestar.com.

TRADE AGREEMENTS AND PUBLIC-PRIVATE PARTNERSHIPS

Many argue that protecting the health care system can be ensured only by a traditional approach, where governments purchase and pay directly for the services (Grieshaber-Otto & Sinclair, 2004). This is the "single-payer" model, which is the current Canadian model, albeit with some private finance and delivery.

In contrast to this traditional and established Canadian model, public-private partnerships (P3s) are a particular form of health care commercialization. Some consider P3s to be particularly risky, since they cover a substantial range of health care services (National Union of Public and General Employees, 2006). A particular concern is that P3s have a strong potential to enable foreign corporations to use trade policy rules to misrepresent key aspects of Canadian health care policy (Grieshaber-Otto & Sinclair, 2004). Further, trade treaty rules tend to favour the rights of the foreign investor, which requires host governments to financially compensate.

THE EFFECTS OF GLOBALIZATION: IMPACT ON THE LABOUR MARKET

Since NAFTA came into being, Canada has lost numerous jobs in the manufacturing sector, and now 25 percent of the jobs in the Canadian labour market are low-paying (Innocenti Research Centre, 2005; Tal, 2015). This is one of the highest percentages of low-paying jobs among advanced economies. Such changes have contributed to a widening gap between high-income groups and low-income groups; these changes have effectively increased health inequalities (Yalnizyan, 1998, 2007; Coburn, 2001). Other countries involved in agreements, particularly the United States and the United Kingdom, have similarly experienced a growth in inequalities in income distribution and health outcomes.

At one time, Sweden and other countries with a social democratic tradition seemed to be less vulnerable to the negative effects of globalization. This appeared to be the case because these countries had a collectivist orientation to public policy development (Swank, 2002, 2010). As a result, they had more developed welfare state apparatuses that could mediate the adverse effects of economic globalization. All of these countries have a social democratic tradition that seemed to provide resistance to neoliberal market-driven policies. This and other evidence on social spending suggests that some political traditions appear to be more susceptible to the negative effects of globalization (Banting & Myles, 2013).

Box 11.8: Proposed MRI Project Renews Privatization Debate
By Angela Hall
Leader Post

No ground has been broken for the proposed project, no pricey equipment is in place, and no stamps of government approval have been made.

But even before details are clear about the latest proposal to put the first privately-owned magnetic resonance imaging (MRI) machine in Saskatchewan, it has renewed general debate about the private sector's role in the province's health-care system.

The recently elected Saskatchewan Party government says the idea of private facilities delivering some publicly funded health services isn't new, but any proposals to expand what's currently done would need to be closely examined.

"I think the debate is 'Do we want to pragmatically look at ways that can reduce wait times for diagnostics?'" Premier Brad Wall said to reporters this week.

"That might include (the provincial government) not owning every single MRI. Right now they don't in terms of X-ray technology, in terms of other diagnostics, the government doesn't have to own it all."

However, the premier said offering medical services such as an MRI for a fee "seems to be outside the *Canada Health Act*," and is [an] area where the government doesn't want to tread.

Wall said he will look at what proposal comes forward from Kawactoose First Nation, which this week along with Siemens Canada announced plans for a health centre in east Regina that would include MRI services. Officials at a news conference Monday said patients would not be able to jump to the front of the queue by paying out-of-pocket, but rather that the proposed centre would work with the existing system.

However, the provincial NDP says that even if the province pays for MRI scans that take place in a facility it doesn't own in the same way it does for those in a public hospital, there are questions about the effectiveness of such a system.

Health critic Judy Junor said private facilities could hurt publicly funded hospitals by luring away trained health professionals, citing that as one problem in Ontario before private MRI clinics were ultimately purchased back into the public fold.

"You can buy the machine, that's the easy part. It's whose [sic] going to work it on a day to day basis," Junor said.

Meanwhile, University of Saskatchewan health economist Allen Backman doubts that a private MRI service could stay afloat without offering both insured and non-insured services.

"What it means is that they would take public patients paid for by the government ... but they would also have to take private patients who pay in order to get in ahead of [the] line or who pay for services that aren't ordinarily funded by government insurance, things like preventative full body scans," Backman said.

Such a move in Saskatchewan would "really mean a new direction in health care," he said.

A few provinces have already headed in the direction of offering MRIs for a fee. In Alberta, patients have long had the option of purchasing such a scan outside of the public system at one of six private clinics, according to Alberta Health. A Vancouver-based company, meanwhile, refers patients willing to pay for certain services, including MRIs, to private facilities that can do the job fast.

Clients from Saskatchewan that contact the company seeking MRIs typically end up in Alberta for the scan, said Richard Baker, the businessman who founded Timely Medical Alternatives.

The last time a Saskatchewan group proposed a private MRI machine was in 2004 when Muskeg Lake First Nation said it wanted to own and operate an MRI unit on its Saskatoon reserve—either through an agreement with the then-NDP government or possibly by charging patients. Plans for a wellness and diabetes centre there were announced last year but without an MRI component. Muskeg Lake officials this week declined comment.

Source: Hall, A. (2008, February 15). Proposed MRI project renews privatization debate. *Leader Post,* p. A3.

Recent data show, however, that social democratic countries are becoming more susceptible to the pressures of economic globalization. Figure 9.1 shows how the different welfare regimes are converging on these selected health and social indicators. Could it be that even social democratic welfare states are becoming less redistributive? If so, what are the implications for the health and social well-being of populations? These findings do not negate the capacity of the political system to protect its citizens from the negative effects of globalization if the political system intrinsically values the social safety net. Some researchers found that democratic countries with developed welfare states experienced lower poverty rates and better health in general (Alesina & Glaeser, 2004; Navarro & Shi, 2002).

CONCLUSIONS

Economic globalization and neoliberalism are prominent forces that have effectively changed the role of governments in advanced Western economies. As a result, they have restructured society. Economic globalization, associated with the ongoing expansion of the market economy, has been linked to a decline in the depth and quality of the welfare state (Leys, 2001; Banting & Myles, 2013; Schrecker & Bambra, 2015).

Indeed, the rise of neoliberalism and economic globalization has led to concerns about the maintenance of a public health care system and health-related policies that promote health and health equity. The CETA and TPP agreements raise further concerns about the impact on the health care system and the achievement of health equity in Canada.

CRITICAL THINKING QUESTIONS

1. What is economic globalization? What does it mean for the social determinants of health and health policy?
2. How can national governments, such as the Canadian federal government, resist global pressures?
3. What role can citizens play in challenging neoliberal policies?
4. What are the supposed benefits of free trade agreements for Canadians? What are some of the threats to the health care system and the health of Canadians inherent within these treaties?
5. What are some of the reasons governments agree to these trade agreements?

FURTHER READINGS

Grieshaber-Otto, J., & Sinclair, S. (2004). *Bad medicine: Trade treaties, privatization, and health care reform in Canada*. Ottawa: Canadian Centre for Policy Alternatives.

Jim Grieshaber-Otto and Scott Sinclair examine a recurring theme in Canada's health care debate: the role of private financing and for-profit delivery of health care. They explore Canada's international trade-treaty obligations

and how these interact with this important issue. Available online at www.
policyalternatives.ca.

Labonte, R., & Schrecker, T. (2007). Globalization and social determinants
of health: Introduction and methodological background (Part 1 of 3).
Globalization and Health, 3(5), 1–10.
Labonte, R., & Schrecker, T. (2007). Globalization and social determinants
of health: The role of the global marketplace (Part 2 of 3). *Globalization and
Health, 3*(6), 1–17.
Labonte, R., & Schrecker, T. (2007). Globalization and social determinants
of health: Promoting health equity in global governance (Part 3 of 3).
Globalization and Health, 3(7), 1–15.
    These three articles sketch out the implications of economic globalization
for the social determinants of health. By doing so, they bring to light the
processes by which larger economic forces shape the form that health and
health inequalities take in different nations.

Leys, C. (2001). *Market-driven politics.* London: Verso.
    Market-Driven Politics is an analysis of global economic forces and national
politics in two fields of public life that are both fundamentally important and
familiar to everyone—television broadcasting and health care. Public services
like these play an important role because they both affect the legitimacy of the
government and are targets for global capital.

Navarro, V. (Ed.). (2007). *Neo-liberalism, globalization, and inequalities:
Consequences for health and quality of life.* Amityville, NY: Baywood Press.
    This book assembles a series of articles that challenges neoliberal
ideology. Written by well-known scholars, these articles question each
of the tenets of neoliberal doctrine, showing how the policies guided by
this ideology have adversely affected human development in the countries
where they have been implemented.

Schrecker, T., and Bambra, C. (2015). *How politics makes us sick: Neoliberal
epidemics.* Houndsmill, UK: Palgrave Macmillan.
    Since the early 1980s, neoliberalism or "market fundamentalism" has
dominated politics and economics across the globe. The authors consider the
effects of over three decades of these policies, with particular reference to the
US and the UK. They focus on obesity, insecurity, austerity, and inequality,
arguing that each represents a "neoliberal epidemic"—neoliberal because they
are implicated in the rise of neoliberal politics.

RELEVANT WEBSITES

Globalization and Health
www.globalizationandhealth.com

The journal *Globalization and Health* publishes manuscripts that consider the positive and negative influences of globalization on health. *Globalization and Health* is affiliated with the London School of Economics.

Globalization and Health Equity
www.globalhealthequity.ca

The Globalization and Health Equity Research Unit is established within the Institute of Population Health at the University of Ottawa. The research group examines how contemporary globalization (post-1980) is affecting social determinants of health and the health status of different population groups within and among nations.

Globalization Knowledge Network
www.globalhealthequity.ca/projects/proj_WHO/index.shtml

The Globalization Knowledge Network examines how globalization's dynamics and processes affect health outcomes. These include trade liberalization, integration of the production of goods, consumption and lifestyle patterns, and household-level income. The uneven distribution of globalization's gains and losses and the impact it has on inequities will be analyzed to inform policies aimed at mitigating the actual and potential harmful effects of globalization on health.

Progressive Economics Forum (PEF), Globalization Section
www.progressive-economics.ca/category/globalization

The PEF aims to promote the development of a progressive economics community in Canada. The PEF brings together over 125 progressive economists working in universities, the labour movement, and activist research organizations. This site provides information about PEF, its research and education products, and ways to contribute to its growth and success through membership, meetings and conferences, and their annual student essay contest.

REFERENCES

Alarcon-Gonzalez, D., & McKinley, T. (1999). The adverse effects of structural adjustment on working women in Mexico. *Latin American Perspectives, 26*, 103–117.

Alesina, A., & Glaeser, E.L. (2004). *Fighting poverty in the US and Europe: A world of difference.* Toronto: Oxford University Press.

Armstrong, P. (2006). Gender, health, and care. In D. Raphael, T. Bryant, & M. Rioux (Eds.), *Staying alive: Critical perspectives on health, illness, and health care* (pp. 287–303). Toronto: Canadian Scholars' Press.

Armstrong, P., & Armstrong, H. (2002). *Thinking it through: Women, work, and caring in the new millennium.* Halifax: Canadian Institutes of Health Research (CIHR), Nova Scotia Advisory Council on the Status of Women, and Atlantic Centre of Excellence for Women's Health (ACEWH).

Armstrong, H., & Armstrong, P. (2003). *Wasting away: The undermining of Canadian health care.* Toronto: Oxford University Press.

Armstrong, H. & Armstrong, P. (2010). *Wasting away: The undermining of Canadian health care* (2nd ed.). Toronto: Oxford University Press.

Armstrong, P., Amaratunga, C., Bernier, J., Grant, K., Pederson, A., & Wilson, K. (2002). *Exposing privatization: Women and health care reform in Canada.* Toronto: Garamond.

Bakker, I. (1996). Introduction: The gendered foundations of restructuring in Canada. In I. Bakker (Ed.), *Rethinking restructuring: Gender and change in Canada* (pp. 3–25). Toronto: University of Toronto Press.

Banting, K., Hoberg, G., & Simeon, R. (1997a). Introduction. In K. Banting, G. Hoberg, & R. Simeon (Eds.), *Degrees of freedom: Canada and the United States in a changing world* (pp. 3–19). Montreal & Kingston: McGill-Queen's University Press.

Banting, K., Hoberg, G., & Simeon, R. (Eds.). (1997b). *Degrees of freedom: Canada and the United States in a changing world.* Montreal & Kingston: McGill-Queen's University Press.

Banting, K., & Myles, J. (2013). *Inequality and the fading of redistributive politics.* Vancouver: UBC Press.

Broadbent Institute. (2014). *Haves and have-nots: Deep and persistent wealth inequality in Canada.* Ottawa: Broadbent Institute.

Bryant, T. (2003). A critical examination of the hospital restructuring process in Ontario, Canada. *Health Policy, 64*, 193–205.

Bryant, T., Raphael, D., Schrecker, T., & Labonte, R. (2011). Canada: A land of missed opportunity for addressing the social determinants of health. *Health Policy, 101*, 44-58.

Canadian Doctors for Medicare. (2011). *Neat, plausible, and wrong: The myth of health care unsustainability.* Toronto: Canadian Doctors for Medicare.

Cao, X., Prakash, A., & Ward, M.J. (2007). Protecting jobs in the age of globalization: Examining the relative salience of social welfare and industrial subsidies in OECD countries. *International Studies Quarterly, 51*(2), 301–327.

Cerny, P. (1993). The deregulation and re-regulation of financial markets in a more open world. In P. Cerny (Ed.), *Finance and world politics: Markets, regimes, and state in the post-hegemonic era* (pp. 51–85). Aldershot: Edward Elgar.

Cerny, P. (2014). Globalization and the resilience of neoliberalism. *Critical Policy Studies, 8*(3), 359–362.

Coburn, D. (2000). Income inequality, social cohesion, and the health status of populations:

The role of neo-liberalism. *Social Science & Medicine, 51*(1), 135–146.

Coburn, D. (2001). Health, health care, and neo-liberalism. In P. Armstrong, H. Armstrong, & D. Coburn (Eds.), *Unhealthy times: The political economy of health and care in Canada* (pp. 45–65). Toronto: Oxford University Press.

Coburn, D. (2004). Beyond the income inequality hypothesis: Globalization, neo-liberalism, and health inequalities. *Social Science & Medicine, 58*, 41–56.

Cornia, G.A. (2005). *Policy reform and income distribution*, ST/ESA/2005/DWP/3. New York: United Nations Department of Economic and Social Affairs.

Cypher, J.M. (1979). The transnational challenge to the corporate state. *Journal of Economic Issues, 13*(2), 513–542.

Deaton, A. (2004). *Health in an age of globalization.* Washington: Brookings Institute.

Dicken, P. (2003). *Global shift: Reshaping the global economic map in the 21st century* (4th ed.). New York: Guilford Press.

Elson, D. (2002). Gender justice, human rights, and neo-liberal economic policies. In M. Molyneux & S. Razavi (Eds.), *Gender justice, development, and rights* (pp. 78–114). Oxford: Oxford University Press.

Elson, D., & Cagatay, N. (2000). The social content of macroeconomic policies. *World Development, 28*, 1347–1364.

Evans, R.G. (1997). Going for the gold: The redistributive agenda behind market-based health care reform. *Journal of Health Politics, Policy, and Law, 22*(2), 427–465.

Grieshaber-Otto, J., & Sinclair, S. (2004). *Bad medicine: Trade treaties, privatization, and health care reform in Canada.* Ottawa: Canadian Centre for Policy Alternatives.

Innocenti Research Centre. (2005). *Child poverty in rich nations, 2005. Report Card No. 6.* Florence: Innocenti Research Centre.

Jenkins, R. (2004). Globalization, production, employment, and poverty: Debates and evidence. *Journal of International Development, 16*, 1–12.

Kirby, M.J. (2002). *The health of Canadians: The federal role.* Ottawa: Standing Senate Committee on Social Affairs, Science, and Technology.

Labonte, R., & Schrecker, T. (2007a). Globalization and social determinants of health: Introduction and methodological background. Part 1 of 3. *Globalization and Health, 3*(5), 1–10.

Labonte, R., & Schrecker, T. (2007b). Globalization and social determinants of health: Promoting health equity in global governance. Part 3 of 3. *Globalization and Health, 3*(7), 1–15.

Labonte, R. & Schrecker, T. (2007c). Globalization and social determinants of health: The role of the global marketplace. Part 2 of 3. *Globalization and Health, 3*(6), 1–17.

Langille, D. (2004). The political determinants of health. In D. Raphael (Ed.), *Social determinants of health: Canadian perspectives* (pp. 283–296). Toronto: Canadian Scholars' Press.

Langille, D. (2008). Follow the money: How business and politics define our health. In D. Raphael (Ed.), *Social determinants of health: Canadian perspectives* (2nd ed.) (pp. 305–317). Toronto: Canadian Scholars' Press.

Leys, C. (2001). *Market-driven politics.* London: Verso.

Mazankowski, D. (2001). *A framework for reform: Report of the Premier's Advisory Council on Health.* Edmonton: Government of Alberta.

McBane, M. (2014, January 28). CETA threats to public health care in Canada. Remarks to the House of Commons Standing Committee on International Trade Study of the Canada-European Union Comprehensive Economic and Trade Agreement (CETA). Ottawa: Canadian Health Coalition. Retrieved from healthcoalition.ca.

Millen, J.V., & Holtz, T.H. (2000). Dying for growth, Part I: Transnational corporations and the health of the poor. In J.Y. Kim, J.V. Millen, A. Irwin, & J. Gershman (Eds.), *Dying for growth: Global inequality and the health of the poor* (pp. 177–223). Monroe, ME: Common Courage Press.

Millen, J.V., Lyon, E., & Irwin, A. (2000). Dying for growth, Part II: The political influence of national and transnational corporations. In J.Y. Kim, J.V. Millen, A. Irwin, & J. Gershman (Eds.), *Dying for growth: Global inequality and the health of the poor* (pp. 225–244). Monroe, ME: Common Courage Press.

National Union of Public and General Employees. (2006). *Public-private partnerships: What they are, why they're a bad idea.* Retrieved from www.nupge.ca.

Navarro, V. (Ed.). (2004). *The political and social contexts of health.* Amityville, NY: Baywood Press.

Navarro, V., & Shi, L. (2002). The political context of social inequalities and health. In V. Navarro (Ed.), *The political economy of social inequalities: Consequences for health and quality of life* (pp. 403–418). Amityville, NY: Baywood Press.

Organisation for Economic Co-operation and Development. (2014). *Society at a glance 2014: OECD social indicators—The crisis and its aftermath.* Paris: Organisation for Economic Co-operation and Development.

Organisation for Economic Co-operation and Development. (2015). *Health at a glance 2015: OECD health indicators.* Paris: Organisation for Economic Co-operation and Development.

Petchesky, R.P. (2003). *Global prescriptions: Gendering health and human rights.* London: Zed Books.

Rachlis, M. (2004). *Prescription for excellence: How innovation is saving Canada's health care system.* Toronto: HarperCollins.

Raphael, D. (2008). *Social determinants of health: Canadian perspectives* (2nd ed.). Toronto: Canadian Scholars' Press.

Raphael, D., & Bryant, T. (2006a). Maintaining population health in a period of welfare state decline: Political economy as the missing dimension in health promotion theory and practice. *Promotion and Education, 13,* 236–242.

Raphael, D., & Bryant, T. (2006b). The state role in promoting population health: Public health concerns in Canada, USA, UK, and Sweden. *Health Policy, 78,* 39–55.

Raphael, D., & Bryant, T. (2015). Power, intersectionality and the life course: Identifying the political and economic structures of welfare states that support or threaten health. *Social Theory and Health, 13*(3–4), 245–266.

Raphael, D., Renwick, R., Brown, I., Steinmetz, B., Sehdev, H., & Phillips, S. (2001). Making the links between community structure and individual well-being: Community quality of life in Riverdale, Toronto, Canada. *Health and Place, 7*(3), 17–34.

Schram, A., Labonte, R., & Khatter, K. (2014). The Trans-Pacific Partnership agreement and public health: Why we should be concerned. *Open Medicine, 8*(3), e100–e101.

Schrecker, T., & Bambra, C. (2015). *How politics makes us sick: Neoliberal epidemics.* Houndmills, UK: Palgrave Macmillan.

Sinclair, S. (2015, October 9). *The TPP and the cost of drugs.* Ottawa: Canadian Centre for Policy Alternatives. Retrieved from www.behindthenumbers.ca.

Sparr, P. (2000). *Mortgaging women's lives: Feminist critiques of structural adjustment.* London: Zed Books.

Statistics Canada. (2004). *Income of Canadian families: 2000 census.* Ottawa: Statistics Canada.

Sutcliffe, B. (2004). World inequality and globalization. *Oxford Review of Economic Policy*, *20*(1), 15–37.

Swank, D. (2002). *Global capital, political institutions, and policy change in developed welfare states*. New York: Cambridge University Press.

Swank, D. (2010). Globalization. In F.G. Castles, S. Leibfried, J. Lewis, & H. Obinger (Eds.), *The Oxford handbook of the welfare state* (pp. 318–330). Oxford: Oxford University Press.

Tal, B. (2015, March 15). Employment quality—Trending downward. *Canadian Employment Quality Index*. Toronto: CIBC World Markets. Retrieved from research. cibcwm.com/economic_public/download/eqi_20150305.pdf.

Teeple, G. (2000). *Globalization and the decline of social reform: Into the twenty-first century*. Aurora, ON: Garamond Press.

Walkom, T. (2011, April 20). Harper and the subtle erosion of medicare. *Toronto Star*. Retrieved from www.thestar.com/news/canada/2011/04/20/walkom_harper_and_the_subtle_erosion_of_medicare.html.

Williamson, J. (1990). *Latin American adjustment: How much has happened?* Washington: Institute for International Economics.

Woodward, D., & Simms, A. (2006). *Growth isn't working: The unbalanced distribution of benefits and costs from economic growth*. London: New Economics Foundation.

Yalnizyan, A. (1998). *The growing gap: A report on growing inequality between the rich and poor in Canada*. Toronto: Centre for Social Justice Foundation for Research and Education.

Yalnizyan, A. (2007). *The rich and the rest of us*. Ottawa: Canadian Centre for Policy Alternatives.

Chapter 12

THE FUTURE OF
HEALTH POLICY IN CANADA

INTRODUCTION

This book has discussed several themes and issues for understanding current directions in health care and health policy in Canada and in other countries. These themes have identified a number of shifts in health policy since the development of the federal health care program—or medicare—in Canada from 1961 through to the present.

This chapter highlights the key issues and concepts explored in the volume and their relevance for understanding health policy in Canada. As discussed, numerous forces have shaped health policy, including the health professions, economic interests such as the pharmaceutical industry, social movements, and the growth of the market as a significant economic force shaping health policy issues. This chapter emphasizes the links between health and social policies and the efforts by Canadian governments to resist challenges to linking health and social policies. It proposes future directions in health for consideration.

POLIS VERSUS THE MARKET

The polis versus the market has been an important theme throughout this volume. Chapter 1 distinguished between the polis, or collectivist approaches, and market-oriented approaches to public policy. The polis refers to an ideal political society in which citizens are engaged in the political process (Stone, 1988, 2012). They participate in decisions to ensure the social and economic security of citizens, and the well-being of the population as a whole.

In contrast, the market refers to a society in which individuals engage in exchanges to satisfy their welfare (Stone, 1988, 2012). People compete with one another to obtain basic goods and services. They try to obtain goods at the lowest cost to themselves. The market distorts politics and public service because the focus is on profit and the functioning of the market, leading to the growth of health inequalities. The polis represents the ultimate political society, in which the collective decides on issues that affect society as a whole and shares risk across the population. The concept of the polis is reflected in the development of medicare and other programs that formed the Canadian welfare state. Embedded in the polis is the notion of sharing risk across the population.

The market, however, represents individualist approaches toward social and health policy issues. In this model of society, people are more reliant on their incomes to obtain the necessities of life. The shift to economic globalization and neoliberalism reflects this model of society. Market-oriented policies lead to an emphasis on individual responsibility for health, and hence a minimal state role in health provision, as reflected in the biomedical and lifestyle approaches to health presented in chapter 2. This policy orientation can lead to greater inequalities in income and health outcomes (Schrecker & Bambra, 2015). Those with lower incomes, populations of colour, women, and other vulnerable groups tend to be at greater risk of having poorer health. Indeed, privatized care and market strategies more generally have not tended to deliver better care (Nichols, Ginsburg, Berenson, Christianson, & Hurley, 2004; Rachlis, 2004, 2005; Rachlis & Kushner, 1995). This may lead to consideration of increasing state intervention to improve health care. The impact of privatization on health policy and health care has been well documented by Armstrong (2010), and Armstrong and Armstrong (2002, 2010), among others (Coburn, 2015; Schrecker & Bambra, 2015).

The dichotomy between the state and the market underlies many of the current health care debates in Canada and elsewhere. The focus seems to preclude consideration of broader health considerations and a recognition that health policy is more than managing and financing the health care system.

THE KEYNESIAN WELFARE STATE

The welfare state—and the creation of a public health care system in Canada and other developed economies—represents a collectivist approach to health and social policy adopted following the Second World War. The state is actively involved in health and social provision, particularly in housing, social services (e.g., income support), and health care. In Canada, the first public health care program was established in Saskatchewan in 1947. The federal health care program, medicare, was established in 1966. Health care is paid for through general revenues, and thus is provided on the basis of need, not ability to pay. Medicare and the other program components of the welfare state help redistribute wealth and other resources from high-income to low-income populations in Canada. As redistributive policy, it runs counter to the market and market-based policies.

Esping-Andersen (1990) devised one of the most used welfare state typologies to differentiate between social democratic, liberal, and conservative welfare regimes. Of the three regimes, social democratic regimes—primarily in the Nordic countries—have tended to have the most generous health and social benefits, as they have a commitment to reduce poverty. Conservative, also termed corporatist, regimes (e.g., Belgium, France, Austria) emphasize the role of the family in social provision, but provide more generous benefits than liberal welfare states (Australia, Canada, New Zealand, United Kingdom, and United States).

Of the all the liberal regimes, the United States is the only country without a public health care system. Prior to the implementation of the Affordable Care Act (ACA), or Obamacare, some American employers provided health insurance benefits to employees. A key aim of the ACA was to insure all Americans (Hall & Lord, 2014). This was achieved by requiring all Americans to purchase health insurance from the private health insurance industry, or face a steep fine. Some critics argue that the act has in fact had little impact on the insurance coverage of about three-quarters of the American population (Hall & Lord, 2014). Its main impact is reducing the proportion of uninsured people to roughly half. This has been achieved by expanding Medicaid to cover this group, or subsidized private insurance provided by a new government exchange. The ACA has created a regulated private health care market. In short, it "reforms the market so that it advances rather than undermines health policy goals" (Hall & Lord, 2014, p. 2).

It would seem that the liberal regimes are more susceptible to neoliberalism, which has seen a resurgence in recent years, and economic globalization. This resurgence requires minimal state involvement in health and social provision. Many observers have associated economic globalization and neoliberal policies with the decline of the welfare state and redistributive politics (Teeple, 2000; Labonte & Schrecker, 2007a, 2007b, 2007c; Banting & Myles, 2013). Esping-Andersen (1990) identified political ideology as an important determinant of the extent of the welfare state in a country. Kwon and Pontusson (2008) found that left party government effects on the welfare state fade under globalization and labour power declines. In contrast, left political parties can have greater influence on social spending—and hence social security—when labour power is high and stable.

In Canada, municipal governments usually have responsibility for public health. Provincial and territorial legislation specifies the mandatory services and programs that local public health units must provide. Mandatory programs include anti-tobacco, infant and maternal health, dental, school-based programs, infection control, and sanitation. In recent years, however, provincial and territorial governments have emphasized conservative approaches to public health, forcing a shift from community-based health promotion programs to biomedical focuses on sanitation and disease and infection control. These focuses contribute to an emphasis on individual risk behaviours and individualized approaches to health intervention. Some public health units advocate on social determinants of health and health equity.

INDIVIDUAL RESPONSIBILITY FOR HEALTH

The shift to market-oriented health care has driven the emphasis on individual responsibility for health, as reflected in the biomedical and lifestyle perspectives on health presented in chapter 2. The lifestyle perspective emphasizes personal behavioural changes as contributing to health. Governments frequently invoke the lifestyle and individual responsibility message to justify their reduced role in social provision. Governments admonish citizens to adopt healthy lifestyles that include exercise, a nutritious diet, moderate alcohol consumption, and smoking cessation. Nettleton (1997) refers to these elements as the "holy trinity of risks" (p. 319)

The lifestyle message is a pervasive and top-down approach to health, emphasizing the expertise of the health professions and others to advise on a healthy lifestyle that will reduce risk factors for chronic diseases, such as cardiovascular disease and type 2 diabetes. The emphasis on lifestyle and individual responsibility tends to exclude consideration of the social determinants of health, such as income and employment security, housing, and education, among others. The lifestyle and biomedical approaches individualize health and tend to justify the state's reduced role in health and social provision.

The dominant health message masks a larger issue that needs to be addressed if governments want to reduce health expenditures. The emphasis on individual risk factors and market-oriented health approaches reflect the influence of neoliberalism and economic globalization.

BARRIERS TO THE DEVELOPED WELFARE STATE: NEOLIBERALISM AND ECONOMIC GLOBALIZATION

Neoliberalism, as the dominant political ideology in Canada and other countries, provides the rationale for economic globalization. Coburn and others define neoliberalism as a market ideology that advocates an unfettered market as the source of all innovation and social provision (Coburn, 2000, 2001, 2004; Teeple, 2000; Jenkins, 2004; Schrecker & Bambra, 2015; Cerny, 2014). Neoliberalism and economic globalization are not new ideas. Capitalism has always been global in character (McNally, 2006). What makes the current phase of neoliberalism and globalization distinct is the development of corporate monopolies and the concentration of vast wealth. This has led to increased commodification of health care and increasing health inequalities. Health care is seen as an investment opportunity for foreign, private, for-profit health care providers.

Thus, the market has redefined public services and the role of government. It requires deregulation and hence a minimal government role. It extols the virtues of an unregulated market in health care provision. Yet there is little evidence to support claims that private care is better and more efficient. These developments have contributed to widening income gaps within so-called globalized economies and concomitant inequalities in health outcomes within the populations of these economies.

THE IMPACT OF TRADE AGREEMENTS ON HEALTH CARE AND HEALTH POLICY

The origins of the current emphasis on market strategies in health care further reflect the rise of neoliberal policies and economic globalization (Teeple, 2000). In Canada, the United Kingdom, and other Western countries, market-oriented strategies have been adopted to reduce government expenditures on health, and ostensibly to preserve the public health care system. Market-based strategies include public-private partnerships (P3s); user fees for assorted health services; and allowing private, for-profit health care providers to deliver health care services. These changes are driven by the belief that allowing a parallel private health care system to develop will relieve some of the pressure on the public system. P3s represent a particular type of health care commercialization. Because they can cover a considerable range of health care services, they represent a risk that foreign corporations will bend important elements of

Canadian health care policy by using trade policy rules to claim that Canada is depriving these foreign entities of a profit (Grieshaber-Otto & Scott, 2004). Much evidence, cited in this volume and elsewhere, shows that such measures reduce access to health care for vulnerable, low-income populations. These populations will do without health care they may need if they are required to pay user fees. Evans (1997) and others have shown that user fees and private health care in general are not cost-efficient and are inferior in quality compared to public health care services. Indeed, as discussed in chapter 6, the single-payer system synonymous with Canada is cost-efficient and delivers higher-quality care than private, for-profit care.

If medicare is fraying at the edges—with reports of long wait times for care or people being sent to the United States at provincial and territorial governments' expense for care that is not available in Canada—many have argued that its problems can be attributed to reduced federal transfers for health care to the provincial and territorial governments. It may also be an issue of resource allocation within the system. Canada ranks as one of the highest health spenders, so perhaps what is needed is better management of resources and different approaches to treatment, professional responsibilities, and means of controlling costs, such as those associated with pharmaceuticals (Lexchin, 2007).

GROWING INEQUALITIES IN HEALTH

Another important theme related to the growth of health care markets in Canada and other countries is growing inequalities in health outcomes (Townsend, Davidson, & Whitehead, 1992; Yalnizyan, 2006; Schrecker & Bambra, 2015). Health inequalities grow out of the shift from redistributive policies to market-based policies described above (Leys, 2001; Teeple, 2000). This is so because the state can influence the health and well-being of citizens through public policies (Raphael, 2006, 2008; Raphael & Bryant, 2006a, 2006b). Indeed, health policy observers have attributed growing inequalities between the developed and developing world, and between rich and poor populations within developed economies such as Canada, the US, and the UK, to economic globalization. In addition, research shows that left political parties are more likely to invest in programs and services that help contribute income, thereby reducing income-related health inequalities (Cao, Prakash, & Ward, 2007; Swank, 2002, 2010; Tjepkema, Wilkins, & Long, 2013). Figure 12.1 shows the child poverty rates in different countries.

The Future of Health Policy in Canada 371

Figure 12.1: Child Poverty Rates in 2008 and 2012

Country	2008	2012
Chile	31.4	22.8
Poland	14.5	22.4
Australia	13.0	19.2
Slovakia	11.1	16.7
Switzerland	14.7	19.5
Norway	5.3	9.6
Republic of Korea	16.8	13.4
Finland	12.0	8.8
Turkey	33.0	30.2
Japan	21.7	19.0
Canada	23.2	20.8
Romania	32.9	30.6
Belgium	17.2	16.4
Sweden	12.9	12.1
Austria	14.9	14.2
New Zealand	18.8	18.4
Czech Republic	13.2	12.8
Germany	15.2	15.0
Israel	35.1	35.6
Bulgaria	25.5	26.1
Malta	20.4	21.0
Netherlands	12.9	13.9
Portugal	22.8	23.8
Denmark	9.1	10.2
United Kingdom	24.0	25.6
Slovenia	11.6	13.4
United States	30.1	32.2
Cyprus	14.0	16.7
Hungary	19.7	22.6
France	15.6	18.6
Mexico	29.3	34.3
Estonia	17.1	22.2
Italy	24.7	30.4
Luxembourg	19.8	26.3
Spain	28.2	36.3
Lithuania	22.8	31.1
Ireland	18.0	28.6
Croatia	15.8	27.6
Latvia	23.6	38.2
Greece	23.0	40.5
Iceland	11.2	31.6

Child poverty rate
■ 2008 ■ 2012

Source: UNICEF Office of Research. (2014). Children of the recession: The impact of the economic crisis on child well-being in rich countries. *Innocenti Report Card 12*, UNICEF Office of Research, Florence.

THE NEW INSTITUTIONALIST PERSPECTIVE ON THE PROSPECTS FOR HEALTH CARE REFORM IN CANADA: THE IMPACT OF CANADIAN FEDERALISM

From a new institutionalist perspective, institutions structure political debate and the range of solutions that policy-makers will consider to address public problems (Hall, 1993; Hall & Taylor, 1996). In health care, for example, Canadian federalism has sometimes led to innovations, such as the creation of medicare, but it has also resisted change, as evidenced by the focus on health care as opposed to health equity (Hutchison, Abelson, & Lavis, 2001).

Federal and subnational institutions can impede meaningful reforms of the health care system, particularly in relation to resourcing and managing medicare. The strife between the federal and provincial/territorial governments over the financing of health care has led to little productive debate on how to change the system to improve and sustain it. The two levels of government, therefore, structure health care debate and can limit the range of solutions that will be considered to reform the system and improve service and health outcomes. This strife seemed to intensify during the Harper Conservative regime (2006 to 2015) (see Box 12.1).

Box 12.1: Why Canadian Politicians Don't Talk about Health Care
By Thomas Walkom, National Affairs
Toronto Star

Health care is a major issue concerning voters. Yet with the federal election just a few months away, it has barely been addressed.

When pollsters ask Canadians to name the issue that concerns them the most, health care routinely tops the list. It regularly outpaces jobs and the economy. It always trumps terrorism. It leaves issues like the Senate scandal in the dust.

Canadians approve heartily of medicare. An Ipsos-Reid poll released this week calculated that 75 per cent think Canada's health system is the best in the world—a fairly typical finding.

But these same polls also find that voters worry about Canada's health-care system falling behind, in areas ranging from prescription drugs to home care to nursing homes. Yet so far in this unofficial federal election campaign—and with one important exception—health care has received barely a mention.

That exception comes courtesy of New Democrat Leader Tom Mulcair. Last year, he made a very public promise that he would "use any budget surplus" to reverse planned Conservative spending cutbacks on health care. Those cutbacks, which the provinces say will cost their health-care systems $36 billion over a decade, are not due to come into effect until next year, well after the October election.

In theory, all Canadian political parties are wedded to medicare. Even Conservative Prime Minister Stephen Harper, a former aficionado of two-tier health, pays obeisance to Canada's publicly funded system. But at the same time, federal politicians are wary of spending money on services like health that are delivered by provinces.

From its inception in 1968, national medicare has been bedevilled by this tension. From time to time, Ottawa cuts back its contribution in order to save money. Then, a few years later, it is shamed into upping it. Finally, when the public furor subsides, it cuts back again—usually by making technical changes to the almost incomprehensible health transfer formula. The last shaming occurred in 2004 when, under public pressure, then Liberal Prime Minister Paul Martin agreed to increase health-care transfers to the provinces by 6 per cent a year. The last backtrack occurred in 2011 when Harper's Conservatives announced that, as of 2016, they would replace this flat 6 per cent annual hike with a formula designed to save Ottawa billions. As the parliamentary budget officer later noted, the Conservative move would allow the federal government to shift more of its debt load to the provinces.

The downside of this shift, however, is that cash-strapped provinces either have to increase their health spending (and hence their debt loads) or cut back services.

In most cases, the provinces choose to cut back services such as home care, hospital care, physician care and nursing homes.

That, in turn, emboldens the critics of medicare. This fall, for instance, a B.C. court is slated to hear yet another constitutional challenge to Canada's universal public health-insurance system. This one was launched by British Columbia physician Brian Day, who says laws to limit extra-billing contravene the Charter of Rights and Freedoms.

A paper written for the Canadian Centre for Policy Alternatives concludes that the Day case, while not the first constitutional attack on medicare, is by far the most serious. It would be interesting to know if any of Canada's federal political parties have an opinion about the issues in play here. The parties will undoubtedly make some reference to health care when their formal platforms are released. It is not always clear what these references mean.

During the 2011 campaign, for instance, Harper's Conservatives promised to "renew" the existing federal-provincial health accord and "continue reducing wait times," pledges they arguably didn't keep. In that same campaign, Jack Layton's NDP promised to reduce the price of drugs "as finances permit." In this campaign, aside from Mulcair's bold promise to give the provinces more money, we've heard very little on health care. It would be useful to hear more.

For instance: All three major parties, including the Harper Conservatives, have flirted with the idea of setting up a national pharmacare program to provide sick people with necessary drugs. Are any of them willing to follow through?

Source: Walkom, T. (2015, June 17). Why Canadian politicians don't talk about health care. *Toronto Star*. Retrieved from www.thestar.com.

This volume has lamented the continuous wrangling over health care between the two levels of government. Of particular concern is the unilateral Harper-Flaherty formula announced in December 2012. Prime Minister Harper and his finance minister, Jim Flaherty, announced that they would continue to increase federal health transfers by 6 percent until 2016/17. After 2017, any increases will be tied to economic growth, including inflation, to about 4 percent, and never drop below 3 percent. The Harper Conservatives ran on a platform that included increasing health transfers to the provincial and territorial governments. This plan was silent on how much they would increase these transfers.

A new federal Liberal government was elected in October 2015, promising to be different from the Harper administration. During the election campaign, Liberal leader Justin Trudeau promised a new partnership with provincial and territorial governments on health care and "a new federal commitment to expanding, investing in health care" (Liberal Party of Canada, 2015). He promised to renegotiate the health accord and include a long-term funding agreement. It is as yet unclear when this will be undertaken. But, will the Trudeau Liberals change the approach to ensure equitable access to health care services and promote the social determinants of health?

While not perfect, the health accords provided some direction on health policy. Most importantly, they recognize the government's important role in health care provision. The Social Union Framework Agreement and the health accords provided a rallying point for civil society actors such as the labour movement, health advocacy organizations, and others to lobby the federal,

Box 12.2: Liberal Party of Canada's New Health Accord

We will make home care more available, prescription drugs more affordable, and mental health care more accessible.

Canada's publicly-funded universal health care system is a source of pride for Canadians—and a source of economic security for the middle class and those working hard to join it. When Canadians are in good physical and mental health, they are able to work better, be more productive, and contribute more fully to our economy while living healthier, happier lives.

Despite our health care system's value and importance, it has been more than a decade since a Canadian Prime Minister sat down with provincial and territorial Premiers to strengthen the program, and ensure that it can meet current needs and the challenges that come with an aging population.

We will restart that important conversation and provide the collaborative federal leadership that has been missing during the Harper decade. We will negotiate a new Health Accord with provinces and territories, including a long-term agreement on funding.

As an immediate commitment, we will invest $3 billion, over the next four years, to deliver more and better home care services for all Canadians. This includes more access to high quality in-home caregivers, financial supports for family care, and, when necessary, palliative care.

To help families care for their loved ones at home, we will make the Employment Insurance Compassionate Care Benefit more flexible and easier to access, so that it provides help for more than just end-of-life care.

We will also develop a pan-Canadian collaboration on health innovation, and will improve access to necessary prescription medications. We will join with provincial and territorial governments to buy drugs in bulk, reducing the cost Canadian governments pay for these drugs, and making them more affordable for Canadians.

We will make high-quality mental health services more available to Canadians who need them, including our veterans and first responders.

To eliminate systemic barriers and deliver equality of opportunity to all Canadians living with disabilities, we will consult with provinces, territories, and other stakeholders to introduce a *National Disabilities Act*.

Source: Liberal Party of Canada. (2016). *A new health accord.* Retrieved from www.liberal.ca.

provincial, and territorial governments to protect health care. Governments' recent inaction suggests that such accords must be supported by concrete action by both levels of government (see Box 12.3).

Box 12.3: Health Care Renewal in Canada: Measuring Up? What Governments Promised: A Summary

2003 First Ministers' Accord on Health Care Renewal

In February 2003, the prime minister and premiers signed an accord on health care renewal, worth $36 billion over five years. They pledged to increase access to health care providers, diagnostic procedures and treatments, home and community care services, and necessary drugs. They also agreed to establish the Health Council of Canada.

The 2004 10-Year Plan to Strengthen Health Care

In September 2004, the prime minister and premiers signed a second health care agreement which committed an additional $41 billion in federal funds over the next 10 years. In it, they reconfirmed their commitment to the principles of the Canada Health Act and also promised to collaborate, share best practices, and be accountable to the public with respect to the progress of renewal. The Health Council was given additional responsibilities to report on the health status of Canadians and on health outcomes.

Aboriginal Health Transition Fund

In September 2004, a special meeting of First Ministers and national Aboriginal leaders announced a $200 million Aboriginal health transition fund, to be created over five years. The fund was designed to improve the integration of federal and provincial health services, improve access to health services, make available health programs and services that are better suited to Aboriginal peoples, and increase the participation of Aboriginal peoples in the design, delivery, and evaluation of health programs and services.

2005 Annual Conference of Ministers of Health

At this conference, the ministers of health made a number of important commitments regarding drug coverage and pharmaceuticals management, including accelerating work on options for catastrophic drug coverage, developing a common drug review, and working toward a national formulary. As well, they agreed on a set of goals for improving the health of Canadians.

2005 Kelowna Accord and Blueprint on Aboriginal Health

In November 2005, a two-day summit of first ministers was held in Kelowna, British Columbia. At this meeting the federal government pledged $5 billion over five years to improve the lives of Aboriginal peoples in the areas of health care, housing, and education. The leaders from 19 jurisdictions, including the government of Canada, every province and territory, and five national Aboriginal groups (the Assembly of First Nations, the Inuit of Canada, the Métis National Council, the Congress of Aboriginal Peoples, and the Native Women's Association of Canada) agreed to the tenets of this commitment, subject to further discussion on the funding and how it was to be spent.

The Blueprint on Aboriginal Health, a 10-year transformative plan to help close the gap in health outcomes between Aboriginal peoples and the general Canadian population, was tabled at this meeting. The federal government committed to use the blueprint in creating Aboriginal health programs; since then, no funding has been committed to the blueprint by the federal government. As a collective, the provinces and territories have not indicated their commitment to the blueprint as their framework for the development or implementation of such programs.

2006 First Ministers' Conference

In the 2004 10-Year Plan to Strengthen Health Care, governments committed to establish a ministerial task force to develop and implement a national pharmaceuticals strategy (NPS), including coverage for catastrophic drug costs, and to report on progress by June 30, 2006. At the conclusion of the Council of the Federation meeting in St. John's on July 28, 2006, the premiers accepted a task force report on the NPS and directed provincial and territorial health ministers to release a report by September 2006 on the status of NPS and to "continue to work on key elements ... with a special focus on the Catastrophic Drug Program."

On September 21, 2006, the provincial and territorial ministers of health released a progress report. The federal minister did not participate in the release. The report recommended, among other things, that the task force focus further on policy, design, and costing analysis for options for catastrophic drug coverage.

Source: Health Council of Canada. (2007). *Health care renewal in Canada: Measuring up?* (p. 6). Toronto: Health Council of Canada.

FUTURE DIRECTIONS: HEALTH CARE REFORM

Reforming health care and health policy provides some avenues for altering government approaches to health to promote better health outcomes for the population as a whole. Many provincial and territorial efforts to reform the health care system have tended to focus on market-based strategies, to the exclusion of public-based solutions.

Romanow recognized public support for medicare. He argued that the public health care system is sustainable and urged moving forward to "transform ... it into a truly national, more comprehensive, responsive and accountable health care system" (Romanow, 2002, p. xv). Moreover, Romanow reiterated the need for a publicly funded and administered system while also recognizing the need to reform and improve the health care system. Further, Romanow noted that most Canadians are satisfied with the care they receive and see little need to privatize. He affirmed the role of the state in health care provision.

As noted in chapter 7, Mazankowski and Kirby endorsed a larger role for local authorities in health (Kirby, 2002; Mazankowski, 2001). Kirby, however, called for a strong federal role in financing medicare.

Governments have justified the adoption of commercial strategies that fundamentally restructure health care, and their implications for access to health care are presented not only as necessary to reduce public spending, but also as inevitable (Bakker, 1996). Governments in Canada, the United Kingdom, and other countries with public health care systems have deregulated or privatized elements of health care in order to save money. They have done so to attract investment, facilitate the process of commodification, and maintain their competitiveness in the global economy (Leys, 2001). These changes may lead governments to reduce health expenditures to deal with moribund civil services. These actions, together with reduced senior government financing, appear to be elements of a larger agenda to meet the requirements of economic globalization.

Opting for private measures or an expanded role for the private sector is an ideological position. It prescribes roles and relationships for private institutions and government within a society. The private institutions identified to improve health care represent the market and market-oriented strategies, such as user fees, medical savings accounts, and P3s. This orientation is consistent with Stone's (1988, 2012) market model. P3 arrangements involve transferring a public service to a private provider to design, build, and deliver. In the end, the new service will belong to a private corporation. Critics argue that once these arrangements are in place, it will be almost impossible to reverse them and bring these goods or services back into the public realm and there is little evidence that market strategies will improve health care in particular, or social welfare in general (Rice, 1997; Woodward & Simms, 2006). Many have documented the economic influences of the single-payer system—synonymous with Canadian medicare—and its ability to enhance social welfare (Yalnizyan, 2006; Gaffney, Woolhandler, Angell, & Himmelstein, 2016).

These is also institutional resistance to expanding the system not only to provide sufficient resources to support core functions of medicare, but also to expand the system's scope to include dental care, home care, and pharmacare, as recommended as early as 1964 by Emmett Hall's first report to the federal government (Canada, 1964). Mazankowski and Kirby only recommended catastrophic drug coverage and were opposed to expanding the scope of medicare to include home care and dental services (Kirby, 2002; Mazankowski, 2001). Yet, there is growing support for a national pharmacare program. This could be an important focus in coming years (see Box 12.4).

Box 12.4: National Pharmacare has Large Support across Canada, Poll Says
By Jane Taber
Globe and Mail

Nearly one-quarter of Canadians say they or someone in their home can't afford prescribed drugs and are splitting pills and skipping doses to make the medicine go further—or not renewing or even filling prescriptions, according to a new poll.

In addition, 36 per cent of the Canadians surveyed reported they have friends or family members who are having trouble paying their drug costs; Atlantic Canadians and British Columbians struggle the most. The Angus Reid Institute poll also found that one in five Canadians spend $500 or more a year on prescriptions—and nearly half of those surveyed are worried they won't be able to afford the drug costs 10 years from now. It's no surprise that the survey—the first to take such a deep look at the affordability and accessibility of prescription drugs across the country—also found overwhelming support (91 per cent) for a national pharmacare program.

The study, released Wednesday, comes as Canada's premiers are in St. John's for their annual summer conference, where they will discuss the issue, and as Canadians prepare for the federal election in the fall. The debate for a national pharmacare program has been going on for decades—Canada is the only country with a universal health-care system that doesn't cover prescription drug costs. But lately the idea has been gaining traction. Last month, Ontario Health Minister Eric Hoskins and some of his provincial and territorial colleagues called for the idea of a national program to be a federal election issue.

The Angus Reid Institute, a non-partisan, not-for-profit polling organization, joined ranks with Vancouver-based Mindset Foundation, a Canadian charity that has been commissioning research on problems of accessing medicine for the last six years, to take a comprehensive look at the issue. Both organizations contributed equally in the project.

"I don't think anyone anticipated … that high number of people coming back and actually saying this is an [issue] for us," says Shachi Kurl, senior vice-president of the Angus Reid Institute. The institute, noted Ms. Kurl, is not pushing for a national program. The study, she said, is "an attempt to understand the real experiences of Canadians when it comes to drug costs."

Steve Morgan, director of the Centre for Health Services and Policy Research at the University of British Columbia, who helped analyze the data, called the results "striking." "We have known in the past that approximately one in 10 Canadians doesn't fill their prescriptions … because of the cost of the prescription to the family," Dr. Morgan said, referring to a Statistics Canada study and one other from 2007, on which he was the senior author. "What we now know is this affects nearly one in four families in Canada."

The poll of 1,556 Canadians was conducted between July 2 and 6. It has a margin of error of plus or minus 2.5 percentage points, 19 times out of 20, the pollster says.

Dr. Morgan noted there are regional differences in costs given the various drug schemes across the country. "But there is no province where you can say that there is nobody put at that kind of risk in Canada," he said. "We have a problem across all provinces in terms of access to medicines that are being prescribed. We are the only developed country with universal health care that basically ends as soon as the doctor hands the patient a prescription to fill."

More than 23 per cent of respondents said that in the last 12 months they or someone in their home did not "take their medicines as prescribed because of cost." Fourteen per cent said they did not fill a prescription; 10 per cent did not renew one, and 15 per cent said they cut pills or skipped doses.

The survey found that 29 per cent of British Columbians do not take their drugs because of costs. "This is possibly because government in B.C. offers only 'catastrophic' drug coverage and may also reflect the higher cost of living in this region," according to the report.

About 26 per cent of Atlantic Canadians face the same problem as on the West Coast—the report says it could be the result of the "limited nature of provincial drug plans" in the region.

Despite the support for a plan, there are some concerns: 51 per cent of respondents are worried that giving away prescription drugs for free will lead to abuse, including 66 per cent who voted for the Conservatives in the last election. And how to pay for a national plan also troubles Canadians. In the survey, respondents rejected the notion it be financed through a hike in the GST or income tax. Rather, a hike in the corporate tax rate to its 2010 rate of 18 per cent is more palatable, with 52 per cent of respondents saying any potential program should be run jointly by the federal government and provinces.

Source: Taber, J. (2015, July 15). National pharmacare has large support across Canada, poll says. *The Globe and Mail.* Retrieved from www.theglobeandmail.com.

DEFICIT-REDUCTION-DRIVEN HEALTH CARE REFORM

Chief among the key dynamics that influence health care and health policy in Canada is an emphasis on deficit reduction among Canadian governments since the 1980s (Maioni, 2003). The focus on deficit reduction and health care seems to have precluded consideration of alternative approaches to health care reform, in particular strategies that consider how to improve the health of the population in addition to concerns about health care.

Some of the public's concerns and perceptions have shaped the debate about health care (Mendelsohn, 2002). First, the Canadian public hears that the health care system as it is currently organized (i.e., with public financing and private provision) is unsustainable. Second, the media and politicians propagate the view that the system is in crisis. Finally, the first two perceptions promote the argument that some form of privatization is the only solution to address the problems of the health care system.

Recent polls show somewhat conflicting results. One poll showed that most Canadians prefer a mixed model of health care, whereby they would have the option of purchasing private care (Stechyson, 2012). The same poll also showed that when given a choice between not-for-profit and for-profit models, four out of five Canadians preferred a not-for-profit health care model.

Another poll showed that 65 percent of Canadians want fixed federal health care funding to the provincial and territorial governments, rejecting the Harper-Flaherty plan to tie health care transfers to economic growth (Canadian Health Coalition & Nanos Research, 2013). The poll also showed that 4 out of 10 Canadians are concerned about affording or having access to health care as a senior. More than 6 in 10 Canadians are willing to pay higher taxes to expand medicare to include home care and prescription medications. It is clear that Canadians continue to value medicare, but want it strengthened through a strong federal government role in financing the system.

NEW DIRECTIONS FOR HEALTH POLICY: SOCIAL DETERMINANTS OF HEALTH

As emphasized throughout this volume, public health refers to healthy public policy, health care services, building strong communities, protecting citizens from environmental threats, and promoting healthy behaviours (Raphael & Bryant, 2006a, 2006b). Much of the emphasis since the Second World War has been on health care provision. Until the 1970s and 1980s, little attention had been paid to social determinants such as housing, income, and education, and their impact on population health and well-being. Yet Canadian and other national governments developed housing and other programs to ensure that families and individuals were able to meet their basic needs (Myles, 1998). To reflect interest in the welfare of the population, the federal government established the federal department Health and Welfare Canada in the immediate postwar period. The name of the department recognized the close relationship between health and social policies in improving and maintaining the health and social well-being of the population.

For several decades, Canadian governments and professional associations such as the Canadian Public Health Association emphasized the importance of the social determinants of health—that is, living conditions—and the importance of healthy public policies in promoting and maintaining the health and well-being of a population. The social determinants emphasize a model of health that is consistent with the political economy approach to health, as defined in chapter 2. The social determinants are the material conditions of living (or simply living conditions), such as income security, employment security, education, food security, housing security, and access to health care services, among others. This model conceptualizes health as related to social structures, such as public policies that strongly influence health and well-being. The social determinants reinforce a belief in collective well-being and state or government provision of services such as health care, as in the Keynesian welfare state.

Moreover, an emphasis on social determinants requires public policies that will enhance population health. In short, the social determinants of health approach requires government intervention to ensure quality health and social programs and to maintain the health of a population. In addition, much research evidence supports a state role in improving the health of a population (Deaton, 2004; Schrecker & Bambra, 2015; Raphael & Bryant, 2015). Many lists of social determinants have been devised by such organizations as the World Health Organization and the Canadian Institute for Advanced Research. However, those lists that emphasize public policy as strong influences on the social determinants of health are most helpful in explicating the importance of a state role in health and social provision.

During the 1980s and early 1990s, Canada was a world leader in health promotion and innovative approaches to public health (Restrepo, 1996). Canadian researchers made significant contributions to the health promotion principles of equity and participation, and the focus in the population health field on the social determinants of health. However, the 1990s marked a departure from progressive approaches to public health. Canada now lags behind other countries in applying its own concepts for promoting health and well-being (Canadian Population Health Initiative, 2002; Schrecker & Bambra, 2015). Behavioural and lifestyle approaches, as defined in chapter 2, have become the new mantra.

Addressing the social determinants requires redistributive social policy changes—that is, policies that redistribute wealth from higher-income groups to the poorest income groups. Health policy as defined in the social determinants of health approach is broader than merely being concerned with the health care system and the delivery of quality health care services across a population, as is the focus in Canada (Bryant, Raphael, Schrecker, & Labonte, 2011). Health policy is also concerned with the determinants of or influences on population health. Canada has yet to learn this lesson about the importance of implementing redistributive policies to improve the overall health of the Canadian population.

THE STATE ROLE IN HEALTH CARE PROVISION

The research cited in the previous sections underscores the important role of the state in not only managing and financing the system to ensure that all citizens have access to health care services, but also to protect national standards. Such standards ensure that all citizens, regardless of where they live in the country, have access to high-quality health care services. When the national health care program in Canada was first established in 1961, governments were committed to cost-sharing the program to ensure universal access and a high quality of care. The reluctance to act highlights the political and economic forces that influence health policy in Canada. There is a need for guidance on the key issues affecting health policy and health care.

The federal, provincial, and territorial governments must move beyond concerns of deficit reduction and devise measures to strengthen medicare. Consistent with a social determinants of health approach, they must also pursue prevention, initiate efforts to reduce poverty, and enact public policies that address the social determinants of health.

THE ROLE OF CIVIL SOCIETY IN HEALTH POLICY AND THE DEMOCRATIC PROCESS

Many different forces and groups in civil society—such as the pharmaceutical industry, the health professions (particularly doctors), and others—act on the political system to influence health policy outcomes. Canadian social movements such as the Canadian Health Coalition, the Ontario Health Coalition, the Canadian Centre for Policy Alternatives, and other civil society organizations have played a critical role in health care and health policy by drawing attention to efforts to privatize health care services (Bryant & Raphael, 2015). They have provided public education on key policy issues that affect health care and health policy in general. Such groups advocate community-based health care to ensure accessibility for marginalized populations in Canadian society. They have also played a role in bringing health inequalities, the social determinants of health, and the impact of income distribution on health outcomes into the health policy discourse in Canada.

Social movements and public policy organizations, such as the Canadian Centre for Policy Alternatives and the Canadian Policy Research Networks, play a critical role in ensuring government accountability to the population in protecting medicare. Social movements also play an important part in ensuring democratic process and government accountability for their actions. These organizations need to be strengthened to ensure their continued vigilance of social and health issues that affect all Canadians and future generations of Canadians.

CONCLUSIONS

This volume has drawn attention to many key issues and tried to expand the understanding of health policy. Health policy is not simply about managing the health care system. It is also concerned with the government's role in improving and maintaining the health of the population.

Health policy is about power, politics, and process. It is driven by values and conflict among different groups in society about how government dollars should be spent on health issues. Health policy is as ideological as other public policy areas, if not more so. It is about intergovernmental relations and the capacity of the two levels of government to move beyond deficit-reduction health reform to resolve long-standing health policy issues through transparent deliberations that enable civil society actors to have input into how these issues should be addressed.

REFERENCES

Armstrong, P. (2010). Gender, health, and care. In T. Bryant, D. Raphael, & M. Rioux (Eds.), *Staying alive: Critical perspectives on health, illness and health care* (2nd ed.) (pp. 331–346). Toronto: Canadian Scholars' Press.

Armstrong, P., & Armstrong, H. (2002). *Thinking it through: Women, work and caring in the new millennium.* Halifax: Canadian Institutes of Health Research (CIHR), Nova Scotia Advisory Council on the Status of Women, and Atlantic Centre of Excellence for Women's Health (ACEWH).

Armstrong, P., & Armstrong, H. (2010). *Wasting away: The undermining of Canadian health care* (2nd ed.). Toronto: Oxford University Press.

Bakker, I. (1996). Introduction: The gendered foundation of restructuring in Canada. In I. Bakker (Ed.), *Rethinking restructuring: Gender and change in Canada* (pp. 3–25). Toronto: University of Toronto Press.

Banting, K., & Myles, J. (Eds.). (2013). *Inequality and the fading of redistributive politics.* Vancouver: UBC Press.

Bryant, T., & Raphael, D. (2015). Opening policy windows with evidence and citizen engagement: Addressing the social determinants of health inequalities. In G. Carey, K. Landvogt, & J. Barraket (Eds.), *Creating and implementing public policy: Cross-sectoral debates* (pp. 25–40). New York: Routledge.

Bryant, T., Raphael, D., Schrecker, T., & Labonte, R. (2011). Canada: A land of missed opportunity for addressing the social determinants of health. *Health Policy, 101*(1), 44–58.

Canada. (1964). *Royal Commission on Health Services, vol. 1 & 2.* (E. Hall, Chair). Ottawa: Royal Commission on Health Services.

Canadian Health Coalition & Nanos Research. (2013). *Canadians on public healthcare.* Submitted to the Canadian Health Coalition by Nanos, November 2013 (Submission 2013-453). Toronto: Nanos Research.

Canadian Population Health Initiative. (2002). *Canadian Population Health Initiative brief to the Commission on the Future of Health Care in Canada*. Ottawa: Canadian Institute for Health Information.

Cao, X., Prakash, A., & Ward, M.J. (2007). Protecting jobs in the age of globalization: Examining the relative salience of social welfare and industrial subsidies in OECD countries. *International Studies Quarterly, 51*(2), 301–327.

Cerny, P.G. (2014). Globalization and the resilience of neoliberalism. *Critical Policy Studies, 8*(3), 359–362.

Coburn, D. (2000). Income inequality, social cohesion and the health status of populations: The role of neo-liberalism. *Social Science & Medicine, 51*(1), 135–146.

Coburn, D. (2001). Health, health care, and neo-liberalism. In P. Armstrong, H. Armstrong, & D. Coburn (Eds.), *Unhealthy times: The political economy of health and care in Canada*. Toronto: Oxford University Press.

Coburn, D. (2004). Beyond the income inequality hypothesis: Globalization, neo-liberalism, and health inequalities. *Social Science & Medicine, 58*, 41–56.

Coburn, D. (2015). Income inequality, welfare, class and health: A comment on Picket and Wilkinson, 2015. *Social Science & Medicine, 146*, 228–232.

Deaton, A. (2004). *Health in an age of globalization*. Washington: Brookings Institution Press.

Dicken, P. (2003). *Global shift: Reshaping the global economic map in the 21st century* (4th ed.). New York: Guilford Press.

Esping-Andersen, G. (1990). *The three worlds of welfare capitalism*. Princeton: Princeton University Press.

Evans, R.G. (1997). Going for the gold: The redistributive agenda behind market-based health care reform. *Journal of Health Politics, Policy and Law, 22*(2), 427–465.

Gaffney, A., Woolhandler, S., Angell, M., & Himmelstein, D. (2016). Moving forward from the Affordable Care Act to a single-payer system. *American Journal of Public Health, 106*(6), 987–988.

Grieshaber-Otto, J., & Scott, S. (2004). *Bad medicine: Trade treatries, privatization and health care reform in Canada*. Ottawa: Canadian Centre for Policy Alternatives.

Hall, M.A., & Lord, R. (2014). Obamacare: What the Affordable Care Act means for patients and physicians. *British Medical Journal, 349*, g5376.

Hall, P.A. (1993). Policy paradigms, social learning, and the state: The case of economic policymaking in Britain. *Comparative Politics, 25*(3), 275–296.

Hall, P.A., & Taylor, R.C.R. (1996). Political science and the three institutionalisms. *Political Studies, 44*(5), 936–957.

Hutchinson, B., Abelson, J., & Lavis, J. (2001). Primary care in Canada: So much innovation, so little change. *Health Affairs, 20*(3), 116–131.

Jenkins, R. (2004). Globalization, production, employment and poverty: Debates and evidence. *Journal of International Development, 16*, 1–12.

Kirby, M.J. (2002). *The health of Canadians: The federal role*. Ottawa: Standing Senate Committee on Social Affairs, Science and Technology.

Kwon, H.Y., & Pontusson, J. (2008). *Unions, globalization and the politics of social spending growth in OECD countries, 1962–2000*. Princeton, NJ: Princeton University Press.

Labonte, R., & Schrecker, T. (2007a). Globalization and social determinants of health: Introduction and methodological background. Part 1 of 3. *Globalization and Health, 3*(5), 1–10.

Labonte, R., & Schrecker, T. (2007b). Globalization and social determinants of health: Promoting health equity in global governance. Part 3 of 3. *Globalization and Health*, *3*(7), 1–10.

Labonte, R., & Schrecker, T. (2007c). Globalization and social determinants of health: The role of the global marketplace. Part 2 of 3. *Globalization and Health*, *3*(6), 1–10.

Lexchin, J. (2007). No excuse for denying drug coverage: It's time to end Canadians' long wait for pharmacare. *The CCPA Monitor*, *14*(December). Ottawa: Canadian Centre for Policy Alternatives.

Leys, C. (2001). *Market-driven politics*. London: Verso.

Liberal Party of Canada. (2015). *A new health accord*. Retrieved from www.liberal.ca.

Maioni, A. (2003). Romanow: A defence of public health care, but is there a map for the road ahead? *Policy Options*, *4*(2), 50–53.

Mazankowski, D. (2001). *A framework for reform: Report of the Premier's Advisory Council on Health*. Edmonton: Government of Alberta.

McNally, D. (2006). *Another world is possible: Globalization and anti-capitalism*. Winnipeg: Arbeiter Ring Publishing.

Mendelsohn, M. (2002, November). Canadians prepared to accept medicare reform in primary care. *Policy Options*, *23*(8), 27–29.

Myles, J. (1998). How to design a "liberal" welfare state: A comparison of Canada and the United States. *Social Policy and Administration*, *32*(4), 341–364.

Nettleton, S. (1997). Surveillance, health promotion, and the formation of a risk identity. In M. Siddell, L. Jones, J. Katz, & A. Peberdy (Eds.), *Debates and dilemmas in promoting health* (pp. 314–324). London: Open University.

Nichols, L.M., Ginsburg, P.B., Berenson, R.A., Christianson, J., & Hurley, R.E. (2004). Are market forces strong enough to deliver efficient health care systems? Confidence is waning. *Health Affairs*, *23*(2), 8–21.

Rachlis, M. (2004). *Prescription for excellence: How innovation is saving Canada's health care system*. Toronto: HarperCollins.

Rachlis, M. (2005). *Public solutions to health care wait lists*. Ottawa: Canadian Centre for Policy Alternatives.

Rachlis, M., & Kushner, C. (1995). *Strong medicine: How to save Canada's health care system*. Toronto: HarperCollins.

Raphael, D. (2006). The State's role in promoting population health: Public health concerns in Canada, USA, UK, and Sweden. *Health Policy*, *78*, 39–55.

Raphael, D. (2008). Introduction to the social determinants of health. In D. Raphael (Ed.), *Social determinants of health: Canadian perspectives* (2nd ed.) (pp. 2–19). Toronto: Canadian Scholars' Press.

Raphael, D., & Bryant, T. (2006a). Maintaining population health in a period of welfare state decline: Political economy as the missing dimension in health promotion theory and practice. *Promotion and Education*, *13*, 236–242.

Raphael, D., & Bryant, T. (2006b). The State's role in promoting population health: Public health concerns in Canada, USA, UK, and Sweden. *Health Policy*, *78*, 39–55.

Raphael, D., & Bryant, T. (2015). Power, intersectionality and the life course: Identifying the political and economic structures of welfare states that support or threaten health. *Social Theory & Health*, *13*(3–4), 245–266.

Restrepo, H.E. (1996). Introduction. In Pan American Health Organization (Ed.), *Health promotion: An anthology* (pp. ix–xi). Washington, DC: Pan American Health Organization.

Rice, T. (1997). Can markets give us the health system we want? *Journal of Health Politics, Policy and Law*, *22*(2), 383–426.

Romanow, R. (2002). *Building on values: The future of health care in Canada*. Saskatoon: Commission on the Future of Health Care in Canada.

Schrecker, T., & Bambra, C. (2015). *How politics makes us sick: Neoliberal epidemics*. Houndmills, UK: Palgrave Macmillan.

Stechyson, N. (2012, June 26). Canadians want choice in how they access health care: Poll. *Edmonton Journal*. Retrieved from www.edmontonjournal.com.

Stone, D. (1988). *Policy paradox: The art of political decision making*. New York: W.W. Norton & Company.

Stone, D. (2012). *Policy paradox: The art of political decision making* (3rd ed.). New York: W.W. Norton & Company.

Swank, D. (2002). *Global capital, political institutions, and policy change in developed welfare states*. New York: Cambridge University Press.

Swank, D. (2010). Globalization. In F.G. Castles, S. Leibfried, J. Lewis, H. Obinger, & C. Pierson (Eds.), *The Oxford handbook of the welfare state* (pp. 318–325). Oxford: Oxford University Press.

Teeple, G. (2000). *Globalization and the decline of social reform: Into the twenty-first century*. Aurora, ON: Garamond Press.

Tjepkema, M., Wilkins, R., & Long, A. (2013). Cause-specific mortality by income adequacy in Canada: A 16-year follow-up study. *Health Reports*, *24*(7), 14–22.

Townsend, P., Davidson, N., & Whitehead, M. (Eds.). (1992). *Inequalities in health: The Black Report and the health divide*. New York: Penguin.

Woodward, D., & Simms, A. (2006). *Growth isn't working: The unbalanced distribution of benefits and costs from economic growth*. London: New Economics Foundation.

Yalnizyan, A. (2006). *Controlling costs: Canada's single-payer system is costly—but least expensive*. Ottawa: Canadian Centre for Policy Alternatives.

COPYRIGHT ACKNOWLEDGEMENTS

Card 12, UNICEF Office of Research, Florence. Copyright © UNICEF, 2014. Reprinted with permission.

Box 12.1: Walkom, T. (June 17). Why Canadian politicians don't talk about health care. *Toronto Star*. Retrieved from www.thestar.com. Copyright © Toronto Star, 2015.

Box 12.2: Liberal Party of Canada. *A new health accord*. Retrieved from www. liberal.ca. Copyright © Liberal Party of Canada, 2016.

Box 12.3: Health Council of Canada. *Health care renewal in Canada: Measuring up?* (p. 6). Copyright © Health Council of Canada, 2007.

Box 12.4: Taber, J. (July 15). National pharmacare has large support across Canada, poll says. *The Globe and Mail*. Retrieved from www.theglobeandmail.com. Copyright © The Globe and Mail, 2015.

INDEX